TEACHING THE PURSUIT OF SCIENCE

JOHN H. WOODBURN

Walter Johnson High School, Bethesda, Maryland

ELLSWORTH S. OBOURN

Specialist for Science, U.S. Office of Education

TEACHING THE PURSUIT OF SCIENCE

THE MACMILLAN COMPANY, NEW YORK
COLLIER-MACMILLAN LIMITED, LONDON

Library of Congress catalog card number: 65–14075

THE MACMILLAN COMPANY, NEW YORK
COLLIER-MACMILLAN CANADA, LTD., TORONTO, ONTARIO

Printed in the United States of America

Designed by Susan Sien

ACKNOWLEDGMENTS

It would be virtually impossible for us to acknowledge all our many obligations to publishers, organizations, colleagues, students, and other individuals. We can here only enumerate some examples of the help we have received.

For the illustrations, we are indebted, first, to The Rand Corporation for permission to reproduce the wash sketches of scientists. Mr. Kirk Ditzler, a student at Dartmouth College, prepared the line sketches of scientists and science educators. Other illustrative materials were provided by the U.S. Department of Health, Education and Welfare, and the U.S. Atomic Energy Commission.

For examples of teachers' instructional materials we thank Mr. A. G. Applegarth; Mr. Nathaniel Hoff; Mr. Paul Johnson; Mr. M. Eugene Mittel; Mr. Fred Moore; Miss Loretta Olver; Mrs. Darnall Schardl; and Mr. Jay A. Young.

For examples of student responses to class assignments we thank Miss Mary Lynn Hendrix, Miss Jane Levine, Mr. William Murray, and Miss Charlene Woodburn, all of whom have been students in the public schools of Montgomery County, Maryland.

For the textual quotations appearing in the book we are indebted to the following publishers, organizations, and individuals: American

v

Association for the Advancement of Science; American Association of Physics Teachers; American Book Company; Division of Chemical Education, American Chemical Society; American Institute of Physics; Mr. Bernard Barber; Biological Sciences Curriculum Study; P. Blakiston and Sons Publishing Co.; Central Association of Science and Mathematics Teachers; Chemical Bond Approach Project; Chemical Education Material Study; *The Clearing House;* Teachers College, Columbia University; Mr. William H. Cornog; Earth Science Curriculum Project; Mr. V. E. Eaton; Educational Services Incorporated; Elementary School Science Program; Elementary School Science Project; Mr. Frederick L. Ferris, Jr.; Frontiers of Science Foundation of Oklahoma, Inc.; Harvard University Press; *Journal of Research in Science Teaching;* Arthur D. Little, Inc.; Mr. J. Stanley Marshall; McGraw-Hill Book Company; Mr. Julius Sumner Miller; National Aeronautics and Space Administration; The National Association of Biology Teachers; National Association for Research in Science Teaching; National Association of Secondary-School Principals; National Science Teachers Association; National Society for the Study of Education; Mr. Harold K. Schilling; Scholastic Magazines, Inc.; *School Activities Magazine; Science Education; Science Education News;* Science Service, Inc.; *Scientific American;* Mr. M. W. P. Strandberg; Mr. Joseph Turner; The University of Chicago Press; Mr. Jerome B. Wiesner; Mr. Ralph P. Winch; and Mr. Stanley P. Wyatt.

We are further grateful to the following students for their contributions toward making this a science teaching methods textbook of value: Mr. Wade Biggs, Miss Donna Hardy, and Mr. Robert Smoot. These people evoked the early spirit of the book, as well as the title.

For his reading of the page proof, we are indebted to Mr. James Miers.

And for assistance by no means limited to matters editorial, we thank Honora Obourn and Ruth Woodburn.

JOHN H. WOODBURN
ELLSWORTH S. OBOURN

CONTENTS

II

GETTING THE FEEL
OF WORKING IN SCIENCE 115

III

PURSUIT OF SCIENCE IN CLASSROOM
AND TEACHING LABORATORY 165

The pursuit of science springs from a striving which the mind is impelled to follow, a questioning that will not be suppressed.

—Sir Arthur Eddington

Introduction

We have discovered that it is actually an aid in the search for knowledge to understand the nature of the knowledge we seek.[1]

Sir Arthur Eddington 1939

I confess that I do not see much danger to learning in giving the prime emphasis to method. By emphasis upon method, I mean upon critical *method—upon criteria of evidence, norms of validity, rules of consistency, on "how we actually think" and "how we ought to think" in whatever field of study we want students to be informed about.*[2]

Sidney Hook 1959

The common concern with teaching students the "right answers" not only fails to give proper emphasis to science

1

as a powerful means of seeking understanding but it also fails to make meaningful many of the concepts and generalizations that are taught. Concepts gain meaning to the student as he uses them in trying to find in a complex and unordered phenomenon some few significant aspects that can be studied more intensively. Generalizations gain meaning to him as he uses them in seeking to explain some perplexing phenomenon. A major objective, then, in science teaching is to help students develop the ability to carry on the whole process of scientific inquiry, including raising questions, identifying particular problems growing out of these questions, suggesting possible explanations, making relevant observations and collecting relevant data, interpreting the data, and restating the explanations and the new questions and problems that result from this cycle of inquiry.[3]

Ralph W. Tyler 1960

To many it is not knowledge but the quest for knowledge that gives the greater interest to thought—to travel hopefully is better than to arrive.[4]

Sir James Jeans 1942

Hitherto the nature and methods of original scientific inquiry have been insufficiently studied, and the success achieved in it has, therefore, been attributed too much to accident, to strong imagination, and exceptional natural ability; and too little to the less brilliant qualifications of steady thought, self-development, industry, and perseverance. No pretence, however, is made to impart by extraneous aid the faculties of imagination and invention, and the quick preception of difference and resemblance. But whilst great aptitude for scientific discovery must, like any other rare and peculiar ability, be born in the man, it is certain that it may, like those other natural abilities, be assisted by advice and developed by experience; and to supply such advice is one of the objects of this treatise.[5]

G. Gore 1878

The student should be disabused of the common misconception that a collection of facts is either the beginning or the goal of scientific inquiry. Emphasis must be placed on the theoretical motivations that underlie the gathering of data, upon the selective character of observation and experiment, and upon the need to analyze and interpret the primary data of observation before they can be admitted as significant fact. Moreover, the student should be made to recognize that the concepts to which he is introduced have not been obtained by a process of simple abstraction from empirical data, but that they are intellectual creations, often suggested by the data, and are the products of a constructive imagination.[6]

Ernest Nagel 1959

Traditionally, teachers of the sciences have claimed that their courses have taught the students "rigorous thinking" or "creative" or "critical" thinking, or "the scientific method." P. W. Bridgman speaks for many of us when he writes that there is no such thing as the scientific method, that in so far as there is any method to science at all, it consists of nothing more than doing "one's damnedest with one's mind, no holds barred."[7]

I. Bernard Cohen 1952

Surely there is little doubt that some parts of the so-called "scientific method" can be defined. . . . But there is usually an almost total neglect of the really challenging aspects of the scientific endeavor—the "simple" matter of recognizing what the problem is, the "simple" operations of framing reasonable hypotheses and of devising "unequivocal" experiments by which to test these hypotheses. There is so much here of art, rather than of science in the usual sense, that it is difficult, if not impossible, to include these considerations in what is commonly regarded as "the scientific method." Yet it is just the sense of these creative operations —the nuances that engender them, their subtlety and their strengths and weaknesses—that must be conveyed to the student if he is to acquire any appreciation of the nature of science.[8]

Leonard K. Nash 1952

A student does not learn to "learn for himself" merely by being told to do so. . . . Hence, the enquiring classroom is one in which the questions asked are not designed primarily to discover whether the student knows the answer but to exemplify to the student the sorts of questions he must ask of the materials he studies and how to find the answers.[9]

Joseph J. Schwab 1962

3

Perhaps the best way for the authors to introduce the subject of this
book is to explain why they have given it the title it bears. It deals with
the tactics and strategy of classroom and laboratory instruction in
science, hence the words *teaching* and *science*. The key word in the
title is *pursuit*. This word was chosen after long and serious contemplation because it conveys both content and process meanings. Thus, this
book attempts to bring the reader's concept of the total scientific endeavor into a perspective that will lead directly toward the development
of efficient, effective science-teaching procedures, procedures that promise not only to develop within the minds of students an appreciation of
the knowledge and inventions that are the results of science, but also
to cultivate the processes of inquiry and to practice the modes of
thought and abilities of the mind that seem to be peculiarly exercised
in the pursuit of scientific knowledge and inventions.

To sense the rationale within which the book has been written, the
reader is asked to imagine the pursuit of science as taking place inside
a sparkling crystal ball. In this ball, generations of scientists and science
teachers enthusiastically invest their lives in the pursuit of their individual facets of sicence. The ball is furnished with intricate apparatus,
and the people seem to possess a highly functional yet somewhat specialized vocabulary. There is a pattern in the way the people go about
their work, and their whole activity radiates an air of importance.
Imagine now having a vantage point from which to view the whole of
this transparent ball—a view of the whole of science, its spirit, the
interrelation of its parts, the patterns in its structure and methods, and
its fundamental significance.

Obviously, no such crystal ball exists, nor can this book or any
other single volume provide the vantage point to serve its imagined
purpose. Each reader must devise his own vantage point from which
to construct his own image. This book can only point to and present
one interpretation of some of the various concepts of the scientific
endeavor that have been provided by historians, philosophers, logi-
cians, and other types of scholars who have attempted to examine and
identify various features of the total pursuit of science. Thus, the
citations that introduce each section serve the very important function
of inviting the reader to seek out and study the complete works from

4

which the citations are drawn, and gain a knowledge of those authors' concepts of science. From this study may come an image of what science really is.

Concurrently with attempting to make a theoretical examination of the pursuit of science, the reader is encouraged to make his own excursion into science. Examples are discussed in which other people have made their initial attempts at finding or selecting problems for investigation, elaborating working hypotheses, planning experiments or other appropriate investigations, and reporting the results of their efforts. These discussions are doubly of interest to science teachers: they not only illustrate various features of science as a human endeavor but also provide a preview of the kind of guidance young people may be expected to need during their early ventures into science.

The final section of this book cites examples of classroom practices and procedures wherein special attention is given to the teaching of science as a human endeavor or pursuit. The argument here is that solutions to pedagogical problems can be derived from one's comprehension of the scientific endeavor. The authors have built into this book the thesis that the methods of science can suggest the designs for the science teacher's lectures, his use of teaching films, his lecture demonstrations, laboratory exercises, or whatever other aids to learning or types of lessons he chooses to use. Class-motivating techniques, for example, are sought in the motives and drives that keep astronomers glued to their telescopes, geologists digging in the earth's rocks, psychologists trapped in their learning mazes, and physicists, biologists —in fact, all kinds of scientists—locked in their laboratories. Similarly, blueprints for lesson plans are sought in the pathways that scientists create as they seek adequate descriptions of phenomena; design, conduct, and interpret experiments; and attempt to relate the results of their experiments to the ultimate welfare and intelligence of mankind.

The examples of classroom practices and procedures that are included in Section III, although drawn from actual teaching situations, are not presented as finished formulas. Each reader is encouraged to build on these examples and to invent or adapt practices and procedures appropriate for his own lecture hall, laboratory, or classroom. By developing lessons that are true to the spirit of science and consistent with its methods, teachers whose fortunate choice of a career permits them to initiate young people into the intellectual pursuit known as science, should come to know the full dimensions of their career and to enjoy the great satisfactions to be derived therefrom.

References

1. Sir Arthur Eddington. *The Philosophy of Physical Science.* Ann Arbor, Mich.: University of Michigan Press, 1958, paperback edition, p. 5. First published 1939.

2. Sidney Hook. *Education in the Age of Science,* edited by Brand Blanshard. New York: Basic Books, 1959, p. 14.
3. Ralph W. Tyler. "The Behavioral Scientist Looks at the Purposes of Science Teaching," in *Rethinking Science Education,* Fifty-Ninth Yearbook, National Society for the Study of Education, 1960. Chicago: University of Chicago Press, 1960, pp. 31–32.
4. Sir James Jeans. *Physics and Philosophy.* Ann Arbor, Mich.: University of Michigan Press, 1958, p. 217. First published 1942.
5. G. Gore. *The Art of Scientific Discovery.* London: Longmans, Green & Company, 1878, p. ix.
6. Ernest Nagel. *Education in the Age of Science,* edited by Brand Blanshard. New York: Basic Books, 1959, p. 192.
7. I. Bernard Cohen. *General Education in Science,* edited by I. Bernard Cohen and Fletcher G. Watson. Cambridge, Mass.: Harvard University Press, 1952, p. 84.
8. Leonard K. Nash. *General Education in Science,* edited by I. Bernard Cohen and Fletcher G. Watson. Cambridge, Mass.: Harvard University Press, 1952, p. 99.
9. Reprinted by permission of the publisher from Joseph J. Schwab and Paul F. Brandwein, *The Teaching of Science.* Cambridge, Mass.: Harvard University Press, Copyright 1962, by the President and Fellows of Harvard College. P. 67.
10. William Whewell. *History of the Inductive Sciences.* London: John W. Parker, 1847, p. xvii.

I

THE SPIRIT,
STRUCTURE,
AND FUNCTION
OF SCIENCE

Assuming that the reader has already studied one or more branches
of science, he knows the vital role the scientific enterprise plays in
the modern world. The human enterprise of science can advance
no more rapidly than it is caused to by the people who pursue it.
Unless each generation includes an adequate number of young
people who are imbued with the spirit of science, trained in its
methods, and aware of its function in a culture, science cannot
advance.

To teach enables one not only to know the satisfactions of gaining knowledge but also those satisfactions which come from arous-
ing interests and developing traits which enable others to gain
knowledge. It has been said often that next to being able to say
a discovery is one's own is to be able to say the discovery was made
by one's student. The teacher enjoys the opportunity not only to
guide his students over memory-rich, well-travelled roads of science
but also into the uncharted trails toward discoveries yet to be
achieved.

Science teachers enjoy an extremely decisive role in the total

7

endeavor of science, and it is the intent of this book to help both new and established teachers explore and enjoy the satisfactions of the full dimensions of this role.

1

Science–
Its Characteristics
and Aims

Science is the attempt to make the chaotic diversity of our sense experience correspond to a logically uniform system of thought.[1]

A. Einstein   1940

Science is the interpretation of nature and man is the interpretor.[2]

G. Gore   1878

Science is the study of those judgments concerning which universal agreement can be obtained.[3]

Norman Campbell   1921

In the sciences, thought is progressive: the later stage corrects the earlier and includes the truth of the earlier.[4]

Report of the Harvard Committee 1945

Nature, with all her regularities and irregularities, might have been just as real even if there were no men to observe and to study her. But there could have been no science without human beings, or beings like them. It is the spirit of man brooding over the stream of natural events that has given birth to science.[5]

A. Wolf 1925

Science . . . leads us to classifications and systems independent of the individual thinker, to sequences and laws admitting of no play room for individual fancy. . . . That form of popular science which merely recites the results of investigations, which merely communicates useful knowledge, is from this standpoint bad science, or no science at all. . . . If any such work gives a description of phenomena that appeals to his imagination rather than to his reason, then it is bad science. The first aim of any genuine work of science, however popular, ought to be the presentation of such a classification of facts that the reader's mind is irresistibly led to acknowledge a logical sequence—a law which appeals to the reason before it captivates the imagination. Let us be quite sure that whenever we come across a conclusion in a scientific work which does not flow from the classification of facts, or which is not directly stated by the author to be an assumption, then we are dealing with bad science. Good science will always be intelligible to the logically trained mind, if that mind can read and translate the language in which science is written.[6]

Karl Pearson 1892

Science is used so loosely these days to account for all manner of things—from the why of nature to the despair of the poet, from the highest reaches of man's intellect to the deadening of humanistic culture, from the preservation of civilization to its destruction . . . it is not surprising that control of nature is frequently confused with man's intellectual desire to understand it . . . the utility of science looms so large in the affairs of men as to shadow its esthetic values.[7]

Morris H. Shamos 1961

The edifice of science not only requires material, but also a plan . . . without the material, the plan alone is but a castle in the air—a mere possibility; whilst the material without a plan is but useless matter. . . . In the work of science, the artisan, architect, and creator are very often one and the same individual; but sometimes, as in other walks of life, there is a difference between them; sometimes the plan is preconceived, sometimes it follows the preparation and accumulation of the raw material. Free access to the edifice of science is not only allowed to those who devised the plan, worked out the detailed drawings, prepared the materials, or piled up the brickwork, but also to all those who are desirous of making a close acquaintance with the plan, and wish to avoid dwelling in the vaults or in the garrets where the useless lumber is stored.

Knowing how contented, free, and joyful is life in the realm of science, one fervently wishes that many would enter its portals.[8]

Dmitri Mendeleev   1868

Perhaps the greatest injustice that can be done to science is to regard it merely as a collection of facts, and the practice of science as little more than the routine accumulation of minutiae. It is true that science deals with hard, inflexible facts, but it has also to do with very general ideas and abstract principles; and it is the co-ordination of these ideas and observed facts that is the essence of modern science. Facts alone do not constitute a science. Nature study *is not the same as the* study of nature.[9]

Morris H. Shamos   1960

Whoever rejects faith in the reality of atoms and electrons or the electro-magnetic nature of light waves or the identity of heat and motion, cannot be found guilty of a logical or empirical contradiction; but he will find it difficult to advance physical knowledge.[10]

Max Planck   1913

For indeed it is one of the lessons of the history of science that each age steps on the shoulders of the ages which have gone before. The value of each age is not its own, but is in part, in large part, a debt to its forerunners. And this age of ours if, like its predecessors, it can boast of something of which it is proud, would, could it read the future, doubtless find also much of which it would be ashamed.[11]

Sir Michael Foster   1901

11

A WORKING DEFINITION

It seems appropriate to begin an examination of the pursuit of science by stating a definition of science. Actually, to comprehend the meaning of science is the ultimate goal of this study, and an attempt to define science at the initiation of its study can yield only a working definition which, hopefully, will point toward this ultimate goal.

Science is that human endeavor that seeks to describe, with ever-increasing accuracy, the events and circumstances that occur or exist within our natural environment. Science, successfully pursued, yields a minimum number of natural laws, which can be seen operating in all of nature's phenomena. To recognize these laws in action reduces events and circumstances in nature to orderly, predictable occurrences. By this recognition, mankind finds in nature no cause for abject homage or terrifying fear but faces his environment with understanding, appreciation, and increasing power to control.

Science is one of the things men do. It is an undertaking marked by initiative, energy, boldness, dynamism, and intrepid drive. The pursuit of science refers not merely to the data acquired by the scientist but also to the means of its acquisition. The men and women of each generation who devote their lives to the pursuit of science become a part of the scientific endeavor. To these people, science becomes a way of life, and their way of life becomes an aspect of the pursuit of science—an aspect that must be included in an attempt to comprehend the total spirit, structure, and function of science.

The accuracy of any one generation's description of a phenomenon tends to be limited by the accuracy with which the phenomenon can be observed and the interrelationships between its parts and other phenomena. Each generation develops what it considers to be satisfactory descriptions of the natural phenomena that it recognizes. At the same time, each generation seems to produce a few individuals who question the adequacy of accepted descriptions of phenomena. Quite often these same individuals are prone to notice and pursue clues which lead to the identification of heretofore undescribed phenomena. Thus, science becomes a self-correcting and self-generating human endeavor.

In his pursuit of science, the scientist uses specialized tools and instruments. All too often these things become symbols of the scientific endeavor. But science is basically an intellectual activity, and its products are intellectual representations of the phenomena of nature. It is true, of course, that these intellectual representations lead almost automatically to the design of machines or the development of practices that enable mankind to predict, manage, or control the aspect of nature that is intellectually described.

Science as the Discovery of Relations

The scientist's interest in nature goes beyond the simple recital of events and circumstances precisely described. These descriptions in themselves do not constitute science so much as do the relations between occurrences in nature. These relations may be of several kinds. There are the relations between different things, between the parts of one thing, and between properties possessed or evidenced by several things. The scientist, upon discovering these relations, formulates statements that describe them. These statements become the theorems, laws, and principles of science.

Science as a Knowledge-Generating Process

Upon completion of an investigation, it is characteristic of the scientist to set his findings down in readable form for the benefit of fellow scientists and humanity in general. The treatises built in this way constitute a great monument to the inquiring mind of the scientist. Knowledge is not a gift bestowed upon mankind by some benevolent deity. Man obtains his knowledge of the universe through painstaking and often frustrating pursuit thereof.

The additions to scientific knowledge that a scientist may make are of several types. First, he may add new facts to those already known concerning an occurrence in nature. Second, there exists for the scientist a vast quantity of data collected through years of research. These data are subject to being described with increased accuracy due to improved instruments, mathematical operations, or other aids to investigation. Third, a scientist may be able to extract a heretofore-unidentified relationship between already-established facts—truly the forte of the scientist.

Almost any excursion into the underscribed realms of nature will result in increasing man's store of knowledge. The scientist is bound to learn from the venture, even if only an alertness to fruitful versus barren techniques or procedures. Usefulness is not a prerequisite to the generation of knowledge. There may be only one person who benefits immediately from a description of a bit of nature. Nevertheless, knowledge has been generated. The body of organized knowledge generated by the pursuit of science is drawn upon by the scientist during his training in science, and is useful as a jumping-off point from which he launches his own investigations.

Does the Scientist Create Science?

It has already been emphasized that science is a human endeavor. Science involves reason, imagination, and a host of other faculties that are peculiar to human beings. At the same time, it is argued that science is a discovering process that ferrets out relationships existent in nature. Thus, the question of whether man discovers or creates science arises. The question really revolves around the definition of science. If science is man's endeavor to discover, analyze, and describe the universe, then the inference is that facts, laws, and principles—the content of science—exist in nature, and the role of the scientist is that of discoverer. This interpretation seems to go too far in the direction of nominalism and can be avoided by arguing that it is the discovery, analysis, and description of nature that is truly the scientific endeavor —an endeavor that can be looked upon as the creation of science.

Science and Philosophy

There was a time when the words *science* and *philosophy* denoted practically the same intellectual endeavor. Today, common usage is likely to assign widely separated meanings to these words; nevertheless, in the minds of some people there is no complete separation between the pursuit of science and the pursuit of philosophy. Furthermore, to these people, to effect separation between the two pursuits would be detrimental to the advancement of both. Other people believe that philosophy carries so many vestiges of misdirected contemplations and internally derived misconceptions that it can have only a retarding influence on the advancement of science.

There is by no means complete agreement that science should concern itself solely with "how" events and circumstances occur in nature restricting itself to sheer descriptions of these phenomena and relegate the "why" of nature to philosophy. Nor is it agreed that the fact-centered logic of science has no counterpart in philosophical contemplations.

Distinctions between the two endeavors, science and philosophy, appear most clearly when the end products of the two endeavors are examined. Scientific investigations lead all investigators eventually to agree on the nature of that which is being investigated. Philosophy, on the other hand, does not require all philosophies to embrace identical systems. The two disciplines differ markedly in the nature of their proofs of hypotheses. In most instances, the hypotheses of philosophy are subject only to analysis by reason, whereas science combines reason with other proving procedures, principally experimentation. The statements of science that take the form of "If . . . then . . . ," when based on facts and provable by experiment, must be accepted as being valid. When statements contain words meaning "good" or "bad" or "right" or "wrong," the statements enter the domain of philosophy.

The day is past when philosophers attempted to designate great areas of human experience or whole blocks of natural phenomena as being beyond the proper realm of science. Today, no events or circumstances in nature are prohibited as the subject of scientific investigation, and, in our advanced state of civilization, the scientist and philosopher work mind-to-mind to provide truly meaningful descriptions of the universe and man's role therein. Philosophy provides critical examination of the principles, logic, and conclusions of science. Science, in turn, helps to hold philosophy close to actual human experience. The mutual interests of these two human pursuits complement each other and hold promise of giving mankind an increasingly complete and satisfying orientation to the world.

THE ROLE OF CHANCE
IN THE PURSUIT OF SCIENCE

The number of discoveries and inventions in science that have occurred unexpectedly is large enough to cause some authors to infer that sheer chance is a significant element in the pursuit of science. If chance is thought of in the language of unplanned and unexpected, the inference is not entirely inconsistent with the spirit of science. On the other hand, to embody chance in the sense of luck, fate, or fortune does seem to contradict the true nature of the scientific endeavor.

The so-called chance discovery is much more likely to occur with the trained than the untrained investigator. Such a discovery cannot be made unless the investigator notes the significance in an unplanned or unexpected observation. What might be a truly remarkable outcome of an experiment, if not anticipated, might not be recorded by an uninformed investigator, or followed with confirming experimentation. The chance discovery is most likely to be made by the scientist who persists in bench work, especially if he experiments with a wide variety of ideas in novel ways. To be sensitive to unexpected clues, the scientist must be able to absorb and retrieve his knowledge without having it too firmly locked into fixed ideas. Equally essential is the habit of contemplating even the most minor variations from the expected results.

It is the unusual that happens in the course of a routine experiment that leads to an unusual hypothesis. If a new fact is revolutionary, it could scarcely have been foreseen in the light of past knowledge. In this sense, the investigator should solicit the unexpected observation and cherish it when it occurs—not as one would woo Lady Luck, but by creating sensitive systems in which clues to subtle and elusive phenomena might be discernible.

What are sometimes publicized as being chance discoveries could well have arisen as the normal outcome of mental activity. The point where conscious and subconscious mental exertion merge has not been clearly marked, and if it is true that mental activity does include these two types of contemplation, sudden and dramatic conversion from subconscious to conscious mental activity could easily be interpreted as a function of chance.

Human nature being what it is, there is a kind of motivation gained from feeling that almost anyone may join the fortunate people who have enjoyed the fruits of "accidental" discoveries. Such a feeling approaches sheer nonsense, however, if a person who has enjoyed good luck in one endeavor or another decides to try his luck at science. It is interesting, in looking for the true role of chance in the pursuit of science, to identify the hypotheses actually being investigated at the time of such discoveries: usually these hypotheses suggest the high degree of training and experience possessed by the men or women to whom such "accidents" are likely to happen. The characteristics, knowledge, and skills possessed by these people must not be lost sight of.

For Discussion and Further Study

1. It is said that truth does not change, it is man's conception of truth that changes. Is this saying consistent or inconsistent with the authors' definition of science?

2. If science is a duality consisting of product and of process, are there unifying concepts that would integrate the parts?

3. Are there sharp differences between the concepts of science quoted in the introduction of this chapter?

4. What issue underlies the argument regarding science's being a discovery versus a creative or inventive process?

5. It is said that only the very young and the very old scientist tends to philosophize. Does the saying have validity or significance?

6. Analyze a discovery or invention that seems to have been influenced by chance, and document your interpretation of the role chance played.

7. What attitude should a teacher take toward students, colleagues, supervisors, or parents who insist that science is the "accumulated knowledge of the ages" and any approach to teaching science as anything else is soft-minded?

8. Contemplate the probable effectiveness of overt versus subtle efforts to inculcate the spirit, structure, and function of science in the minds of students.

9. What opportunities exist in typical communities to give students glimpses of the spirit, structure, and function of science?

References

1. Albert Einstein. "Considerations Concerning the Fundamentals of Theoretical Physics," *Science,* **9** (1940), p. 487.

2. G. Gore. *The Art of Scientific Discovery*. London: Longmans, Green & Company, 1878, p. 2.
3. Norman Campbell. *What is Science?* New York: Dover Publications, 1952, p. 27. First published 1921.
4. Harvard Committee. *General Education in a Free Society*. Cambridge, Mass.: Harvard University Press, 1945, p. 62.
5. A. Wolf. *Essentials of Scientific Method*. New York: Macmillan Company, 1925, p. 17.
6. Karl Pearson. *The Grammar of Science*. New York: Meridian Books, 1957, p. 10. First published in 1892; revised in 1900; and published in final edition in 1911.
7. Morris H. Shamos. "Science for Citizens," *Saturday Review*, 44 (September 16, 1961), pp. 68–69.
8. Dmitri Mendeleev. *The Principles of Chemistry*, 1868. Quoted by the Rand Corporation, *Scientific American*, 204 (June 1961), p. 2.
9. Morris H. Shamos. "Science and the Humanities," in *Rethinking Science Education*, Fifty-Ninth Yearbook, National Society for the Study of Education. Chicago: University of Chicago Press, 1960, p. 5.
10. Max Planck. Quoted in William H. George, *The Scientist in Action*. London: William and Newgate, 1936, p. 271.
11. Sir Michael Foster, *History of Philosophy*, 1901. Quoted by the Rand Corporation, *Scientific American*, 200 (June 1959), p. 2.

2

The Domain of Science

Religion belongs to that realm that is inviolable before the law of causation and therefore closed to science. The scientist as such must recognize the value of religion as such, no matter what may be its forms, so long as it does not make the mistake of opposing its own dogmas to the fundamental law upon which scientific research is based, namely, the sequence of cause and effect in all external phenomena. In conjunction with the question of the relations between religion and science, I might also say that those forms of religion which have a nihilist attitude to life are out of harmony with the scientific outlook and contradictory to its principles. All denial of life's value for itself and for its own sake is a denial of the world of human thought, and therefore in the last analysis a denial of the true foundation not only of science but also of religion. I think that most scientists would agree to this, and would raise their hands against religious nihilism as destructive of science itself.

There can never be any real opposition between religion and science; for the one is the complement of the other. Every serious and reflective person realizes, I think, that the religious element in his nature must be recognized and cultivated if all the powers of the human soul are to act

18

*together in perfect balance and harmony. Science enhances
the moral values of life, because it furthers a love of truth
and reverence—love of truth displaying itself in the constant endeavor to arrive at a more exact knowledge of the
world of mind and matter around us, and reverence, because every advance in knowledge brings us face to face
with the mystery of our own being.*[1]

Max Planck   1932

*There are no distinct natural boundaries that divide the
sciences, not even between the physical and biological sciences; yet the accumulated knowledge of a century ago
was already so vast as to compel specialization. As a result
the branch of knowledge once termed "natural philosophy"
has been split into a number of seemingly independent
sciences. Each has its own fundamentals, its own terminol-
ogy and techniques, and to some extent its own Weltansicht
or world view. Each is so demanding that its scholars find
it extremely difficult, except in rare instances, to move effectively from one scientific field to another.*

*. . . Actually there is a structure to science—a logical
sequence that recognizes certain first principles as common
to all of science yet acknowledges varying degrees of complexity among natural phenomena. In this sense physics,
dealing as it does with most basic kind of phenomena, is
the "simplest" of the sciences. At the opposite extreme, concerned with matter in its most complex state of organization and at the highest level of sophistication, lie the life
sciences. Between the two fall other physical sciences such
as chemistry, geology, meteorology, and various branches or
combinations of these.*[2]

Morris H. Shamos   1961

*Science is concerned with the general conditions which are
observed to regulate physical phenomena; whereas religion
is wholly wrapped up in the contemplation of moral and
aesthetic values.*[3]

Alfred North Whitehead   1925

*For I agree wholeheartedly with the critics of science in the
belief that the training of generations of scientists in mere
science, without making them familiar with the world of
human behavior, would be harmful to the cause of civiliza-*

19

tion. Whether we like it or not, scientists will participate more and more in the leadership of society in the future. Also there is hardly a doubt by now that the contribution of the scientists to a political life has been more on the side of peace and tolerance than have the contributions of the students of law or government or, for that matter, of philosophy proper.[4]

Philipp Frank   1949

Science in itself furnishes none of the ends of action; in so far as the knowledge of the scientist is concerned, it is immaterial whether what we know of high explosives is used to build a great reservoir to make the desert blossom as the rose, or to construct giant shells to snuff out the lives of an entire city. As a man the scientist may, nay, must, make some preference; but the grounds for that preference are not to be found in physics.[5]

Columbia Associates in Philosophy   1923

The creative spirit is one and indivisible. It cannot live and work under servitude or external control. . . . If we are right in holding that the most urgent business of our age is to devise better laws of conduct in the arts of human government, within and beyond the limits of nationality, success depends upon stimulating in as many spots as possible the largest number and variety of independent thinkers, constructing and maintaining among them the best conditions of free intercourse and cooperation and finally enabling their creative thought to play freely in criticism and in reform upon the existing modes of political and economic life.[6]

John Atkinson Hobson   1926

THE SCOPE OF SCIENCE

An attempt to look into the total array of interrelated and overlapping human endeavors and to construct boundaries of the domain of science necessitates arbitrary reference to the definition of science. Recalling the working definition of science developed in the opening pages of this section, science cannot be pursued where men are absent. Expressed positively, the domain of science is characterized by the presence of and, thus, may exist wherever mankind exists. Only intel-

lectual representations of the phenomena of nature are attempted in
the pursuit of science. From this is derived another of the boundaries of
the domain of science: namely, the pursuit must be intellectual. The
third boundary prescribed by its definition is that science limits its
interests to naturally occurring phenomena.

Each of these derived boundaries is individually exclusive. Dealing
with a natural phenomenon in manner other than intellectual goes
beyond the domain of science. Such an endeavor could be art, music,
literature, technology, or other, equally valuable activity, but it would
not be science. Furthermore, only those intellectual treatments of natural phenomena in which the treatment is consistent with the rigor
imposed by the methods of science can be included in the domain of
science.

The boundary between naturally occurring events and circumstances
and those that are contrived by or develop from man's activities, is less
apparent. This boundary is easily described when considering phenomena in earth and astronomical science, in fact, the whole array of
physical sciences. This is equally true in the biological sciences until
those phenomena are considered in which man, either as a species or
as an individual, plays a significant role. Nothing more than arbitrary
decisions allocate many phenomena either to the domain of natural or
to the domain of social sciences. Obviously, phenomena that arise from
the interaction of man's activities with purely naturally occurring phenomena can be allocated to either domain. For these borderline phenomena, a scientist knows he is approaching the boundary of his
domain when the phenomenon being investigated tends to take on
more of the characteristics of those that arise from the interaction of
men with men than from the interaction of man with nature.

Social, political, ethical, and similar phenomena are simply beyond
the domain of science. This does not mean that their domains are any
less important than is the domain of science, but it does mean that
their pursuits are different human endeavors. Men who pursue these
phenomena are likely to be sensitive to a different complex of motivations and to be adept at different kinds of mental processes. Furthermore, successful pursuit of social and ethical phenomena yields satisfactions which differ from those which derive from the description and
interpretation of purely naturally occurring events and circumstances.

FIELDS OF SCIENCE AND
HOW THEY ARE RELATED

Nature is not compartmentalized. The fields of science are simply
groupings of phenomena, and the divisions are largely conventional.
The broad scope of science has prompted mankind to divide it into

fields or branches in which the phenomena are sufficiently related to permit one man to achieve a satisfying degree of competence and familiarity with the phenomena that are prescribed or assigned to the field; the resources of even the most profoundly gifted single scientist are limited.

However, although each phenomeon is likely to require specialized instruments and procedures for its investigation, there are more similarities than differences in the tactics and strategy of investigations ordinarily associated with the various fields of science. The geologist, for example, shares many of the traits of the astronomer. All scientists tend to exercise the same powers of the mind during the pursuit of what would appear to be widely diverse phenomena. The same satisfactions can be enjoyed from constructing an adequate description of an event or circumstance regardless of what realm of nature is the predominant scene of the phenomenon.

SCIENCE FOR ITS OWN SAKE VERSUS SCIENCE IN THE SERVICE OF MANKIND

It is scarcely in keeping with the spirit of science to place science in opposition to technology. Although Archimedes may have been expressing a point of view of his generation when he said, "The work of an engineer and every art that ministers to the needs of life are ignoble and vulgar," such a point of view is difficult to defend in modern society.

In the seventeenth and eighteenth centuries, when the scientist was likely to be his own lens grinder or toolmaker, he was at once scientist and technologist. Today when the technologist comprehends the fundamental goals, basic assumptions, principle operating conceptions, and general methodology typically subscribed to by the scientist, he, too, is at once scientist and technologist. To seek to know only for the sake of knowing how condemns one to the role of technologist, but to become intrigued by a puzzling event or circumstance and abandon oneself to the sheer joy of discovery can change this label to *scientist*. Thus it is more the attitude of the investigator than the nature of his investigation that distinguishes the two mutually interdependent human endeavors, science and technology.

THE PROGRESS AND FUTURE OF SCIENCE

Science does not seem to progress uniformly with the passage of time; nor do all groups and nationalities of mankind advance science at the same rate. It is easier, however, to make this observation than it is to isolate the events and circumstances that advance or retard the progress of science.

The greatest single factor that affects the advance or retardation of the pursuit of science is the subtle, pervasive mental resistance to new ideas. The reluctance to allow a new idea to displace a cherished belief is all too familiar, not only to the creator of the new idea but also to the people who have promoted and perpetuated belief in the ideas being replaced.

New facts are not easily accepted even when they can be correlated with the existing body of accepted beliefs. Premature discoveries are usually neglected and lost or, at best, subjected to excessive skepticism and conservatism. This is true even when the new idea does not overtly threaten entrenched authority or vested interests either intellectual or material. Obscurantism and authoritarianism are not yet dead in many of the evironments in which science operates, and the pursuit of science in these environments requires diplomacy and tact if the pursuit is to advance.

The rate of growth of science seems to be closely related to the incidence of original thinking, to the invention of improved means of observing and measuring the features of a phenomenon, and the invention of more comprehensive or precise mathematical procedures. Abnormally large increases in the rate of growth of science sometimes follow the announcement of a single theory or conceptual theme. These bursts of growth suggest that the scientific endeavor is fed by a more or less constant force and the product of the endeavor, if temporarily dammed up by a particularly resistant phenomenon, will burst forth when an adequate description of this phenomenon is finally achieved.

For Discussion and Further Study

1. To what extent do each of the following provide valid boundaries of science: (a) Science exists wherever mankind exists; (b) Science's representations of the phenomena of nature are uniquely intellectual; (c) The interaction of man and nature marks the boundary between natural and social science.

2. Is Max Planck realistic when he claims there can be no genuine opposition between science and religion?

3. Are the motivations that drive people to pursue social, ethical, or political phenomena different from those that seem to drive people in the pursuit of natural phenomena?

4. To what extent would one expect to find similarities or differences in the tactics and strategy used in meteorology versus astronomy, physics versus space biology, chemistry versus physics, zoology versus paleontology, or physics versus oceanography?

5. Is the degree of scientific literacy of the public mind a significant factor in determining the advancement of science?

6. How can a teacher know when unprepared or misguided students are coaxing him to leave his subject?

7. What criteria determine whether or not class time should be used to promote or administer a community-sponsored project?

8. What significance do the ideas expressed by Morris H. Shamos have for relationships between the sciences in school science departments?

9. Should teachers clarify, emphasize, or de-emphasize the apparent boundaries between the fields of science?

References

1. Max Planck. *Where is Science Going?* New York: W. W. Norton & Company, 1932, p. 168.
2. Morris H. Shamos. "Science for Citizens," *Saturday Review,* 44 (September 16, 1961), pp. 68–69.
3. Alfred North Whitehead. *Science and the Modern World.* New York: The Macmillan Company, 1925, p. 258.
4. Philipp Frank. *Modern Science and Its Philosophy.* Cambridge, Mass.: Harvard University Press, 1949, pp. 260–61.
5. Columbia Associates in Philosophy. *An Introduction to Reflective Thinking.* Boston: Houghton Mifflin Company, 1923, p. 214.
6. John Atkinson Hobson. *Free Thought in the Social Sciences,* 1926. Quoted by the Rand Corporation, *Scientific American,* 205 (September 1961), p. 2.

3

The Characteristics
of Scientists

Science is the creation of scientists and every scientific advance bears somehow the mark of the man who made it. . . . The creative scientist, whatever his field, is very deeply involved emotionally and personally in his work, and . . . he himself is his own most essential tool.[1]

Anne Roe   1961

The philosopher should be a man willing to listen to every suggestion, but determined to judge for himself. He should not be biased by appearances; have no favorite hypothesis; be of no school; and in doctrine have no master. He should not be a respecter of persons but of things. Truth should be his primary object. If to these qualities be added industry he may indeed go and hope to walk within the veil of the temple of Nature.[2]

Michael Faraday   1791–1867

True philosophers, who are only eager for truth and knowledge, never regard themselves as already so thoroughly in-

formed, but that they welcome further information from whomsoever and from wheresoever it may come; nor are they so narrow minded as to imagine any of the arts or sciences transmitted to us by the ancients in such a state of forwardness or completeness that nothing is left for the ingenuity and industry of others. On the contrary, very many maintain that all we know is still infinitely less than all that still remains unknown.[3]

William Harvey 1628

The primary qualities of research workers are those of character; innate creativeness, a flair for and a deep belief in the processes of investigation and the worth of investigation as a career; curiosity; integrity; dependability; endurance. These can be recognized only through personal acquaintanceship of an indefinite duration and can seldom be fully appreciated except by men who share the same characteristics.[4]

C. P. Haskins 1948

Next in importance to the skilful use of a gifted mind in research comes dexterous employment of the human hand. To the mental qualifications of scientific knowledge, imagination, and invention, it is almost indispensable to add aptitude in mechanical matters, and cleverness in experimental manipulation. Great manipulative ability can be acquired only by long practice, which should be commenced at an early age. . . . In scientific study also, as in other abstruse meditations, the mind soon becomes exhausted by intense thinking, but is usually relieved by preparing and making experiments.[5]

G. Gore 1878

If any student comes to me and says he wants to be useful to mankind and go into research to alleviate human suffering, I invariably advise him to go, rather, into charity. Research wants egotists, real egotists, who seek their own pleasure and satisfaction, but find it in solving the puzzles of nature. . . . A scientific researcher has to be attracted by these blank spots on the map of human knowledge, and if need be, be willing to give his life to fill them in.

As for myself, I like only basic problems, and could

26

characterize my own research by telling you that, when I settled in Woods Hole and took up fishing, I always used an enormous hook. I was convinced that I would catch nothing anyway, and I thought it much more exciting not to catch a big fish than not to catch a small one.[6]

Albert Szent-Gyorgi 1961

The strong liking for turning disorder into order carries such individuals through the searching period which their tolerance for ambiguity permits them to enter. The strong egos . . . permit regression to prelogical forms of thought without serious fear of failure to get back to logical ones. Preoccupation with things and ideas rather than with people is obviously characteristic of natural scientists, and even of some social scientists. . . . To understand what he does, one must try to know what his work means to him. The chances are that he does not know or care to know. Indeed he does not need to know. We do.[7]

Anne Roe 1961

Personally I am inclined to agree with Schopenhauer in thinking that one of the strongest motives that lead people to give their lives to art and science is the urge to flee from everyday life, with its drab and deadly dullness, and thus to unshackle the chains of one's own transient desires, which supplant one another in an interminable succession so long as the mind is fixed on the horizon of daily environment.[8]

Albert Einstein 1932

It seems to be characteristic of the research temperament that during peak periods of intensely concentrated effort— peaks which may last for a year, or more in rare cases— normally sociable, percipient individuals become increasingly shy and retiring. The ability of any man to make contacts freely and graciously is likely to be seriously curtailed during such periods of severe mental application, and his laboratory director should protect and aid him during such times.[9]

C. P. Haskins 1948

HOW AUTHORS
SEE THE SCIENTISTS

Not yet has there been identified a precise set of traits of character that are adequate to distinguish scientists from their fellowmen. Similarly, it is impossible to define a combination of characteristics that will convert the would-be or pseudo scientist into a truly creative, effective scientist. There are, however, some qualities and traits which are very likely to be considered whenever the behavior of scientists is being discussed.

Factors most commonly mentioned in connection with the motivation of the scientist include an insatiable curiosity, inquisitiveness about natural phenomena, an interest in data for their own sake, and a desire to organize data into laws or qualified statements of uniformity with the, perhaps, remote hope that these data will contribute to human welfare.

Another point of view divides scientific workers into three categories, with each category suggesting a motivating factor. The naturalist seeks knowledge purely for its own sake. It is sufficient for him to find the satisfactions he feels at each discovery, and he doesn't seem to care if his findings have any value beyond that which he derives from them. The iconoclast, the breaker of images, is one who is rebelling against authority, trying to prove the old idols false. He desires to convince others of the truth revealed to him. The third type includes most of the men of science: these are the men and women who, by critical inquiry into the origin of nature's strengths and weaknesses, hope to discover the means of describing, interpreting, and, perhaps, subduing nature.

Few discussions of the characteristics of scientists fail to mention fertile inventiveness, strong imagination, or other elements of creativeness. Furthermore, scientists, are invariably described as being knowledgeable, enlightened, informed, and capable of exercising sound judgment and prudent foresight. They possess a high level of mental energy. There is general agreement that scientists are capable of high degrees of perseverance, but for some scientists, the characteristic of patience is less appropriately applied than would be the characteristic of an almost frantic impatience.

Although biographers are prone to dramatize and glamourize the scientist, especially when writing for a popular or semi-popular audience, their writings are worthy of some consideration by those who would attempt to characterize scientists. The paragraphs which follow are drawn from this source.

The scientist admits the limits of his knowledge and the arbitrary nature of many of his concepts and definitions. He is not so prone to exaggerate nor so quick to form opinions. He is not sure he is always right and sometimes not sure he is ever right. Seldom is he self-satisfied or happy-go-lucky. Seldom do we find a scientist who is an egotist engrossed in dreams of self-grandeur and importance, and never does he play upon his inadequacy to comprehend scientific material.

When selecting data, the scientist has powers to cull the important from the unimportant, the slanted from the unprejudiced, be it in the laboratory or in a newspaper. He is willing to probe things that may make "right-thinking" people uncomfortable. He shies away from dogma. He tries sometimes to rise above his prejudices. He depends on fact and not fabrication. He hates untruth and half-truths. He is determined not to jump to conclusions and retains skepticism toward conclusions based on one or a few observations. He is willing to change an opinion or conclusion if later evidence shows it to be wrong.

The scientist would like other people to think for themselves. He prefers to gather his own facts, but is willing to use facts obtained by others. He respects other people's ideas, opinions, and ways of life even though they differ from his own.

The scientist is interested in seeing the overall unity of the universe, the relation of things one to another. He is actively curious about the world in which he lives. He admires but is not swallowed up by the complexity of the vast world of which he is but a small portion. He possesses a broad and often comprehensive perspective of the world. Seldom, if ever, is he superstitious or fatalistic in his explanations.

The scientist is favorable toward change if he considers it a change for the better. He does not rush to repair any chinks that may develop in his prejudices or hallowed traditions. He is not a slave to habit, nor does he exhibit a tendency to take things for granted unless they are established as assumptions basic to some pursuit.

The scientist is capable of abstract thinking and is not likely to panic when confronted with a tough problem.

HOW SCIENTISTS SEE THEMSELVES

How scientists see themselves has been explored by Harrison G. Gough.[10] He believes that "it is a matter of common observation in most fields of endeavor where high-level or professional talents are involved, e.g., in music, writing, athletics, etc., that stylistic differences as well as competence differences exist among practitioners." To identify these differences among research scientists, Gough assembled a list of phrases and statements that would encompass the range of approaches found among working scientists and would delineate the essential differences between one man and another. He admits that his conclusions remain, at best, subjective and inferential. It is equally inferential that any group of people can be compartmentalized. Gough's work does, however, provide a tentative and probable description of eight types of research scientists. These types are:

TYPE 1: THE ZEALOT. This man is dedicated to research activity; he sees himself as a driving, indefatigable researcher, with exceptional mathematical skills and a lively sense of curiosity; he is seen by others as tolerant, serious-minded and conscientious, but as not getting along easily with others and as not being able to "fit in" readily with others.

TYPE 2: THE INITIATOR. This man reacts quickly to research problems, and begins at once to generate ideas; he is stimulating to others and gives freely of his own time; he sees himself as being relatively free of doctrinaire bias—methodological or substantive—and as being a good "team" man. Observers describe him as ambitious, well-organized, industrious, a good leader, and efficient; they also characterize him as being relatively free of manifest anxiety, worry, and nervousness.

TYPE 3: THE DIAGNOSTICIAN. This man sees himself as a good evaluator, able to diagnose strong and weak points in a program quickly and accurately, and as having a knack for improvising quick solutions in research trouble spots; he does not have strong methodological preferences and biases, and tends not to be harsh or disparaging towards others' mistakes and errors. Observers see him as forceful and self-assured in manner, and as unselfish and free from self-seeking and narcissistic striving.

TYPE 4: THE SCHOLAR. This man is blessed with an exceptional memory, and with an eye for detail and order. However, he is not a research perfectionist nor an endless seeker for ultimates. He readily seeks help when blocked in his work, and feels he can adapt his own thinking to that of others. He is well-informed in his field, and is not given to bluffing. Observers describe him as conscientious and thorough, and as very dependable.

TYPE 5: THE ARTIFICER. This man gives freely of his own time, and enjoys talking shop with other researchers. He is aware of his own limitations and does not attempt what he cannot do. He sees himself as having a special facility for taking the inchoate or poorly formed ideas of others and fashioning them into workable and significant programs. Observers see him as honest and direct, getting along well with others, and as unusually observant and perceptive and responsive to nuances and subtleties in others' behavior.

TYPE 6: THE ESTHETICIAN. This man favors analytical over other modes of thinking, and pefers research problems which lend themselves to elegant and formal solutions. His interests are far-ranging, and he tends to become impatient if progress is slow or if emphasis must be put upon orderliness and systematic detail. His own view of experience is primarily an esthetic one. Observers see him as clever and spontaneous, but as undependable and immature, lacking in patience and industry, and indifferent about duties and obligations.

TYPE 7: THE METHODOLOGIST.   This man is vitally interested in methodological issues, and in problems of mathematical analysis and conceptualization. He is open about his own research plans and enjoys talking of them to others; he has little competitive spirit and tends to take a tolerant view of research differences between himself and others. Observers characterize him as a considerate, charitable person, free from undue ambition; at the same time they report a certain moodiness and an occasional tendency toward complications and difficult behavior.

TYPE 8: THE INDEPENDENT.   This man eschews "team" efforts, and dislikes and avoids administrative details connected with research work. He is not a driving, energetic research man, although he does have a lively sense of intellectual curiosity. He prefers to think in physical and structural models, rather than in analytical and mathematical ways. Observers describe him as active and robust in manner and hardheaded and forthright in judgment; he appears relatively free from worry and self-doubt, but inclined to behave impolitely or abruptly.

QUALITIES OF THE SCIENTIST THAT RECUR PERSISTENTLY

To summarize this section, the following statements present those traits of character that seem to recur most often where attempts are made to characterize the scientist:

(a) The scientist has an insatiable curiosity, inquisitiveness, and spirit of adventure, and a desire to investigate things that capture his curiosity.

(b) The scientist is independent in thought, seeks to improve status quo, and is ready to abandon the disproved.

(c) He has a fertile inventiveness, a strong imagination, and is creative.

(d) The scientist is knowledgeable, enlightened, and informed, and possesses sound judgment and prudent foresight.

(e) The scientist has high mental energy and is capable of extreme degrees of perserverance.

For Discussion and Further Study

1. Assess your traits with reference to the eight types of scientists reported in this section. Is your self-analysis defensible? Is Gough's compartmentalization defensible?

2. Do elements of Gough's characterizations of types of scientists show through the conversation of your colleagues and students?

3. How would two teachers differ if they embraced opposite opinions on the validity of the saying: Scientific traits of mind cannot be taught, they can only be caught?

4. How should a teacher respond when he is told that a student "just was not cut out to be a scientist"?

5. Should a science teacher be expected to reflect the traits of the scientists during out-of-class relations with colleagues and employers?

6. How far should a teacher go in calling attention to the degree to which students reflect the characteristics of practicing scientists?

7. On what characteristics do the greatest number of scholars who have studied the functioning scientist seem to agree? Disagree?

8. Does the literature contain points of view regarding the traits and characteristics of scientists that are not represented among the quotations in the introduction to this chapter?

References

1. Anne Roe. "The Psychology of the Scientist," *Science*, 134 (August 18, 1961), pp. 456–59.
2. Michael Faraday. Quoted in Sir Richard Gregory, *Discovery, or the Spirit and Service of Science*. New York: The Macmillan Company, 1924, p. 121.
3. William Harvey. *Letter to the Royal College of Physicians*, 1628.
4. C. P. Haskins. *Research in Industry*, edited by C. C. Furnas. Princeton, N.J.: D. Van Nostrand Company, 1948, p. 187.
5. G. Gore. *The Art of Scientific Discovery*. London: Longmans, Green & Company, 1878, p. 313.
6. Albert Szent-Gyorgi. "Secret of the Creative Impulse," *The New York Times Magazine*. July 30, 1961.
7. Anne Roe. "The Psychology of the Scientist," *Science*, 134 (August 18, 1961), pp. 456–59.
8. Albert Einstein. From Prologue of Max Planck, *Where is Science Going?* New York: W. W. Norton & Company, 1932, p. 8.
9. C. P. Haskins. *Research in Industry*, edited by C. C. Furnas. Princeton, N.J.: D. Van Nostrand Company, 1948, p. 192.
10. Harrison G. Gough. *How Scientists See Themselves*. Paper (mimeographed) read at the annual meeting of the Western Psychological Association, April 24, 1958, Monterey, California.

4

Powers of the
Mind at Work in Science

*It requires a very unusual mind to undertake the analysis
of the obvious.*[1]
       Alfred North Whitehead 1925

*Part of the pleasure of discovery consists in the perception
of new similarities and differences, contradictions, and intellectual difficulties; the acquisition of new intellectual
and individual power by the reduction of the unknown to
the known. Part also consists in the suitability of the occupation to the individual; the pleasures of activity, of
pursuit, of anticipation, of success; the charm of mystery,
and the excitement of uncertainty as to what will come
next; and the anticipated value of the final result. . . . The
great and primary sources of error are the imperfect action
and limited extent of all our powers, and especially that
of the intellect. In order to avoid error and arrive at truth,
all our lower powers require to be regulated and corrected
by the higher ones; the bodily powers by the senses, the
senses by perception and attention by comparison, and
comparison by reason and inference. . . . To believe we*

33

know that which, on account of its uncertainty or of our finite powers, we cannot know, is a greater error than to remain ignorant, because it misleads us; and the proper name for such a state of mind is conceited ignorance.[2]

G. Gore 1878

To find no contradiction in the union of old and new; to contemplate the Ancient of Days and all His Works with feelings as fresh as if all had then sprang forth at the first creative fiat; characterizes the mind that feels the riddle of the world, and may help to unravel it. To carry on the feelings of childhood into the powers of manhood; to combine the child's sense of wonder and novelty with the appearances which every day for perhaps forty years had rendered familiar . . . this is the character and privilege of genius, and one of the marks which distinguish genius from talents. And, therefore, it is the prime merits of genius, and its most unequivocal mode of manifestation, so to represent familiar objects, as to awaken in the minds of others a kindred feeling concerning them, and that freshness of sensation which is the constant accompaniment of mental, no less than of bodily, convalescence.[3]

Samuel Taylor Coleridge 1817

When we pass from the known to the unknown by an act of imagination, we first conceive known ideas, and then by purely mental acts compare, infer, divide, combine, or permutate them, and in each case, form a resulting new mental conception, and this is the so-called "creative" process.[4]

G. Gore 1878

Nature is a spectacle continually exhibited to our senses in which phenomena are mingled in combinations of endless variety and novelty. Wonder fixes the mind's attention; memory stores up a record of each distinct impression; the powers of association bring forth the record when the like is felt again. By the higher faculties of judgment and reasoning the mind compares the new with the old, recognizes essential identity, even when distinguished by diverse circumstances, and expects to find again what was before ex-

34

perienced. It must be the ground of all reasoning and inference that what is true of one thing will be true of its equivalent, and that under carefully ascertained conditions nature repeats herself.[5]

W. Stanley Jevons 1873

The cultivated powers of the free mind . . . involve the processes of recalling and imagining, classifying and generalizing, comparing and evaluating, analyzing and synthesizing, and deducing and inferring. These processes enable one to apply logic and the available evidence to his ideas, attitudes, and actions, and to pursue better whatever goals he may have. . . . The rational powers of any person are developed gradually and continuously as and when he uses them successfully. There is no evidence that they can be developed in any other way. . . . The teacher has the critical role in enabling the student to achieve these successes, selecting problems which are within his grasp, providing clues and cues to their solution, suggesting alternative ways to think about them, and assessing continuously the progress of the pupil and the degree of difficulty of the problems before him. . . . Also, there is a highly creative aspect in the processes of thought. All the higher mental processes involve more than simple awareness of facts; they depend also on the ability to conceive what might be as well as what is, to construct mental images in new and original ways. . . . Further, the processes of thought demand the ability to integrate perceptions of objective phenomena with judgments of value in which subjective emotional commitments are important elements.[6]

**Educational Policies Commission
of the National Education Association
and the American Association of School Administrators 1961**

Though awareness of anomaly marks the beginning of a discovery, it marks only the beginning. What necessarily follows, if anything at all is to be discovered, is a more or less extended period during which the individual and often many members of his group struggle to make the anomaly lawlike. Invariably that period demands additional observation or experimentation as well as repeated cogitation. While it continues scientists repeatedly revise their expectations, usually their experimental standards, and sometimes their most fundamental theories as well.[7]

Thomas S. Kuhn 1962

What people call applied science is nothing but the application of pure science to particular classes of problems. It consists of deductions from those general principles, established by reasoning and observation, which constitute pure science. No one can safely make these deductions until he has a firm grasp of the principles.[8]

Thomas Henry Huxley

No one is competent to assert things about absolute space and motion; they are pure matters of thought that cannot be produced in experience. . . . No one is warranted in extending these principles beyond the boundaries of experience. In fact, such an extension is meaningless, as no one would possess the knowledge to make use of it.[9]

Ernest Mach   1912

Ready and Faithful Memory

Among the several powers of mind that seem to be particularly involved in the pursuit of science, first to be considered is the exercise of ready and faithful memory. An original thought can come only from materials stored up in the memory. But stored materials must be readily accessible and subject to almost immediate retrieval. To order and retrieve remembered data at the most opportune time is truly an intellectual process quite closely tied to the efficiency with which scientists function.

Detecting Essential Resemblances and Differences

A second mental process consists of detecting essential resemblances and differences. Ahead of this is the ready ability to make a rapid analysis of the total situation in which a phenomenon is assumed to occur. Concomitant events and circumstances must be isolated and tagged with different degrees of probability of being merely coincidental in contrast to being essential antecedents or consequences of the phenomenon up for study.

36

Inferring New Truths

Knowing that some things are true, a third power of mind is exhibited in the ability to infer new truths. At the lowest level, this consists of originality in linking ideas whose connections were not previously suspected. At a higher level, it is the creation of hypotheses out of the dim regions of intuition and the ability to bring them into the bright light of relationships with laws or principles already known or struggling to be identified. At what is perhaps the highest level, the scientist's mind, on occasion, must project known facts into the regions of the unknown and see the picture upon a completely new mental plane.

Comparison

The process of comparison is featured as the fourth power of the mind to be considered here. This power shows up in the ability to compare antecedents with consequences, to avoid confusing facts with assumptions, and to contrast a working hypothesis with a proved conclusion. The various orders in which a collection of facts can be arranged must be compared in order to identify different degrees of logic and to ferret out relationships which are inferred. In many cases, comparison becomes the mental process that precedes immediately the formation of a judgment or the maturity of an attitude.

Discipline and Persistence

Although the pursuit of science becomes a very enjoyable mental process, the successful scientist must possess the power or discipline to force his mind to stick with a problem. This persistence is not of the type exhibited by the stubborn bulldog that refuses to release his grasp of an adversary. It is more that of the pugilist who adroitly maneuvers for a more advantageous position from which to attack his opponent for round after round, ignoring the fatigue and bruises that come with the battle.

And yet in every mind there must be a very personal room set aside for "playing with ideas." It should be a place of joy and refreshment where the imagination can roam freely, a place where any thought that strikes the fancy is allowed, a place one can return to with a adolescent's enthusiasm untethered by convention or autocratic restraint. When the going is rough, it is most difficult to slip away to this room; but that is when creative people have the greatest need for this retreat. It is within this chamber of the mind that creativity and fresh thoughts flourish best.

Faith

Imaginative vision and faith in the ultimate success are indispensable for sustained mental effort. And science can be pursued only by sustained mental effort. Many are the episodes in science in which the investigator was kept groping in the frustration of a problem that refused to be solved. The only relief from the despair of doubt seems to be the faith that the break-through to success will eventually come.

Communication

Although less directly related to the successful completion of an episode in science, productive mental effort is often helped by intellectual intercourse. Until a would-be scientist gains the power to communicate his thoughts, these thoughts are likely to retain disorder and ambiguity. To retrace with a fellow scientist the path along which an investigation has evolved or to describe the circumstances that appear to block further progress can sometimes reveal a way around obstacles. "I never really understood that phenomenon until I taught it" is frequently heard, especially from young people who are beginning their pursuit of science.

Creative Thinking

Creativity in thinking tends to be more of a degree than a variety and will not be treated here other than to cite that the kind of thinking designated as being truly creative is the play of the mind on concepts divorced from personal complacencies, triumphs, and humiliations. Its judgments are concerned with a higher order of decisions than those required for everyday decisions. Its logic is far purer and more objective than the specious arguments formulated to defend cherished beliefs and prejudices.

Suspicion and Criticism

At no time, however, during the communication of his ideas, can a scientist disengage another power of the mind, namely, criticism. It is the essence of the scientific spirit to doubt in order to know what to believe and not merely for the sake of doubting. A perpetual suspicion of results already obtained wages constant battle in a scientist's mind against the confidence with which they are being enhanced by tentative acceptance. Systematic doubt serves as a self-corrective method.

Analysis of an Act of Thought

Although too little is known for sure today about the functioning of the intellect to try to ascribe a pattern to the thought process, there can be a sequence in which the powers of the mind are brought to bear on a problem. An act of thought is likely to begin as a felt difficulty or puzzling state of affairs. This is followed by an analysis and the ordering of all available information that promises to bear on the difficulty or puzzling situation. At almost any time, the mind will come forth with suggestions or possible answers. Penetrating suggestions, however, are more likely to await clear definition of the problem and thorough familiarity with the background in which this and similar problems exist.

Regardless of when the flash of insight occurs, tentative suggestions must be tested for consistency with past circumstances or predicted consequences. Each test which yields confirming evidence moves the thinker toward adopting one rather than another belief, or following one as opposed to another course of action.

Resistance to Thinking

There is a very wide range of variation in human ability to think. Some minds are spectacularly resourceful and some approach being useless. Most men, however, are neither geniuses nor idiots. Resistance to thinking must be distinguished from inability to think at the expected intellectual level.

Many of the things that people do and believe do not require disciplined thought. In fact, so many decisions in each day's course of events are dictated by laws, customs, or habits that many people wonder what hit them when they are confronted with a thought-demanding situation. For these people, resistance to thinking is more likely to be sheer ignorance of the process.

People are more or less subject to all kinds of superstitions, even the most absurd. Once a superstition has been adopted, many people are more likely to protect it than admit to having been mentally duped. Furthermore, if people lack sophistication, many superstitions provide a more plausible and more easily digested solution than would be gained by actually thinking through the situation. Hence there arises another case of resistance to thinking.

The things one experiences tend to cause an individual to occupy a position of mind somewhere between extremely rigid and flexible. Regardless of how large a body of evidence they may have accumulated to bear on a situation, some people rigidly and suspiciously resist allowing the thought process to culminate in changed beliefs or courses of action. At the other extreme are the ultraliberal or free-minded folk whose beliefs and actions sway pleasantly in the lightest mental breeze. These patterns of behavior must be kept in mind when attempting to analyze the effectiveness of any efforts to encourage or exercise the powers of mind.

Instructors are well aware of how persistently students resist the thinking process. Such resistance can best be overcome by making overt efforts to exercise the powers of mind, either singly or in combination, that seem to be operating wherever science is pursued. Once started, most people derive a satisfaction from the exercise that is, in itself, motivation.

For Discussion and Further Study

1. Are there things a teacher can do to improve his ability to discern likenesses and differences in observations?

2. What responsibilities are visited upon science teachers if it is true that discoveries in science stem from the ability to note instances of disconformity or supreme orderliness in naturally occurring events and circumstances.

3. Do the "cultivated powers of the free mind" that are discussed in the quotations in the introduction to this chapter lend themselves to being the overt goal of individual lessons?

4. Is the concept of a personal intellectual retreat where one can "play with ideas" totally incompatible with the realities of teaching, particularly in the public secondary school?

5. Do hunches play a significant role in the scientific endeavor?

6. Does creative thinking in science differ essentially from creative thinking in other human pursuits—art or politics, for example?

7. How should a teacher proceed if he senses that his community will evidence rigidity or resistance to teaching the processes of inquiry and especially so if these processes are directed toward established superstitious or cultural beliefs?

8. Is it true that people, especially students, simply do not like to think or to be made to think?

9. Can the usual forms of class discussion and recitation serve to develop the power of communication?

10. Do causes of intellectual error exist today that were not touched on in this chapter's first quotation from Gore?

References

1. Alfred North Whitehead. *Science and the Modern World.* New York: The Macmillan Company, 1925, p. 6.

2. G. Gore. *The Art of Scientific Discovery*. London: Longmans, Green & Company, 1878, pp. 11, 111.

3. Samuel Taylor Coleridge, *Biographia Literaria*, 1817.

4. G. Gore. *The Art of Scientific Discovery*. London: Longman's, Green & Company, 1878, p. 360.

5. W. Stanley Jevons. *The Principles of Science*. New York: Dover Publications, 1958, pp. 1–2. First published 1873.

6. Educational Policies Commission of the National Education Association and the American Association of School Administrators. *The Central Purpose of American Education*. Washington, D.C.: National Education Association, 1961, pp. 4, 5, 17.

7. Thomas S. Kuhn. "Historical Structure of Scientific Discovery," *Science,* **136** (June 1, 1962), pp. 760–64.

8. Thomas Henry Huxley. Quoted by the Rand Corporation, *Scientific American,* **198** (November 1957), p. 44.

9. Ernest Mach, 1912. Quoted by the Rand Corporation, *Scientific American,* **205** (September 1961), p. 43.

5

The Role of
Observation in Science

It is the essence of good observations that the eye should not only see a thing itself, but of what parts that thing is composed. And if an observer is to become a successful investigator in any department of science, he must have an extreme acquaintance with what has already been done in that particular department. Only then will he be prepared to seize upon any one of those minute indications which often connect phenomena apparently quite remote from each other. His eyes will thus be struck with any occurrence which, according to received theories, ought not to happen; for these are the facts which serve as clues to new discoveries.[1]

F. W. Westaway 1931

What is observed depends not only upon what there is to be observed, but upon the observer, and what he has previously observed.[2]

William H. George 1938

Philosophy is written in that great book which ever lies before our eyes—I mean the universe—but we cannot under-

stand it if we do not first learn the language and grasp the symbols in which it is written. This book is written in the mathematical language, and the symbols are triangles, circles, and other geometrical figures, without whose help it is impossible to comprehend a single word of it; without which one wanders in vain through a dark labyrinth.[3]

Galileo 1610

The careful recording of all details in experimental work is an elementary but important rule. It happens surprisingly often that one needs to refer back to some detail whose significance one did not realize when the experiment was carried out. . . . Apart from providing an invaluable record of what is done and what observed, note-taking is a useful technique for prompting careful observation.[4]

W. I. B. Beveridge 1957

He only sees well who sees the whole in the parts, and the parts in the whole.[5]

J. K. Lavater 1741–1801

Only two kinds of stimulant secure attention with little or no voluntary effort on the part of the observer. These are the smashingly obtrusive, which thrust themselves irresistibly upon our attention by presenting vivid or startling changes to our sense organs and the intrinsically interesting which appeal to our innate wants.[6]

Harold A. Larrabee 1945

In order to be acceptable, a feature of an observation must be: (a) capable of being presented again in similar conditions; (b) if possible, connected with other constants by means of generalizations. . . . An individual observation is said to be publicly verifiable when it could be confirmed by any suitably qualified scientist; it is said to be publicly verified when it has been so confirmed by a sufficient number of other observers.[7]

Max Black 1946

43

When we merely note and record the phenomena which occur around us in the ordinary course of nature we are said to observe. When we change the course of nature by the intervention of our will and muscular powers, and thus produce unusual combinations and conditions of phenomena, we are said to experiment. Experiment is thus observation plus alteration of conditions.[8]

W. Stanley Jevons   1874

Hearsay, reading, and observation, are the three vehicles of information and if judged by present-day results the effectiveness diminishes in the order named, hearsay being far more potent in our working conceptions than observation![9]

William Gould Vinal   1922

Dogmatism has no place in science, and dogmatism about the unknown is especially reprehensible. We live by faith, faith in the order of nature, faith in ourselves, and faith in our fellow men. This faith is our most prevalent motivation, and it is a reliable guide for behavior just in so far as it is founded on knowledge. Where knowledge is lacking we may extrapolate with due regard for the uncertainties arising from the incompleteness of our knowledge. The mystics too often neglect this caution.[10]

Charles Judson Herrick   1956

. . . Scientists believe that there is a hierarchy of facts, and that a judicious selection can be made. . . . The most interesting facts are those which can be used several times, those which have a chance of recurring. . . . It is with regular facts, therefore, that we ought to begin; but as soon as the rule is well established, as soon as it is no longer in doubt, the facts which are in complete conformity with it lose their interest, since they can teach us nothing new. Then it is the exception which becomes important. We cease to look for resemblances, and apply ourselves before all else to differences, and of these differences we select first those that are the most accentuated, not only because they are the most striking, but because they will be the most instructive. . . . But what we must aim at is not so much to ascertain resemblances and differences, as to discover similarities hidden under apparent discrepancies.[11]

Henri Poincaré   1914

44

THE REALITY OF THINGS

Observations are usually concrete ideas, often consisting of a great many simple conceptions combined in a single statement. To observe something is to direct one's senses and perceptive powers to objects, events, or circumstances. Nature can be studied only through the senses. Thus, people can study only the model of nature that the senses and the human mind enable them to construct. Although science can establish criteria by which to determine the reality of objects of thought, science cannot test the validity of the criteria themselves. So long as science remains empirical, it cannot test the truth or falsity of reality or concepts of existence. Thus, there is no proof that any model of nature, consistent though it may be, represents truly the real structure of nature. Acting within this limitation, the pursuit of science operates on the basis of objects, events, and circumstances being as real as are the reproducibility of their descriptions.

MENTAL CONDITIONS OF CORRECT OBSERVATIONS

It is common knowledge that different people viewing the same scene will notice different things. Errors in observation arise not only because observers frequently miss seemingly obvious things but also because they invent false observations. Many errors can be traced to the tendency of the mind to unconsciously fill gaps so that things observed correspond with past experience, knowledge, and conscious expectations. If a transient phenomenon is being observed, accuracy of observation is unlikely to occur unless the phenomenon can be repeated many times. Attention during observation is mandatory. Many phenomena occur in apparent domains of deception, trickery, and fraud wherein irrelevant events and conditions misdirect attention.

Observation implies selection. Unwise choice yields an array of observations that can be so remotely connected that it becomes almost impossible to ferret out their relationships. In general, powers of observation can be cultivated; among the most effective elements of strategy are developing the habit of watching things with an active, inquiring mind, and working with some specific object in mind—at the same time, staying alert for unexpected opportunities.

Optimum conditions for observing facts require that the subject matter fall within the range of human sense organs, aided when necessary by instruments, that it be stable enough to support attention, and occur under circumstances that allow it to be observed without causing the observation process itself to disturb the real nature of what is being observed. The subject matter must be accessible and not obscured by any distorting medium nor inextricably confused with background events and circumstances. The observer's sensory equipment must be neither congenitally defective nor temporarily handicapped. Finally, the observer needs a background of experience with similar subject matter, he should be free from strong personal prejudices, and he must know how to stay on guard against all perils of erroneous inference.

QUANTITATIVE OBSERVATIONS

Only rarely do purely qualitative observations prove to be adequate to produce an accurate description of a phenomenon. In nearly all cases, quantitative observations are required. In fact, in any branch of science, the more accurate measurements are, the more highly advanced is that branch of science.

There are at least three basic procedures underlying measurement. One method assumes that an increase or decrease of the quantity being measured can be equated with a standard unit in some determinate ratio. A second method applies some natural conjunction of events that enables the investigator to compare directly the multiples of the quantity with those of a measuring unit. In the third method, it is not the quantity itself but some other quantity connected with it by known mathematical relations that is observed, and these observations provide an indirect measurement of the quantity.

Accuracy of measurement depends upon the ability to repeat units of exactly equal magnitude so that they can be joined together forming an aggregate that is truly equal to the sum of the parts. Instruments can be used to assist in the quantitative observation of an event or circumstance, but they must have no effect on or control of the observation.

DISTINCTION
BETWEEN OBSERVATION
AND EXPERIMENTATION

There is no sharp transition between observation and experimentation; in fact, there is a kind of "natural experiment" that can be termed experimentation or observation with almost equal accuracy. In general, however, experiments are distinguished from observations because they are deliberately undertaken, and feature artificially arranged, systematically varied factors and the investigation of a specific question. An observation is not elevated to the status of an experiment by simply calling on the aid of an instrument. When a telescope is used to view a distant object, for example, no experiment is performed because no variation of the conditions of the phenomenon is being exercised. Similarly, to observe an atmospheric phenomenon as it evolves concurrently with changing temperature or some other factor within the physical environment allows the investigator to remain in the role of observer, even though what he is observing takes on the character of a "natural" experiment.

For Discussion and Further Study

1. Is there a paradox in the opinion that whereas one learns by observing, the truly successful observer must have extreme acquaintance with the general nature of what is observed?

2. Is the inference of the quotation from Galileo that quantitative relationships exist in nature and are "discovered" rather than created by mathematicians?

3. How can we account for the reluctance of students to keep effective records of the work they do in the laboratory?

4. Does the empirical nature of science preclude proof that any concept is universally true or false?

5. How do the processes of observation and experimentation interact?

6. What kinds of dramatized or camouflaged situations can be devised to demonstrate to students that what is seen depends on who is doing the seeing?

7. Is it possible to analyze a typical demonstration and rank separate observations in the order of greatest significance? Can students be ranked in ability to ferret out significant observations?

8. Cite examples of quantitative observations wherein one type of measurement strategy would be more appropriate than another.

9. Why is one fully verified discrepant observation likely to be more significant than many confirming observations?

10. What should a teacher say during a demonstration: What are the merits of the so-called silent demonstration?

References

1. F. W. Westaway. *Scientific Method*, 4th ed. New York: Hillman-Curl, 1937, p. 196.
2. William H. George. *The Scientist in Action*. New York: Basic Books, 1938, p. 148.
3. Galileo. *Il Saggiatore*, 1610.
4. W. I. B. Beveridge. *The Art of Scientific Investigation*. New York: Random House, 1957, p. 24. First published 1950.
5. Johann Kaspar Lavater. In G. Gore, *The Art of Scientific Discovery*. London: Longmans, Green & Company, 1878, p. 46.

6. Harold A. Larrabee. *Reliable Knowledge*. Boston: Houghton Mifflin Company, 1945, p. 141.
7. Max Black. *Critical Thinking*. Englewood Cliffs, N.J.: Prentice-Hall, 1946, pp. 359–60.
8. W. Stanley Jevons. *The Principles of Science*. New York: Dover Publications, 1958. First published 1873, p. 400 of original printing.
9. William Gould Vinal. Quoted in Francis D. Curtis, *A Digest of Investigations in the Teaching of Science*. Philadelphia: P. Blakiston's Sons & Company, 1926, p. 214.
10. Charles Judson Herrick, 1956. Quoted by the Rand Corporation, *Scientific American*, **205** (October 1961), p. 48.
11. Henri Poincaré, 1914. Quoted by the Rand Corporation, *Scientific American*, **198** (September 1957), p. 79.

6

Finding or Selecting
a Problem

*We have no intention of producing sow's ear silk for the
market. We made this silk purse from a sow's ear because
we wanted to, because it might serve as an example to
clients who come to us with their ambitions or their troubles,
and also as a contribution to philosophy.*

*For over half a century we have been fighting such ex-
pressions as "What's the use?" "It isn't done," "It isn't practical," "We've got no time for theories," and all the other
wretched substitutes for hard, earnest, straight thinking.*

*Things that everybody thinks he knows only because he has
learned the words that say it, are poisons to progress. The
only way to get ahead is to dig in, to study, to find out, to
reason out theories, to test them—and then to hold fast
to that which is good.*[1]
        Arthur Dehon Little 1921

*Good laboratory facilities, good and sufficient equipment,
good lighting and ventilation, adequate floor space, and
provision for ready communication between individuals at
no great effort stand high on the list [of material factors
that contribute to the success of research efforts]. A fairly
extensive library is a tremendous asset to any type of labora-*

tory. . . . The provision of central and decentralized machine shops, woodworking shops, and glassblowing shops are of course also desiderata which are more essential in some types of laboratories than others.

It becomes of prime importance for the research director to analyze and understand the characteristics of his own research staff in particular, and those of scientific research in general. . . . Once the worker has proved his ability and fitness for his job, reasonable assurance of tenure should be given him, and adequate provision should be made for his monetary security and that of his family.[2]

C. P. Haskins   1948

In team research the synergistic effect is pronounced in that A volunteers information to which B can add an additional fact and from which C occasionally is able to synthesize a hypothesis.[3]

Robert G. Chollar   1956

If one knows physics only from a distance, it may appear to be merely strange names and mathematical formulae, and one may come to believe that it is an affair of the learned alone, ingeniously and wisely constructed, but without significance for men of other interests and problems. And yet one could do no worse injustice to physics than to turn away, repelled by this hard shell of technical terms with which it has surrounded itself. Whoever succeeds in looking behind this wall . . . will find there a science full of living problems, full of inner motion, full of the intense endeavor to find answers to the questions of the truth-seeking spirit.[4]

Hans Reichenbach   1930

COURTESY OF THE RAND CORPORATION

SEEKING ONE'S OWN TOPIC

A discussion of how one goes about selecting his own topic for investigation in the pursuit of science, to be consistent with the spirit of this book, must be quite brief though it may seem arbitrarily abrupt. To find or select a topic for an excursion into science, the potential investigator, by one means or another, must assume the characteristics of the scientist: his mind must work as the mind works in the pursuit of science, and he must enter the domain of science and exercise the powers and strategy of observation.

GUIDING OTHERS IN
FINDING OR SELECTING A TOPIC

Much more can be said about how one individual can help other individuals, who are supposedly less experienced in the realm of science, find and select their problems for investigation. This is true even though, ideally, the selection of a topic for study should be influenced only by the interests of the investigator. In practice, teachers, laboratory directors, patrons, or other sponsors of research are required to influence, either openly or subtly, the topic chosen by or assigned to another investigator. Because this book deals primarily with the problems of people who are only beginning their pursuit of science, the emphasis is on helping students find and select topics even though the authors draw heavily on the experiences that have been reported by directors of institutes, laboratories, and other research centers.

How can those who are to influence the choice of topic by another investigator keep their influence consistent with the interests of the person who is to do the actual work? This is a complex question, but it does imply an obvious need to become as fully acquainted as possible with the workers whose choices of topic are to be influenced. Assuming that the counselor has had sufficient experience with the pursuit of science to enable him to recognize and appreciate the characteristics of the scientist, it becomes his function to exploit the characteristics that seem to be latent or only partially developed within the students or workers he is to counsel. Furthermore, the counselor must arouse those characteristics that seem dormant, and compensate, if possible, for any that seem to be lacking.

Individuals in almost any group of people, young or old, naive or sophisticated in the pursuit of science, will differ widely in the degree to which they have developed creativeness, curiosity, integrity, endurance, and the many other qualities that seem to recur in scientists at work. They will also differ widely in basic confidence in the processes of investigation and in their estimation of the worth of investigation as a career. There will be individuals for whom the counselor's primary responsibility will be simply to guide toward worthwhile topics. On the other end of the scale will be individuals so lacking in the feel of science that they will never come up with an idea of their own, and remain totally immune to ideas suggested to them.

Assuming that the counselor's time, energy, and other resources are finite, he must decide how much to invest in the latter group before invoking the expediency of abandoning individuals or assigning them to a supporting role in the scientific endeavor. Fortunately, the pursuit of science is an enterprise so vast as to provide many roles for artists, engineers, writers, historians, sociologists, in fact, for nearly all human endeavors, and thus allows wide scope for students' various interests and personality types. The counselor should be able to give each of his counselees an opportunity to experience some of the satisfactions inherent in the pursuit of science. In a world where so many things of doubtful worth scream for the attention of young people, counselors are at times disturbed by the conjecture that many Einsteins, Harveys, Newtons, and Darwins are lost to the world because they were never caused to feel the satisfactions that come with the pursuit of science.

ENVIRONMENTS IN WHICH TO SEEK TOPICS

Each investigator must feel that he has at least a degree of freedom in finding or selecting the topic for his investigation. Some people hunt most effectively when given full freedom, whereas others seem to want and need an array of possible alternatives from which to choose their "own" topics. The least responsive members of a group may want to be assigned preliminary work, which they hope will lead them to a topic. This preliminary work may involve an appropriate version of "literature search," serving as an assistant to a more precocious or sophisticated person, constructing a needed piece of equiment, repeating significant experiments done by other investigators, or some similarly closely structured assignment.

The exuberant person must guard against frittering away his time and resources on half-baked or meaningless topics, and the sheer novice must learn to avoid the frustrating degradation that comes from seeing his associates whose searches bore fruit earlier and, thus, allowed their work to get under way more promptly. Sometimes an undue hunger for freedom can cause one to become impatient in his search for a worthy topic for his investigation. The very spirit of science imposes inescapable limits and restrictions on the investigator, and this can cause him to be especially impatient with what would seem to be petty administrative and housekeeping restrictions.

The sense of freedom has special significance to the teaching scientist. It is difficult to imagine the teacher's being able to create an environment in which young people will be encouraged to find or select worthwhile topics for investigation unless the teacher, too, has freedom to choose and pursue ideas. Ideally, the science teacher can be a symbol of the pursuit of science in his community. The school laboratory can be his laboratory and he can feel free to use library, greenhouse, darkroom, and all other school facilities not only for his own small-scale investigations but also, assuming that he has proved his right to be a teaching scientist, for the pursuit of investigations that promise to continue throughout several school terms. It is not too idealistic to foresee the day when science teachers will be encouraged to explore ideas even though they show little direct relationship to "company" problems, and supplies and apparatus will be requisitioned solely for the teacher's own research. Time and other resources invested in a science teacher's own research may yield rich dividends to all of the teacher's students.

Overemphasis on extrinsic motivation contradicts the spirit of the pursuit of science and may actually be detrimental to an environment in which topics are to be sought for investigation. The student or worker who has proved his ability and fitness to select an investigation should have reasonable assurance that he will be permitted to pursue the investigation at his own pace and receive recognition for his achievements regardless of company or institutional deadlines.

SPECIAL AREAS FROM WHICH TOPICS FOR INVESTIGATIONS ARISE

The scientific enterprise, although diffuse and very difficult to analyze, was examined many years ago by Gore[5] from the point of view of identifying circumstances that seem to be especially likely to yield topics for investigation. Gore's analysis deserves careful study in its original form, but since it is no longer readily available, excerpts are presented here in outline form. One of his classical examples of each set of circumstances has been cited (paragraphs in italics) and, to show how timeless is his analysis, a second illustration has been drawn from recent science. Obviously, since few episodes in science have their origins in a single circumstance or employ a single plan of attack, many of the illustrative topics could have been used equally effectively to clarify other circumstances or methods of investigation.

I. Discovery from Investigation of Likely Circumstances
  1. Examining Neglected Truths and Hypotheses

The facts discovered by Geber (who was born in the year 830), that iron, lead, and copper became heavier by being heated to redness and cooled in the air, so as to become oxidised; and by Boyle (during the seventeenth century), that tin behaved similarly, remained almost unnoticed, or at any rate uninvestigated and without a true interpretation, until about the year 1778, when Lavoisier inferred their true explanation.

For many, many years people have noticed that under certain circumstances the sight of food calls forth a secretion of digestive juices, but it was not until the twentieth century that Pavlov began investigating this event. His investigations led him to new knowledge about the autonomic control of internal organs and, eventually, to his famous description of the conditioned reflex.

2. Examining Peculiar or Unexplained Truth in Science

The unexplained fact, first noticed by Mr. George Fisher in the year 1818, that the rate of a chronometer was affected by the proximity of a mass of iron; and that of Arago, in 1824, that proximity of plates of various substances, especially metals, affected the oscillation of a magnet, originated Faraday's discovery of magnetic electricity.

Charles Nicolle's description of events leading to the discovery that brought him a Nobel prize includes observations made at the native hospital of Tunis. When visiting this hospital, Nicolle often stepped over the bodies of typhus patients who had come to be admitted but had fallen at the door. He also observed that contagion seemed to be limited to outside the doors of the common medical wards. Typhus developed among the doctors who visited with patients during admission to the hospital and among the employees whose duty it was to collect and launder patients' clothes. Not a single person, however, became contaminated by a typhus patient after the patient had been admitted to a ward, not an attendant nor a doctor.

By asking himself what happened between the hospital doors and the wards, Nicolle realized that entering patients were relieved of their clothes and were shaved and washed. This realization focused attention on something associated with clothing and personal hygiene. By this kind of reasoning, the louse was identified as the carrier of typhus.

3. Investigating Unexplained Phenomena Observed in Manufacturing and Other Operations

It was by examining a specimen of manufactured oxide of zinc which had a peculiar yellow colour that Strohmeyer [1776–1835] was led to the discovery of cadmium.

The origin of penicillin was the contamination of a culture plate of staphylococci by a mold. It was noticed that, for some distance around the mold colony, the staphylococcal colonies had become translucent, and evidently lysis was going on. This was an extraordinary appearance and seemed to demand investigation, so the mold was isolated in pure culture and its properties determined.

4. Investigating Exceptional Cases

The long-established doctrine that expansion is a direct result of rise of temperature is completely disproved by the fact that iodide of silver,

whilst in the solid crystalline state, and being cooled from 16° C. to 13° C.,
enlarges in volume from 1000 to about 1018 Expansion by heat, therefore,
is not a direct effect of the heat, but of a molecular change, produced by
the heat.

Contrary to the impression one gains from casually observing growing
plants, the leaves on many annual plants show changes in shape from
leaf to leaf up the stem. The Russian botantist N. P. Krenke observed
these changes in the cotton plant and suggested that the cycle of leaf
shape in cotton is a measure of physiological age. His work provides
a tentative solution to the complex problem of measurement of
senescence and rejuvenescence, a problem of biology: the cause of
old age.

5. Examining Extreme Cases and Conspicuous Instances

The phenomena of electric discharge and optic spectra in rarefied gases,
rotation of bodies in rarefied media by means of heat, Graham's [1805–
1869] discovery of osmose, etc., are instances of this kind.

For a long time, the Japanese have known about the "foolish seed-
ling" disease which causes young rice plants to grow ridiculously tall.
By 1926 Japanese scientists had found that the disease was caused by
a fungus, *Gibberella jujikuroi,* and, after twelve years of effort, were
able to extract from the fungus a substance they named gibberellin.
Other gibberellins have been discovered, and their oftentimes striking
effects on plant behavior occupied the time of many scientists in the
middle of the twentieth century.

6. Examining Common but Neglected Substances

Dalton's [1776–1884] chemical theory of the rule of multiple combining
proportions of bodies, in accordance with his theory of atoms, was suggested
by his experimental investigation of olefiant gas and carburetted hydrogen.

Soon after the discovery of the heavier isotope of hydrogen during
the early 1930's, E. W. Washburn and E. R. Smith argued that heavier
atoms of hydrogen would collect in the residues from the electrolysis
of water. Their hypothesis was confirmed by examining samples of
water taken from cells where hydrogen and oxygen were being produced industrially by the electrolysis of water.

7. Investigating Peculiar Minerals

A peculiar substance—the red-lead ore of Siberia—had early drawn the
attention of chemists on account of its beauty; and various attempts had been
made to analyse it. Among others, Vauquelin tried his skill upon it in 1789,

*in concert with M. Macquart, who had brought specimens of it from Siberia;
but at that time he did not succeed in determining the nature of the acid
with which the oxide of lead was combined in it. He examined it again in
1797, and succeeded in separating an acid to which, from the beautifully
coloured salts which it forms, he gave the name of chromic. He determined
the properties of this acid, and showed that its basis was a new metal, to
which he gave the name of chromium.*

Puzzled by the deaths of thousands of sheep on Australian ranches
by a disease resembling anemia, ranchers found that feeding large doses
of iron prevented the disease in some cases and not in others. The
difference was traced to the source of the iron. After a series of elaborate
analyses of iron-ore samples from all over the world, it was found
that the iron that helped to cure bush sickness contained tiny amounts
of cobalt.

8. Examining Rare Substances

*Various important discoveries were made in thermo-electricity by Peltier,
Matthiesen, and others, by the aid of the comparatively scarce substances,
tellurium, selenium, and bismuth.*

By 1945–46, B. B. Cunningham and L. B. Werner, working at the
University of California, had learned how to prepare ultramicrochem-
ical quantities of pure compounds of the newly identified rare earth,
americium. By bombarding americium-241 with accelerated alpha
particles, element 243, berkelium, was created.

9. Examination of the Residues of Manufacturing Processes

*By examining the solution of crude platinum in aqua-regia, obtained in
his process of manufacturing that metal, Dr. Wollaston [1766–1828] discovered palladium.*

Following the thermonuclear test explosion of November 1952 at
Eniwetok Atoll, two new heavy isotopes of plutonium and americium,
namely Pu-246 and Am-246, became available. Realizing that nuclides
with such high neutron content could arise only from successive
neutron captures, scientists were immediately alerted to the possibilities
of finding new trans-uranium elements in the explosion residues.
Elements 99, einsteinium, and 100, fermium, were found.

10. Examining the Ashes of Rare Plants and Animals

*It was the distillation of dried urine which led to the discovery of the
element (phosphorus), and the analysis of the ashes of bones which further
led to its abundant production.*

Calculations show that if calcium carbonate forms in sea water at 0°C., it will be enriched in the O-8 isotope by a factor of 1.026 over that in the water, whereas at 25°C., the corresponding factor will be 1.022. By using a mass spectrometer to determine the ratio between O-16 and O-8 in shells of fossil marine organisms, the temperature of pre-existent seas can be determined.

II. Discovery from Devising of Hypotheses and Questions and Testing Them

1. Searching for One Thing and Finding Another

Whilst Columbus, in the year 1492, was searching for a new continent, he discovered the variation of the magnetic needle.

In 1906, Ernest Rutherford and Hans Geiger were attempting to determine accurately the number of alpha particles expelled from one gram of radium. They noticed that about one particle in 8,000 was scattered at an angle of 90° when the radiation impinged on a thin sheet of gold, a fact about as credible as a 15-inch shell's bouncing back from a piece of tissue paper. Thus was born the concept of the atom as containing a positively charged nucleus.

2. Assuming the Truthfulness or Certainty of All the Great Principles of Science

After he had observed the anomalous molecular change which occurs in a stretched wire of iron or steel whilst cooling from a full red heat, Professor Barrett discovered the simultaneous evolution of heat which accompanies that change.

In 1927, Heisenberg invoked the argument that any particle or event that is affected by the processes of observation can never be described with certainty. For example, if a particle that is already in motion suffers recoil from the interaction of a photon and the interaction with the photon is essential to observation of the particle, the velocity of the particle is indeterminant.

3. Assuming That Most of the Principles That Operate in the Simpler Sciences Operate Also in the Complex and Concrete Ones

Although elementary substances and their compounds are divided into electro-positive and electro-negative, chemists, even at the present day, do not seem to formally recognize the existence of two kinds of chemical attraction, viz., that in metals and bases, and that in metalloids and acids, corresponding to their two kinds of electrical property.

The extreme specificity with which one enzyme influences only one chemical reaction promises, if adequately described, to shed much light on the whole physico-chemical nature of the life process. To guide the search for experimental evidence, the "lock and key" analogy has proved to be useful. The enzyme molecule can be visualized as a lock with notches and indentations of a particular pattern; the substrate molecule is the key, and its configurations mesh into the enzyme pattern. When the key enters the lock, deformation of the substrate occurs and new molecules are formed. Knowledge about a key helps to understand the lock and knowledge of either sheds light on the whole enzymatic process.

4. By Assuming that Certain General Statements That Are True of One Force or Substance Are True to Some Extent of Others

Faraday having, in the year 1845, discovered the magnetic rotary polarisation of light, Wartmann, in the following year, succeeded in discovering a similar action with a beam of heat.

Seeking to describe with greater clarity the evolving picture of the atom, Franck and Hertz argued that a slow electron with a given kinetic energy should, on striking an atom at rest, be deflected by the atom practically without loss of energy, rather like a rubber ball striking a hard wall. They devised experiments to observe the impact effects of electrons and thus obtained data that supported Bohr's theory of discrete energy states of the atom.

5. Assuming the Existence of Converse Principles of Action

Magneto-electricity and electro-dynamic induction were discovered in this way. As electric currents produced magnetism, so magnetism was assumed to be able to produce electric currents.

Is it tensions developed in the living cells of the shoots that pulls water to the tops of tall trees? If it is, argued D. T. MacDougal, the trunks should be slightly smaller in diameter during the day when the water is moving more rapidly than at night. The inward pull on the walls of each conducting vessel should add up to an appreciable decrease in diameter of the whole trunk. By designing an extremely sensitive dendrograph, MacDougal found that the trunks of trees are indeed somewhat thinner during the day.

6. Assuming the Existence of Complete Homologous Series

[The idea] of complete homologous series in organic chemistry led to the discovery of a whole multitude of compound substances, including cyanides,

*ethers, alcohols, fatty acids, paraffins, compounds of monad, dyad, triad,
tetrad, and hexad compound radicals.*

Masuto Tahara has observed that the various species of the chrysan-
themum family have different numbers of chromosomes, but that they
are all multiples of nine—namely, 18, 36, 54, 72, and 90. This observation suggested to Ojoind Winge that new species can arise by chromosome doubling, a theory that has been repeatedly confirmed by
using colchicine to produce experimental polyploids. For example,
the relationship has been proved between the 14-chromosome, primitive
einkorn wheat of southeastern Europe, the 28-chromosome emmer
wheat of northern Europe, the 42-chromosome bread wheat of America,
and goat grass, the common weed that grows around the wheat fields in
the Mediterranean region.

III. Discovery by Means of New Experiments and Methods of Working
1. Making or Repeating, in a Modified Form, Experiments Suggested by Other Persons

*Wartmann, in the year 1846, by repeating with rays of heat the experiment
which Faraday in 1845 had made with rays of light, discovered the rotation
of the plane of polarisation of heat rays by magnetism.*

Repeating and extending the work begun in Japan in 1939 by
Kihara and his associates, Eigsti substituted American for Japanese
varieties of watermelons and developed a commercial process for
growing seedless watermelons.

2. Extending the Researches of Others

*Galileo [1564–1642], having heard that Lippershey, A Dutch maker of
spectacles, had constructed and presented to Count Maurice of Nassau an
apparatus which caused distant objects to appear near, repeated his experiment, developed the telescope, and thus laid the foundation of modern
astronomy.*

By removing the prefrontal region of the brain from two chimpan-
zees, Fulton and Jacobsen proved that intelligence was not affected but
that tantrums that used to flare up following frustration no longer
appeared. Moniz and Lima extended this research by severing the
pathway between the prefrontal region and the thalamic center of 50
hopeless mental patients in Portugal. Anxiety states were relieved.

3. Using Known Instruments or Forces in a New Way

*In the production of colours from white light by means of thin films,
Newton [1642–1727], by adopting the device of pressing two glass lenses*

together, was enabled to discover the thickness of the film which was neces-
sary for the production of each colour.

By mounting Geiger-Muller tubes horizontally, with one placed
above the other and connected by a coincidence circuit so that the
system would respond only to ionizing particles passing through all
the counters, Bothe and Kolhörster obtained a cosmic-ray telescope.
This instrument reveals the exact direction a cosmic ray was traveling
when detected.

4. Making Experiments the Converse of Those Already Known

An electric current having been found by Öersted to produce magnetism,
Faraday [1791–1867] adopted this method, and, by a converse form of Öersted's
experiment, discovered the way to produce electric currents by means of
magnetism, and laid the foundation of the branch of science called magneto-
electricity, and all its great technical appliances.

Accepting the premise that amino acids are joined to form protein
molecules by the attachment of the alpha-carbon of one amino acid to
the carboxyl group attached to the alpha-carbon of another with the
elimination of water, a premise supported by the breaking down of
proteins in acid hydrolysis, Fischer argued that progress in this difficult
field, hinged on the discovery of a method which would permit the
experimenter to establish a well-defined sequence whereby amino acids
join together.

5. Subjecting Different Forces or a Series of Substance to Similar New Conditions

By suspending a great variety of substances free to move between the poles
of a powerful magnet, Faraday discovered the universality of magnetism;
Coulomb had previously made a similar attempt.

From about 1920 on, Virtanen investigated the processes that occur
during storage of green fodder. He realized that fermentation produced
various acids and breakdown products which spoil the fodder. By
acidifying the pressed green fodder to a pH below 4, the detrimental
biological processes were arrested and the nutritive value of the fodder
maintained. Virtanen received the Nobel award in chemistry for 1945.

6. Examining the Effects of a Particular Force on Substances

By applying heat to oxide of mercury, Priestley in the year 1774 dis-
covered oxygen, and by heating black oxide of manganese to redness, Scheele
in the following year re-discovered that gas.

In 1932, Cockcroft and Walton accelerated protons by the ionization of hydrogen in a discharge tube and used them to bombard a layer of lithium oxide. Bright sparkles, due to particles ejected from the lithium, were immediately observed on a nearby zinc sulfide screen. These sparkles, being caused by alpha particles, produced the conclusion that an occasional lithium atom captured an alpha particle and thereupon broke into two new helium-atom nuclei. Transmutation of an element had been achieved.

7. Examining the Effect of Mutual Contact of Substances upon Each Other

It was by examining the action of hydrogen and oxygen upon each other, under different circumstances, that the formation of water by synthesis was first discovered.

"Hardened" substitutes for butter can be traced to Sabatier's work done at the turn of the twentieth century. He learned that if the vapors of unsaturated hydrocarbons, together with an excess of hydrogen, were passed over freshly reduced nickel kept at 150–200°C., the fatty acids would be converted into solid fats.

8. Examining the Influence of Time upon Phenomena

The influence of time is seen on the grandest scale in the phenomena of astronomy and geology; here the experiments are made for us, and continued not merely for a few years, but during hundreds, thousands, and even millions of years.

On the morning of August 27, 1883, a violent volcanic explosion converted the island of Krakatoa into a completely lifeless wasteland covered with a thick blanket of smoking pumice and ashes. Realizing that the repopulation of the island required all seeds, spores, and animals to cross a 25-mile stretch of the sea, the island became a perfect "laboratory" in which to study the distribution of plants and animals over the earth. With the passage of time, a clear picture emerged not only of independent means of seed dispersal but also the interrelationships between many species.

9. Investigating the Effects of Extreme Degrees of Force on Substances

In the year 1835, Thilorier solidified carbonic anhydride by the intense cold of its own evaporation.

In 1911, Kamerlingh Onnes, while working with pressures ranging as high as 3,000 atmospheres and very low temperatures, discovered that near absolute zero the electrical resistance of certain metals practically disappears. An electrical current started in a coil of one of these metals may continue to flow for hours or even days. This phenomenon is called superconductivity.

10. Employment of Instruments of Very Great Power

The discovery of electro-magnetism by Öersted, in the year 1819, enabled very powerful magnets to be made, and thus paved the way for discoveries to be evolved by their aid.

Much of the success of the mid-twentieth century satellite projects designed to explore outer space was due to the powerful performance of extremely miniaturized instruments. These instruments could not only record measurements of space factors, but they could also convert these measurements into impulses that could be broadcast back to earth or recorded on magnetic tape in capsules to be recovered after re-entry into the earth's atmosphere.

IV. Discovery by Means of Additional, New, or Improved Observations
1. Additional or New Observations with Known Instruments or Known Methods

DeLuc, in the year 1755, observed that ice, during the act of melting, did not rise in temperature above the freezing-point until it was entirely melted; and Dr. Black confirmed that observation.

Believing that a better understanding of the physiology of the camel can make a valuable contribution to the welfare of people in arid countries, K. Schmidt-Nielsen abandoned the popular belief that camels store water in some kind of reservoir. Extending the usual techniques for collecting data on metabolism and tissue of cellular changes, he discovered that the camel's adaptation to arid conditions is more accurately related to such things as rate of water excretion, fluctuating body temperature, distribution of body fat, and other factors of general physiological interest.

2. Employing New or Improved Modes or Instruments of Observation

It was by the assistance also of greatly increased sensitiveness of the galvanometer which he employed, that Du Bois Reymond was enabled to make his discoveries of electric currents in animal tissues.

Availability of the isotope O-18 enabled Samuel Ruben and Martin Kamen to prove that all of the oxygen liberated in photosynthesis originated in water; none came from carbon dioxide.

3. More Intelligent and Acute Observation

The movements of the magnetic needle, for instance, which revealed the existence of magnetic storms over large portions of the earth, were many of them so small as to be microscopically minute, and required the most acute observation in order to detect them.

While contemplating Libby's C-14 method for dating ancient organic material, E. Thellier and O. Thellier realized that the strength of the earth's magnetic field has been decreasing steadily. This fact was based on measurements of the magnetism of bricks over 1,700 years old. A decreasing magnetic field around the earth would permit an increase in the flux of cosmic rays reaching the earth's atmosphere. From this the Thelliers argued that estimates of the ages of materials by the C-14 method would be too small by as much as 240 years in 1700 years.

4. Combined Efforts of Many Observers

A large amount of discovery in astronomical, magnetical, and meteorological science, and the subject of cosmical spectrum analysis, has resulted from the combined intellectual action of many observers in different parts of the world.

In the late 1950's, a world-wide organization of scientists attacked those phenomena that have world-wide dimensions. By careful advance planning and synchronization of observations, certain phenomena were observed in their totality, whereas only spotty observations could have been possible without such an organization. The coordinated observations bearing on solar activity, ocean currents, geomagnetism and related phenomena gave mankind one of the most accurately interpreted bodies of data ever collected concerning these phenomena.

V. Discovery from the Classification and Comparison of Known Truths
1. Simple Comparison of Facts or Phenomena

In 1820 Brewster, by comparing, discovered the coincidence of position between the geographical points of maximum cold and the terrestrial magnetic poles.

In 1934, E. Fermi and his associates bombarded uranium with slow neutrons, hoping to identify new, heavier elements. His identifying techniques consistently revealed lighter elements in his apparatus, the presence of which seemed to be most easily explained as impurities. By 1939, after repeated examination of the data, L. Meitner and her associate O. R. Frisch came up with the brave, new, and correct interpretation, based on division of the unstable uranium nucleus into two nuclei of approximately equal mass.

2. Comparison of Facts with Hypotheses

It was largely by means of comparison that Goethe, about the year 1790 (and before him Wolff and Linnaeus also, but vaguely), suggested the discovery that all the different parts of a plant are only modified stems and leaves, so altered by surrounding conditions as to fit them to those conditions and to the work to be done.

On January 26, 1939, a group of physicists at a meeting in Washington, D.C., were told of conjectures concerning the fission of uranium by neutron bombardment. Experiments were devised immediately to detect the intense ionization expected from the fission products. An oscillographic record was quickly obtained. Cloud-chamber observations confirmed the hypothesis. In addition, F. Joliot found that the fission fragments were ejected with enough energy to travel the predicted distance.

3. Comparing Facts and Collecting Together Similar Ones

Discovery by generalization, or simply classing together similar substances or phenomena, has constituted a very necessary step in the evolution of knowledge, but is fast being replaced by the more truthful method of classification (or rather arrangement) of bodies and actions in natural series, in accordance with their relations of mutual dependence as cause and effect.

In 1900, C. T. R. Wilson suggested that the puzzling discharge of well shielded electroscopes could be due to unknown rays coming from outside the earth. Another group of scientists observed that electroscopes were similarly discharged on the surface of frozen Lake Ontario, at some distance from the land. In 1910 T. Wulf and A. Gockel further attacked the theory that these rays were coming from radioactive minerals in the earth by showing that at high altitudes, electroscopes were actually discharged more rapidly than at the earth's surface. Still other investigators proved that these as yet undescribed rays could travel through thick layers of metal and even penetrate the depths of mountain lakes. In 1925, R. A. Millikan put all these separate investigations and observations into the single perspective of cosmic rays.

4. Comparing Collections of Facts with Each Other

Sir J. Herschel [1792–1871] discovered that the right-handed or left-handed optical property of crystals correspond with what may be termed their right-handed or left-handed crystalline form.

It was at the turn of the twentieth century that J. J. Thomson improved upon man's concept of electricity as being composed of discrete units rather than matter in an "ultragaseous" state. His concept of the electron grew out of Crooke's work with cathode rays, Faraday's discoveries concerning electrolysis, Townsend's measurements of the electrical charges on individual cloud droplets, and the hypotheses of Stoney and Helmholtz.

5. Arranging a Collection of Facts in Particular Orders, and Comparing the Orders

By comparing together the order of the elements with regard to their conducting power for heat and that for electricity, the important discovery was made that the orders were alike for the two forms of energy, and therefore the conclusion could be drawn that the one phenomenon was related to the other in some intimate way.

During the 1930's, a group of business-minded scientists under Charles F. Kettering realized that housewives would never go for refrigerators unless they used a refrigerant that was safer than the ammonia used in ordinary ice-making machines. Kettering's men knew that the desired compound must have a boiling point between 0° and —40°C., be stable, nontoxic, and nonflammable. By turning to the classified array of facts on the periodic table, their attention was drawn to fluorine. Other information and circumstances led to the idea that dichloromonofluoro-methane would have the desired properties. It did, and the problem was solved.

VI. Discovery by Means of Study and Inference

Lamarck (born in 1747), by the study of such living things as snails, worms, insects, shell-fish, sea-anemones, sponges (to which he gave the name of "invertebrate animals," because they have no backbone), and from the impossibility of determining what were distinct forms or species, was led to infer and discover the defective nature of the theory of distinct species, and to conclude that all the immense variety of animals were not separately created, but were probably evolved by the gradual alteration and differentiation of a few simple forms during the long series of ages; and the differences of climate and of food formed a part of the cause of their change.

Knowing that a moving stream of charged particles is deflected by a magnetic field in a direction perpendicular both to the field and to the direction of their motion, B. Rossi in 1930 argued that more cosmic rays should approach the earth from easterly than from westerly directions. This was proved true in 1935 by T. H. Johnson, using cosmic-ray telescopes. From this he deduced that the particles present in cosmic rays before interacting with nuclei present in the atmosphere, are mainly protons.

VII. Discovery by Means of New or Improved Methods of Intellectual Operation

Poisson, in 1824, by employing the mathematical artifices of Laplace and Legendre, was enabled to obtain general expressions for the attractions and repulsions of a body of any form whatever, magnetised by influence upon a given point, and in the case of spheroidal bodies was able to solve completely the equations which determine these forces.

By being willing to abandon the basic postulate that the description of a particle is the same irrespective of whether a right- or left-handed frame of reference is used, T. D. Lee and C. N. Yang, were able in 1956 to explain experimental results that strongly suggested that neutrons and antineutrons, definitely different particles, were different simply because their spin coordinates were of opposite sign.

VIII. Discovery by Means of Calculations Based Upon Known Truths

By calculation also, Newton "appears to have discovered the method of demonstrating that a body might describe an ellipse, when acted upon by a force residing in the focus, and varying inversely as the square of the distance." By similar means he discovered the specific gravity of the planets, and that the density of Saturn is almost nine times less than that of our earth; also that our earth could not be a perfect globe, and ascertained almost exactly how much it was flattened at the poles. He also found, by similar means, that the precession of the equinoxes was due to the earth not being a perfect sphere, and that the cause of it was the greater attraction of the sun and moon upon the extra mass of matter existing around it at the equator.

In 1946, W. F. Libby realized that cosmic rays bombarding N-14 in the atmosphere would produce C-14, an isotope with a known half-life of 5,600 years. Furthermore, he knew that the C-14 would soon be converted into carbon dioxide and, in turn, be caught up in the photosynthesis carbon cycle. Finally, specimens of new wood from all over the world yield 15.3 counts per minute per gram of carbon from the decay of C-14. From these observations, Libby concluded that the C-14 count from ancient carbonaceous material will permit calculation of the age of the material.

To summarize, the environment most likely to encourage the identification of topics for investigation is rich in clues to naturally occurring events and circumstances, richly furnished with facilities to note and pursue these clues, and inhabited by at least a few people who are radiating the enthusiasm that comes with being able to identify and pursue those clues that lead to worthwhile excursions in science.

EVALUATING A POTENTIAL TOPIC

During the pursuit of science, an investigator's primary attention must be focused on one idea or hypothesis at a time. The investigator is thus reduced to defending his choice of topic for investigation as being the most valuable and important one in which to invest his resources. To predict accurately the ultimate value of any excursion in science is difficult if not impossible. The spirit of science gives each man the right to invest his lifetime examining even trifling matters and especially so because each man is likely to adopt a different set of standards by which to estimate the value of a new discovery or invention. The teaching scientist or laboratory director, however, cannot escape the responsibility of trying to divert students and other workers in science away from trifling matters and toward those that are likely to evolve into great ideas.

Somewhere along any excursion in science the worker must confront himself with an evaluation of his work. Sooner or later he must ask himself: What will be the worth of what I am setting out to do? What is the worth of what I have done? If that which conduces most to the progress of civilization is adopted as a greatest value, the most important episodes in science are not always those that produce the greatest immediate improvement in the comfort and welfare of mankind, but rather those that lead ultimately to the explanation, coordination, and integration of the greatest number of facts. From the principles that grow out of this coordination of facts often come the great breakthroughs by which civilization advances.

An investigator only delays facing up to his own sense of values when he chooses the quick, easy, highly profitable small idea and shies away from a bigger, less manageable, elusive idea that seems to carry with it the haunting appeal of a truly significant challenge. The young or new worker in science must do his share of accumulating "lesser" truths, but there is probably no stimulant or catalyst more effective than having a clear vision of the "great" discovery toward which his work is advancing. Then there is always the question of "ripeness" of an idea. Is it true that some scientists have really suffered under the handicap of being "before their time"? When examined against the total social, economic, and ethical environment in which science is pursued, this question is highly debatable. It is true, of course, that the likelihood of any excursion in science being successfully completed is a function of two sets of factors, only one of which is in the investigator—his characteristics, resources, and facilities. The second set is in the topic chosen for investigation. A group of scientific workers, be they students or practicing research people, is very probably making maximum progress toward agreed-upon goals when the difficulty of the topic under investigation arouses frustrations just short of the breaking point. If the topic seems to take a particularly elusive turn, frustration may exceed tolerance. On the other hand, the satisfactions that accrue from successful completion of even minor facets of an investigation can be adequate to return the worker to attack, with renewed energy, even a bigger problem.

STATING THE PROBLEM

Following closely upon the selection of a topic for investigation is the statement of the problem. The event or circumstance to be investigated, explored, or discovered all too often exists in a misty cloud of predominant ignorance presenting an awesome, unapproachable, sometimes even mystical appearance. Until the investigator can circumscribe the unknown area and identify where known and yet-to-be-known factors impinge on each other, he will remain in the hauntingly frustrating condition of "just-can't-seem-to-get-at-it." Actually, the research worker cannot say he has found or selected a topic for an excursion in science until he has a problem stated in approachable form. The graduate student who is "thinking about doing something on polymerization" or expects to "look into the occurrence of human twins" is quite likely to continue indefinitely to clutter up the university science department.

Basically, inability to fabricate a problem statement is most often traceable to a specific deficiency in one or more of the essential characteristics of the scientist. Lacking successful identification of a specific deficiency, inability to shape up a problem statement can be sometimes overcome by doing additional background reading in the general area of the topic around which the investigation is being planned. In some cases teams of workers, by pooling their efforts, can pin down a loosely conceived problem. Rarely is the statement of a problem done once and for all. By exploratory steps, some taken in the laboratory and some in the library, the problem is narrowed; and eventually a problem statement appears in which the solution becomes obvious, and the desired results become almost inescapable.

Assuming that the investigator has settled on a topic that seems to meet importance, probability, and ripeness criteria, and that the worker is fitted to an investigation of the topic, he should proceed promptly toward wording a problem statement and shaping an attack. Lacking sufficient knowledge to design an investigation or experimentation, he may need to resort to search principles, the topic of the chapter that follows.

For Discussion and Further Study

1. Keeping the total environment of his students in mind, what can a teacher do to increase the likelihood that they will find problems worth investigating?

2. Under what circumstances should a teacher shunt a student away from interest in a problem?

3. Within the limits imposed by the spirit of science, how far can a teacher go in trying to arouse student interest in a problem?

4. Is the science teacher justified in requiring each student to explore an assigned problem sufficiently to insure that the student will know whether the problem interests him?

5. Do the categories of sources of problems as outlined by Gore apply to twentieth century problems?

6. In respect to ultimate selection of their own problems to investigate, what are the positive and negative features of assigning students as apprentices to practicing scientists?

7. What role should a teacher assume when a student wants to take on a sophisticated problem before he has completed the usual prerequisite training?

8. Can students be "trained" to be alert to curiosity-stimulating observations in their environments?

9. Is it possible to trace the segments of science that appear in textbooks to their individual triggering situations?

10. Why do scientists often claim that no clear-cut, single event or circumstance launched them on separate discoveries or inventions?

References

1. Arthur Dehon Little *On the Making of Silk Purses from Sow's Ears.* Cambridge, Mass.: Arthur D. Little, Inc., 1921. Brochure, p. 8.
2. C. P. Haskins. *Research in Industry,* edited by C. C. Furnas. Princeton, N.J.: D. Van Nostrand Company, 1948, pp. 192–93.
3. Robert G. Chollar. *Motivating Industrial Research Personnel,* Research Development Series, Pamphlet No. 2. New York: American Management Association, 1956, p. 10.
4. Hans Reichenbach. *Atom und Kosmos,* 1930. Quoted by the Rand Corporation, *Scientific American,* **200** (February 1959), p. 36.
5. G. Gore. *The Art of Scientific Discovery.* London: Longmans, Green & Company, 1878, pp. 453–612.

7

Search Principles

There are in fact four very significant stumbling-blocks in the way of grasping the truth, which hinder every man however learned, and scarcely allow anyone to win a clear title to wisdom, namely, the example of weak and unworthy authority, long-standing custom, the feeling of the ignorant crowd, and the hiding of our own ignorance while making a display of our apparent knowledge. Every man is involved in these things, every rank is affected. For every person, in whatever walk of life, both in application to study and in all forms of occupation, arrives at the same conclusion by the three worst arguments, namely, this is a pattern set by our elders, this is the custom, this is the popular belief: therefore it should be held.[1]

Roger Bacon   c. 1260

Several different kinds of cultural resistance to discovery may be distinguished . . . the substantive concepts and theories held by scientists at any given time become a source of resistance to new ideas. . . . The methodological conceptions scientists entertain at any given time constitute a second cultural source of resistance. . . . Some scientists, for example tend to be antitheoretical . . . [or to] reject propositions just because they cannot be put in the form of some model. . . . Some scientists are excessively partial to mathematics, others are excessively hostile . . . the religious ideas of scientists themselves constitute, after substantive and methodological conceptions, a third cultural source of resistance to scientific innovation.

In addition to shared idea-systems, the patterns of social interaction among scientists also become sources of resistance to discovery. . . . The first of these . . . is the relative professional standing of the discoveries. . . . Another . . . is the pattern of specialization that prevails in science at any given time. . . . Occasionally, when [scientific] organizations or publications are incompetently staffed and run, they may serve as another social source of resistance to innovation in science. . . . The rivalries of what are called "schools" are frequently alleged to be another. . . . That the older resist the younger in science is another pattern . . . that has often been noted by scientists themselves and by those who study science as a social phenomenon. . . .

That some resistance occurs, that it has specifiable sources in culture and social interaction, that it may be in some measure inevitable, is not proof either that there is more resistance than acceptance in science or that scientists are no more open-minded than other men.[2]

Bernard Barber 1961

Successful conduct of research is associated more with particular mental attitudes and habits of mind than with specialized techniques or procedures, although the latter may be present in certain phases of the work. . . . The specifically creative phases of the research process appear to be relatively loose, informal and personal, having very little in common with the highly structured, rigorously logical, and formal, public description of the results. It seems clear that it is this private, relatively unstructured, and perhaps only partly conscious, process which results in the creation of new ideas and insights. Thus, although analogy and metaphor are definitely prescribed techniques for formal reasoning, they may be among the dominant processes in the intuitive, sometimes illogical, initially random, scanning and searching process for new connections and clues. To be creatively efficient such scanning and searching processes might well need an uninhibited, habitually exercised, capability to consider, and tentatively accept, ideas in direct contradiction to accepted facts, concepts and theories; obviously also, the efficiency of this process would be greater, the larger the universe of relevant data of all sorts available for it.[3]

Jerome B. Wiesner 1963

Scientific research is always concerned with searches of one kind or another. These may be as trivial as searching for the proper setting of three screws to bring a galvanometer into a level position or as large-scale as a search for a cure for cancer.[4]

E. Bright Wilson 1952

COMMON-SENSE STRATEGY

Most of the discussions of the tactics and strategy of the pursuit of science assume that any episode proceeds smoothly from the identification of a problem into the elaboration of working hypotheses and on into the design of experiments or investigations. It is safer to assume, however, that there will be delays between the identification of a puzzling event or circumstance and the elaboration of an hypothesis sufficiently precise to allow the designing of an experiment or the launching of an investigation. Especially for young people who are being initiated into the pursuit of science, this delay can be quite hazardous and prolonged.

Wilson[5] provides some basic "search" principles which can help an investigator proceed efficiently between identification of a problem and the elaboration of a working hypothesis. In general, these principles are simply organized common sense.

"Know as Much as Possible
About the Object of the Search"

Rarely does an investigator set out in search of an explanation or description of an event or circumstance that is entirely unrelated to all other events or circumstances. If the search involves the cause of a strange disease, for example, it can be argued that knowledge concerning the cause of already familiar diseases should point toward the unknown cause. The investigator should know, however, that knowledge pertaining peculiarly to the disease being investigated, if it can be obtained, will be more enlightening than knowledge derived from studying even closely related diseases.

One needs only to think about the huge sums of money and the millions of hours that have been spent searching for the cause or causes of cancer to realize that no guaranteed-to-be-successful procedures can be established for the pursuit of science. There are probably few phenomena about which more is known. Who knows—perhaps the

72

actual cause of cancer is connected to the visible symptoms by a long and quite intangible connection. For reasons such as these, the principle of knowing as much as possible about the object of the search must be constantly tempered with the inherent inconsistency that the investigator does not know for sure what he is looking for. To persistently "search the literature" on apparently related topics could become a treadmill to nowhere.

"Prove, if Possible, That the Object Exists in the Area to be Searched"

This principle can be easily illustrated by calling attention to a situation often encountered by transoceanic air navigators whose destinations are coastal cities. They know it will be no problem to find the coastline, but, assuming they do not hit the city, they must decide whether to turn to the right or to the left. The navigator who wants to play it the safest will alter course while yet far out to sea so as to be sure he can "home in" on the coastline. Obviously, this cautious navigator is willing to sacrifice time and distance for the security of knowing that he will eventually find his destination. Unfortunately, however, solutions in the pursuit of science are not charted on maps. The investigator must settle for only that security that comes from carefully considering all known factors and for hoping that he has included the object of his search in the boundaries of his investigation.

There are phenomena which seem to lack all possibilities of finding a single feature on which the investigator can "home in." Which way should one turn, for example, if he seeks an adequate description or explanation of gravity? Similarly, can an investigator be sure that he can construct a laboratory that will contain each and all of the events and circumstances that accompany the occurrence of a specific disease? Even more haunting is the possibility that the investigator might include a factor that would either mask, counteract, or otherwise obscure the existence of the object of the search.

The boundaries of a pursuit in science can be, at best, a three-dimensional spiral. The investigator begins by examining closely those things that he believes are most likely to circumscribe the solution to his problem or an adequate description of the thing which puzzles him. His continuing investigation expands to include additional factors, but his elevated position enables him to review the pathway along which he has already traveled. Three-dimensional alertness can identify clues that might be worth special investigation, and the spiral perspective keeps the investigator in closest touch with the reasoning that gave the original direction to the investigation.

"Use the Most Efficient
Method of Detection"

This can be a very difficult principle to apply, especially in the pursuit of phenomena in the psychological sciences. If one is attempting to study the development of the ability to design experiments, for example, how can the developing ability be detected? Or if one is investigating the likelihood of extrasensory perception, how does he know that the phenomenon can be detected with sensory procedures?

Invariably, the detection of the object of a search is based on a secondary property or symptom of the object. Slight changes in blood count, temperature, melting point, electrical conductivity, and similar factors are used to keep track of a whole complex of physiological or chemical phenomena. Efficiency of this kind can be gained only at the risk of losing track of the true solution to the problem being studied. The investigator must keep under constant surveillance the validity and reliability of secondary factors being used to observe primary phenomena.

"Be Sure You Would See the
Object if It Were Encountered"

Anyone who has ever put a jigsaw puzzle together can sense both the meaning and the frustration of this principle. Even though all of the surrounding pieces are in place and one can see the exact shape, color, and design of the missing element, it is often quite difficult to pick the piece from its apparent hiding place. The frustration becomes even more haunting when a bystander casually picks up the needed piece simply because he enjoys a better perspective or freshness of observation.

Another lesson may be extracted from the jigsaw metaphor. One takes on an extremely haunting frustration if he thinks that pieces of the puzzle have been lost permanently or have been forced into their wrong positions.

This principle is closely related to knowing as much as possible about the object of the search. Knowing what is desired as the end product of a search is only a part of the story. Many men have earnestly and persistently sought the cause and cure of cancer. They all knew precisely what they hoped to find, but only in terms of hopes and desires. They did not know the precise specifications of what they sought and, thus, may have been in the presence of what they sought without recognizing it. Those who pursue science must not only have a goal in mind but be constantly striving to establish the identifying characteristics of what it is they seek. This is the best insurance that the object will be recognized if encountered.

"Be Sure You Wouldn't See the Object When It Isn't There"

The reverse of this principle is the old proverb: None is so blind as he who will not see. The exaggerated version is: It is so because thus it is so useful. Human nature being as it is, each investigator must be on guard against allowing intense desire to overcome strict objectivity in his observations. Although there is in the pursuit of science a place for persistence, more often it is a case of persistence in search of a point of view than in protection of a hoped-for solution.

There are so many instances where a wavering meter pointer can be read a little high or a little low, where a color change does or does not quite occur, or where a difference becomes or fails to become significant in the normal evolution of investigations, that the investigator must not only discipline himself to avoid shading his observations optimistically, but he must also establish safeguards against overcompensating for desire.

"Search Systematically Instead of Haphazardly"

A few hours spent classifying and ordering one's data can yield large dividends in time saved in the design and execution of experiments. The history of science bears witness to the advantage derived from data that yield central tendencies in contrast to totally divergent observations. When the data derived from an investigation begin to converge, the investigator gains the advantage of establishing boundaries to his pursuit. It is usually more effective to establish this convergence by a systematic design in the accumulation of data than to hope that patterns will emerge as the investigation continues.

Each of the fields of science provides well-established classifications of known facts and relationships. The life sciences have their phylogenetic orders, chemistry has its periodic arrangement of the elements, the physical sciences provide such relationships as the electromagnetic spectrum; and it would be only the inept investigator who did not utilize these kinds of relationships in building system into his pursuits.

If an investigation involves variations of one or more factors, it is axiomatic that the variation should be systematic. The ultimate value of data all too often hinges on interpolation and extrapolation, processes which are almost impossible if the data have not been systematically derived.

"If Possible, Devise a Way of
Determining the Approximate Direction and
Distance of the Object at Every Point of Search"

This principle applies more easily to technological than to pure-science pursuits, because it assumes a known location for the object of the search. If an investigator is seeking, for example, an alloy of prescribed hardness, it is a simple matter to compare the hardness of each experimentally derived sample against the desired end products. How can one determine, however, how close he is to an adequate description of the antecedents of earthquakes or the exact direction in which the true explanation of this phenomenon lies?

"In Many-Dimensional Problems It Is Usually
Necessary to Devise a One-Dimensional Path"

This principle assumes that the investigator can pursue one facet of his work at a time more effectively than to try to keep several facets progressing simultaneously. Obviously, if the phenomenon being studied seems to involve an interplay of several factors, the single line of approach is not appropriate. In any case, to devote one's full time and attention to one factor does enable the investigator to achieve fuller understanding of that factor. If, for example, the object of a search is a new chemical compound, the usefulness of which depends upon narrowly specified properties, it may be appropriate to seek to meet one specification at a time. Drug chemists, however, know all too well how futile it is to synthesize a new drug that possesses the properties which would make it useful only to find that it also has a toxic property. Invariably one or more of the desired specifications become lost in the effort to gain the final property.

"If Possible, Mark the Starting Point,
and Record the Path Actually Followed"

Even the proverbial needle in the haystack can be found if one devises a way to examine each bit of hay and to separate what has been searched through from what remains to be examined. Each hypothesis in any pursuit of science takes the investigator in one or another direction. If the starting point is marked and the end result known, a line of direction is established. Lacking either of these points, the investigator faces the future with no more confidence than he had at the beginning of his investigation. Frustration can become panic when one is groping for the right path and suddenly realizes that he has searched the same place before but can't recall the circumstances.

Carefully recorded observations made along previous investigational pathways can be reviewed when an apparent stalemate is reached in any pursuit. This kind of review can restore the investigator's confidence that some kind of progress is being made and, sometimes, point toward a new and promising path yet to be explored.

"Use a Convergent Procedure"

This principle follows naturally from the preceding one and is closely related to the advice to make a systematic rather than a haphazard search. No greater encouragement can come during the pursuit of science than when the results of several experiments begin to point toward a common conclusion. If it can be done, to design experiments with this convergent characteristic in mind is more effective than to recognize unplanned but hoped-for convergence.

"Search the Most Probable Place First"

This is an appropriate place to recall the common-sense nature of all of these search principles.

"Distribute the Available Time, Facilities, or Effort in Reasonable Proportions in Different Regions"

This principle, although it appears to contradict the preceding one, is quite appropriate during the early phases of an investigation. Exploratory experiments, properly focused, can often avoid expenditure of time and resources on extensive dead-end hypotheses. An exploratory experiment, however, must be done as carefully and interpreted even more adroitly than full-scale experiments. A superficial testing of an hypothesis provides a very effective hiding place for the object of a search, a state of affairs touched on in the next principle.

"Take into Account the Finite Probability of Missing the Object on Passing by It"

Every student in the beginning stages of chemical analysis knows the haunting frustration of wondering whether or not the "unknown" escaped detection at one of the earlier steps in the analytical scheme.

"Consider Any Effect the Search Procedure May Have on the Search Object"

The implications of this principle are very important in the life sciences, especially those phenomena that are primarily psychological.

An investigator must design his experiments exceedingly carefully to insure that the presence of the investigator in itself does not introduce an uncontrolled variable. The possibility that the means of observing phenomena in the physical sciences can approach the magnitude of the forces being observed has led to the principle of indeterminancy, and although these conditions are likely to prevail only in highly sophisticated experiments, the general concept of indeterminancy must be kept in mind.

MAXIMS FROM INDUSTRIAL SCIENCE

Somewhat related to Wilson's search principles are some "tips on how to increase your earning power as an industrial scientist." These ideas and suggestions have been prepared by John O. Percival,[6] and were published in *Chemical and Engineering News* on January 25, 1960. Only excerpts and adaptations will be presented here.

Obtain a clear definition of each problem. It is almost axiomatic that, to get somewhere, it is necessary to know where you want to go.

Follow a work plan. An investigation without a work plan is like a ship without a course.

Plan short cuts. Try to do the last experiment first. Don't delay in getting your feet wet or your hands dirty on a problem. A few crude preliminary experiments often will put you further ahead than a week of theoretical planning.

Strive for simplicity. Analyze your problems and answers to find the simple way, to eliminate the unnecessary, the awkward, and the inefficient.

Balance precision with economics. A man who never makes a mistake never does anything. Yet a man who makes too many mistakes doesn't get another chance.

Keep busy. Be a self-starter. A man who needs to have all details of his work planned and interpreted, or who has to be continually prodded into activity, can never expect a very high rating. Plan your experiments in advance; lay out your work plan days or weeks ahead. Then you can start your work bright and early each morning without stopping to figure out the next step.

Have several problems. The more problems you can handle simultaneously, the greater your progress. While something is aging or baking, you can be starting another project, writing a report, or getting the next experiment ready.

Work safely. Almost all accidents could be eliminated by the use of ordinary common sense and forethought. No one wants to associate with an unsafe worker.

Finish what you start. If jobs are carefully selected in advance, they usually can be finished.

Keep supervisors informed of progress and results. Many executives have risen far in their organizations not only through outstanding skill, but because, in addition, they could talk convincingly, clearly, pleasantly, and understandably.

Be neat and pleasant. Everyone likes the cheerful chap who works with enthusiasm, takes criticism gracefully, spreads praise where due, shares earned credit, shows a personal interest in his fellow workers, carries no wooden objects on his shoulders, and who always remembers the modern version of the Golden Rule, "Treat others as they would like to be treated."

Cooperate. There is no room for secrets, hoarding, or petty jealousies.

Be reliable. Make sure your answers are true, and if there is an element of uncertainty, clearly state the degree of uncertainty.

Write good reports. Nothing points up a report better than leading off not with a work summary but with a brief statement of principal results, conclusions, and recommendations.

Make suggestions. Don't keep your light under a bushel or a beaker. No one can read your mind. New ideas take selling, but if you are convinced, you can convince others. But don't be discouraged if your ideas at first meet resistance ranging from disinterest to downright opposition. That's just human nature.

Grow with the company. Successful men increase their popularity by kindness, their skills by doing, and their knowledge by home study.

For Discussion and Further Study

1. Is the pursuit of science so artistic that to impose common-sense search principles upon students threatens to stultify inventiveness and creativity?

2. Contrast how plodding versus prima-donna students might react to John O. Percival's suggestions.

3. What kind of laboratory exercises can be arranged that will illustrate the nature and wisdom of one or more of Wilson's search principles?

4. Is the science teacher justified in contriving laboratory exercises that will entrap students who contradict the common-sense suggestions included in this chapter?

5. Would the search principles outlined in this chapter apply to approaching persistently elusive pedagogical problems?

6. If the contents of this chapter were translated into reasons for so few practicing scientists' actually achieving proclaimed success, would the inferences be valid?

7. What would be the reaction to the material of this chapter by a person who embraces the "doing one's damnedest, no holds barred" concept of the processes of science?

8. Do the contents of this chapter shed valid light on the problem created by the many graduate students who complete all required course work but never accomplish suitable research projects?

References

1. Roger Bacon. *Opus Majus,* **I**, c. 1260, p. 1.
2. Bernard Barber. "Resistance by Scientists to Scientific Discovery," *Science,* 134 (September 1, 1961), pp. 596–602. Reprinted by permission of the American Association for the Advancement of Science and Bernard Barber.
3. Jerome B. Wiesner. Address delivered at the New York University Conference on Education for Creativity in Sciences. New York City, June 13, 1963. Reprinted by permission of Jerome B. Wiesner.
4. E. Bright Wilson, Jr. *An Introduction to Scientific Research.* New York: McGraw-Hill, 1952, p. 140. Used by permission of McGraw-Hill Book Company.
5. *Ibid.,* pp. 140–145 in part.
6. John O. Percival. "Increase Your Earning Power," *Chemical and Engineering News* (January 25, 1960), pp. 10–13.

8

Hypotheses

Hypotheses are the scaffolds which are erected in front of a building and removed when the building is completed. They are indispensable to the worker; but he must not mistake the scaffolding for the building.[1]

Johann Wolfgang von Goethe c. 1830

An hypothesis is, strictly speaking, a proposition which is put forward for consideration, and concerning the truth or falsity of which nothing is attested until the consideration is completed. It is thus necessarily associated with doubt, but with doubt of a negative rather than a positive kind. With the doubt which consists of a suspense of judgment rather than with the doubt which consists of an inclination to disbelieve.[2]

Norman R. Campbell 1922

Logic, which alone can give certainty, is the instrument of demonstration; intuition is the instrument of invention.[3]

Henri Poincaré 1905

Summing up, then, it would seem as if the mind of the great discoverer must combine contradictory attributes. He must be fertile in theories and hypotheses, and yet full of facts and precise results of experience. He must entertain the feeblest analogies, and the merest guesses at truth, and yet he must hold them as worthless till they are verified in experiment. When there are any grounds of probability he must hold tenaciously to an old opinion, and yet he must be prepared at any moment to relinquish it when a clearly contradictory fact is encountered.[4]

W. Stanley Jevons   1873

The logico-experimental sciences are made up of a sum of theories which, like living creatures, are born, live, and die, the young replacing the old, the group alone enduring. As with living beings, the lifetimes of theories vary in length and it is not always the long-lived ones that contribute most to the advancement of knowledge. Faith and metaphysics aspire to an ultimate, eternal resting-place. Science knows that it can attain only provisional, transitory states. Each theory fulfils its function, and there is nothing more to ask of it.[5]

Vilfredo Pareto   1919

The first process therefore in the effectual study of science must be one of simplification and reduction of results of previous investigation to a form in which the mind can grasp them. The results of this simplification may take the form of a purely mathematical formula or of a physical hypothesis.[6]

James Clark Maxwell   1855

It is interesting to contemplate a tangled bank, clothed with many plants of many kinds, with birds singing on the bushes, with various insects flitting about, and with worms crawling through the damp earth, and to reflect that these elaborately constructed forms, so different from each other, and dependent upon each other in so complex a manner, have all been produced by laws acting around us. . . . Thus, from the war of nature, from famine and death, the most exalted object we are capable of conceiving, namely, the production of the higher animals, directly follows. There is grandeur in this view of life, with its several powers, having been

82

originally breathed into a few forms or into one; and that, whilst this planet has gone cycling on according to the fixed law of gravity, from so simple a beginning endless forms most beautiful and most wonderful have been, and are being evolved.[7]

Charles Darwin 1859

TENTATIVE EXPLANATIONS

Hypotheses are tentatively accepted explanations of phenomena or probable solutions to problems. Hypotheses state that certain relationships exist concerning individual or groups of items, events, or circumstances. These statements are provisional suggestions of possible patterns in a given situation, rather than arrogant insistence that some one particular order must be imposed. Hypotheses are explicitly tentative in character; they are accepted only as mental tools used to fashion what are hoped will turn out to be more substantial explanations of puzzling situations. Hypotheses are triggered by a few facts, and should culminate in a revelation of proved orderliness. Expressed in a metaphor, hypotheses are the temporary bridges that a scientist constructs along his mental pathway between initial curiosity and later acceptable understanding.

Why Hypotheses?

In the pursuit of science, hypotheses, properly used, can suggest new experiments or observations and serve as aids in assessing the significance of an object or events. The hypothesis thus provides a preview of what the end product of any specific investigation is likely to be. The hypothesis provides an opportunity to subject the design of an evolving investigation to the rules of formal logic and deduce various consequences. These rules of formal logic can identify inconsistencies in thinking and suggest increased efficiency in the design of experiments. This is the first point at which logic is utilized in science.

Hypotheses are dangerous if, being too fondly embraced, they cause the investigator to subordinate facts to ideas, to cling to ideas proved useless, or to cling to misconceptions. Playing as they do such a significant role in the pursuit of science, hypotheses must be evaluated against criteria, which may predict fruitfulness versus barrenness, potential rather than stagnation.

THE REQUISITES
OF GOOD HYPOTHESES

A good hypothesis is a useful tool, or guide, in the observation of phenomena for which explanations are being sought. As a tool, therefore, a good hypothesis covers in its proposed explanation all the facts that it is intended to explain. The hypothesis that requires remodeling as each step of the investigation proceeds is not at all efficient, because it fails to reduce the complexity of what is being investigated. Such hypotheses threaten to leave the investigator on a half-built bridge, with nothing to do but return to the beginning of the journey and reconstruct new ideas from the already-explored facets of the investigation.

An exploratory hypothesis reveals its greatest value when it yields fresh predictions of facts that were not envisaged as within its scope when it was formulated. Even though hypotheses tend to be self-correcting and self-generating while under investigation, time spent elaborating the best possible hypothesis during the early stages of inquiry invariably proves to be time well spent.

The antithesis of good hypotheses are those that are dangerously tacit and unconscious. Returning to the metaphor, these are the oftentimes inviting detours, or habitual paths subconsciously followed in preference to a more logical yet less clearly seen mental bridge between the known and the hypothesized. That hypotheses be based on facts and not blindly intertwined with one another is essential. When the hypothesis that is woven from several hypotheses is condemned by experimental findings, it is impossible to identify the specific aspects of the investigation that were faulty. The hypothesis that has been proved to be false quite often advances an investigation as effectively as those that prove to be true. Assuming that the proof is decisive, the false hypothesis may point to something otherwise neglected, something without which a rare phenomenon may have been overlooked. Thus, false as well as true hypotheses may contribute one of the essential qualities for formulating the truly fruitful hypothesis, namely, testability. Perfect and aesthetically satisfying logical structure can be only hoped for in an hypothesis. It is sufficient that the hypothesis suggest some ascertainable difference in order for it to meet the criterion of testability.

By way of summary, a good hypothesis is:

(a) Precise enough to become the solution to a specific problem, yet sufficiently inclusive to yield knowledge that will enable the investigator to handle new and related problems.

(b) Stated so that it can be tested or verified either immediately or eventually.

(c) A clear picture of what the end product of the investigation will be.

(d) Logically consistent, free of ambiguity, and contains no tacit or interlocking assumptions.

(e) The simplest hypothesis that is adequate to embrace the problem.

ORIGIN OF HYPOTHESES

The creator doubtlessly needs a rich background of knowledge to create hypotheses that meet criteria of goodness such as those above. Faced with the same problem, any group of investigators, even though they share similar knowledge, will produce hypotheses differing widely in their basic nature. Even within the restrictions of the basic epistemological assumption of science that there is some order in nature, the normal approach to solving problems involves devising several alternative hypotheses and then sifting them. A single body of facts may be patterned in a great many different ways, reflecting many different frames of reference, and projected toward the creation of many different explanations. What sort of hypothesis originates in the mind of any one investigator depends not only on the agreed-upon facts but also upon a subtle quality synthesized from the past experiences, interests, and purposes of the investigator.

Imagination couples with past experience to produce hypotheses. Some imagination is essential, yet sheer imagination must be tempered with disciplined preparation and effort. This preparation is likely to begin with the spadework of classifying. The investigator is obliged to guess what questions to ask of his data in order to bring out the orderliness or relationships which become the clues to phenomena described by the data. Quite often these clues are identified either by classification of the data or by groupings of the replies obtained to the questions asked of the data.

The origin of hypotheses invariably involves the process of observation. It is observation that holds the hypothesis to reality and only rarely do purely mentally contrived hypotheses turn out to have any basis in the facts of the natural world unless these hypotheses, in one way or another, were triggered in the minds of their creators by some source of curiosity-catching subject matter.

The ideas expressed in the preceding paragraphs suggest that the qualities of mind required to produce hypotheses are in conflict with each other. In a sense, imagination is the antithesis of disciplined ordering of acquired knowledge. Similarly, the process of observation is dedicated to the here and now, not to the conception of what may be. But such seems to be the nature of the origin of hypotheses and perhaps it is this apparent internal conflict which causes the elaboration of the truly noble hypothesis to be such a rare event.

DEVELOPMENT OF HYPOTHESES

Most hypotheses are not yet ready for testing immediately upon being conceived. The tentative nature of hypotheses and the fact that they originate within the speculative realm of mental activity foretell the probability that they will not be stated clearly enough to be testable by the deduce-and-confirm process. In contrast to the absence of rigorous formality in human thinking, the great accumulation of knowledge that constitutes the discipline of logic is rigorously formal. Logic deals with ideal forms of thought and, as such, holds promise of being of special value toward clarifying the raw hypothesis and rendering it suitable for testing. Without this clarification process, the investigator faces the hazard of time and energy wasted in futile attempts to prove the unprovable. Conversion of the raw, freshly conceived hypothesis to the rigorous, testable hypothesis proceeds through the double process of projection against the body of observable facts whereby its utmost possible significance can be exploited and the body of knowledge accumulated in the rules and dicta of formal logic.

There have been instances in which the final form of an hypothesis was envisioned by its creator almost at the time of its conception. These instances, however, are much more likely to occur among the well-established than the newer members of the scientific fraternity, and it is this latter group that is the major concern of those who teach the pursuit of science.

LOGIC AND THE HYPOTHESIS

Probably the most effective step toward recognizing the role that formal logic can play in the clarification of hypotheses is consideration of the pairs of very common words and phrases that students of logic refer to as *connectives*. Three examples are: if . . . then, either . . . or, if . . . and only if. The degree of efficiency with which an hypothesis leads to the design of an experiment or other means of testing is quite likely to be determined by how obviously a pair of connectives has been used within the statement of the hypothesis.

John Stuart Mill, a nineteenth century philosopher and logician, attempted to describe the patterns that seem to exist in statements of hypotheses. These patterns, known as Mill's Methods of Experimental Inquiry, may seem quite clumsy to those who are only beginning the pursuit of science, and quite naive to those who are already caught up in the very complex hypotheses of modern day science. Nevertheless, these methods show nicely how hypotheses develop, and especially how connectives, in one form or another, are used to clarify their statements. Mill's methods of inquiry promise guidance for young people who are only beginning their pursuit of science, particularly if it can be shown how these methods can be combined with formal logic to yield guides for clarification of hypotheses. In some cases, these guides may actually take part in suggesting the content of hypotheses. Mill's methods are:[8]

THE METHOD OF AGREEMENT. If two or more instances of the phenomenon under investigation have only one circumstance in common, [then] the circumstance in which alone all the instances agree is the cause (or effect) of the given phenomenon.

THE METHOD OF DIFFERENCE. If an instance in which the phenomenon under investigation occurs, and an instance in which it does not occur, have every circumstance in common save one, that one occurring only in the former; the circumstance in which alone the two instances differ is the effect, or the cause, or an indispensable part of the cause, of the phenomenon.

THE JOINT METHOD OF AGREEMENT AND DIFFERENCE. If two or more instances in which the phenomenon occurs have only one circumstance in common, while two or more instances in which it does not occur have nothing in common save the absence of that circumstance, the circumstances in which alone the two sets of instances differ is the effect, or the cause, or an indispensable part of the cause, of the phenomenon.

THE METHOD OF CONCOMITANT VARIATIONS. Whatever phenomenon varies in any manner whenever another phenomenon varies in some particular manner, is either a cause or an effect of that phenomenon, or is connected with it through some fact of causation.

THE METHOD OF RESIDUES. Subduct from any phenomenon such part as is known by previous inductions to be the effect of certain antecedents, and the residue of the phenomenon is the effect of the remaining antecedents.

Many people, upon first encountering the statements of Mill's Methods of Experimental Inquiry, turn away from what they prematurely label archaic and awkward expressions. This is to be regretted. All too often these same people will struggle clumsily for many years with a hypothesis or phenomenon which they diagnose as being exceedingly elusive whereas, in reality, the elements of elusiveness could have been brought under control, one by one, by subjecting the overall investigation to Mill's patterns of experimental inquiry.

Many authors make much of what they consider to be the shortcomings of Mill's Methods of Experimental Inquiry. If these methods are taken out of their proper perspective or forced to do more than they can do, they will exhibit very serious "shortcomings." These methods can be invoked only after imaginative and creative thinking has occurred. The methods themselves are no stimulant to thinking; in fact, they tend to discipline free and unbridled seeking of possible solutions to problems and explanations of puzzling circumstances. Returning to the language of connectives, there are those students of the pursuit of science who maintain that investigators should be free to do the *if* kind of thinking without having to anticipate the *then* restriction. This may be quite possible, but awareness of the possibilty should make it less probable.

Mill's Methods of Experimental Inquiry and the use of connectives are, obviously, more mechanical than intellectual. If an investigator sets out with that purpose in mind, Mill's Methods of Experimental Inquiry can be made to yield ridiculous results. Nonscientists, irked by the overzealous scientist who would attempt to project his supremely efficient methods into other human endeavors, especially social and political science, sometimes develop these ridiculous situations into supposedly amusing anecdotes.

It is much more intelligent to recognize Mill's Methods of Experimental Inquiry for what they are. They are a part of, but in no sense the whole spectrum of the tactics and strategy of science. Their use should be mastered by those who would undertake the pursuit of science. How this mastery can be sought receives additional attention on pages 95 and 138.

Mill's Methods and other aspects of formal logic should be kept in mind at all points in the elaboration and clarification of hypotheses. They should be openly invoked whenever deductive inference, that human activity of thinking by which proposition after proposition is accepted or rejected, is used. Inferring is something people may do or fail to do and may do well or badly. It is one's grasp of formal logic that determines whether or not he will end in the tangles to which unrefined hypotheses may lead. In no sense, however, can logic substitute for past experience, imagination, or any of the other requisites for hypothesis elaboration. If misused, logic may cause the investigator to subdue imagination or to wander into that absent-minded tendency to devise systems that are not related to reality. The proper role of logic in hypothesis elaboration seems to be to supplement and to discipline the other powers of the mind during the conception and clarification of hypotheses. Logic serves as both a hidden guide and a conscious director causing the investigator to doubt his facts, his hypotheses, and the relationships which may exist within his data. From these doubts arise the design and conduct of experiments.

For Discussion and Further Study

1. How does courage enter into the creation and publication of hypotheses?

2. Does Campbell's interpretation of the nature of the tentativeness of hypotheses permit an investigator to become enamored of a favored hypothesis?

3. Is the paragraph quoted from Darwin, with which he brought his *Origin of Species* to a close, an hypothesis or a theory?

4. Other editions of Darwin's *Origin of Species* include the phrase: "having been originally breathed by the Creator into a few forms or into one." Does this wording change your answer to Question 3?

5. How do hypotheses differ from assumptions?

6. Can lessons be designed that will teach overtly the criteria of fruitful versus barren hypotheses?

7. If observation, imagination, and logic play entangled roles in the elaboration of hypotheses, is each function equally in need of and subject to discipline?

8. Are Mill's Methods of Experimental Inquiry reflected in the design of twentieth century episodes in science?

9. Elaborate or identify several hypotheses associated with proposed solutions to pedagogical problems, particularly science-teaching-improvement problems. Do these hypotheses meet the criteria of fruitful hypotheses?

10. If a teacher lingers too long at entertaining an array of hypotheses about a phenomenon, should he be accused of not "knowing his subject"?

References

1. Johann Wolfgang von Goethe. Quoted in Philipp Frank, *Modern Science and Its Philosophy*. Cambridge, Mass.: Harvard University Press, 1949, p. 62.

2. Norman R. Campbell. *Physics: The Elements.* Reprinted in Herbert Feigl and May Brodbeck, *Readings in the Philosophy of Science.* New York: Appleton-Century-Crofts, 1953, p. 290.

3. Henri Poincaré. *The Value of Science,* authorized translation by G. B. Halstead. New York: Dover Publications, 1958, p. 23. Originally published 1905.

4. W. Stanley Jevons. *The Principles of Science.* New York: Dover Publications, 1958. First published 1873, pp. 592–93 of original printing.

5. Vilfredo Pareto. *Traité de Sociologie Générale,* 1919. Quoted by the Rand Corporation, *Scientific American,* **197** (December 1957), p. 36.

6. James Clerk Maxwell. Quoted by Phillipp Frank, *Philosophy of Science.* Englewood Cliffs, N.J.: Prentice-Hall, 1957, p. 308.

7. Charles Darwin. *Origin of Species.* New York: Mentor edition, The New American Library of World Literature, 1958, p. 450. Originally published 1859.

9

Experiments

I shall begin by making some experiments before I proceed any further; for it is my intention first to consult experience and then show by reasoning why that experience was bound to turn out as it did. This, in fact, is the true rule by which the student of natural effects must proceed although nature starts from reason and ends with experience, it is necessary for us to proceed the other way around, that is—as I said above—begin with experience and with its help seek the reason. Experience never errs; what alone may err is our judgment, which predicts effects that cannot be produced in our experiments. Given a cause, what follows will of necessity be its true effect, unless some external obstacle intervenes. When that happens, the effect that would have resulted from the cause will reflect the nature of the obstacle in the same proportion as the obstacle is more or less powerful than the cause.[1]

Leonardo da Vinci 1500

Nothing . . . so effectually destroys the motives for research and the pleasure of such occupations, as to find, after having made and published a laborious investigation, that the conclusion was all a mistake.[2]

G. Gore 1878

90

*One of the most difficult decisions which an experimenter
has to make is whether or not to reject a result which seems
unreasonably discordant. . . . The best procedure to use
depends on what is known about the frequency of occurrence
of wild values, on the cost of additional observations, and on
the penalties for the various types of error. . . . There is
often a desire to disregard negative results on the grounds
that conditions were not right or that the operator was not
in the right mood. This is undoubtedly responsible for much
pseudo science, psychic phenomena, and similar material.*[3]

E. Bright Wilson, Jr. 1952

*Men who have an excessive faith in their theories or in their
ideas are not only poorly disposed to make discoveries but
they also make very poor observations. They necessarily observe with a preconceived idea and, when they have begun
an experiment, they want to see in results only a confirmation of their theory. . . . Those who believe too much in
their own theories do not sufficiently believe in the theories
of others. . . . They also make poor observations because
they take into the results of their experiments only what fits
their purpose, by neglecting what is unrelated to it, and by
very carefully avoiding whatever might go in the direction
of the idea they wish to combat.*[4]

Claude Bernard 1865

COURTESY OF THE RAND CORPORATION

*If matter evades us, such as the air and light, because of its
extreme thinness, if objects are located far from us in the
immensity of space, if man wishes to understand the performance of the heavens for the successive periods which
separate a large number of centuries, if the forces of gravity
and of heat be at work in the interior of a solid globe at
depths which will be forever inaccessible, mathematical
analysis can still grasp the laws of these phenomena. It
renders them present and measurable and seems to be a
faculty of the human reason destined to make up for the
brevity of life and for the imperfection of the senses.*[5]

Jean Baptiste Fourier 1822

COURTESY OF THE RAND CORPORATION

WHAT EXPERIMENTS ARE

Experiments are efforts to observe an event or circumstance under
conditions where as many extraneous factors as possible are eliminated

or their probable influence taken into account. These efforts, if successful, accumulate, bit by bit, evidence for or against an hypothesis. In the pursuit of an adequate description of a phenomenon, experiments proceed through continued elimination of irrelevancies while the investigator attempts to ensure that all essential conditions related to the phenomenon remain and that no newly irrelevant factors are introduced by the sheer mechanics of the experiments.

Basic to the validity of experimentation as a procedure in the pursuit of science is the assumption that a specified event or circumstance, if it occurs once with a determined set of antecedent or accompanying events or circumstances, will always occur with these and only these events or circumstances. These conditions of validity suggest a test for the reliability of experimentation as a procedure. An experiment is reliable if it reveals the absolute minimum events and circumstances which must accompany or precede the occurrence of the event being investigated. Reliability is closely related to accuracy. An accurate experiment provides a description sufficiently precise to allow other investigators to reproduce with a bare minimum of trial and error those features of the phenomenon that were described or defined by the experiment.

A large body of knowledge has been accumulated to help an investigator predict how closely his results will agree with results obtained by repeated investigations using different samples or instances of the phenomenon. This knowledge stems from statistical factors associated with randomization and replication. Obviously, if results obtained by investigating only a small sample of an event or circumstance that in nature occurs in large numbers are used to generalize about the total event or circumstance, the generalization can be no more accurate than the experimental sample was representative of the total phenomenon. By providing a kind of insurance against the inevitable prejudices and preferences of the investigator, a sample chosen at random is generally least likely to yield biased results. Similarly, the greater the number of samples investigated, the more likely it is that the results will be reproducible.

Using statistical techniques can increase the efficiency of designing, conducting, and interpreting experiments. With knowledge of the degree of validity required in the results, the size of experimental sample or number of replications required can be anticipated, with subsequent savings in time and other resources. To handle unduly large masses of data, although less hazardous than to attempt to extend inadequate data into too broad generalizations, is inelegant if not downright clumsy.

When apparatus is required for an investigation, each item can introduce a need for new precautions at each phase of planning, conducting, and interpreting experiments. Appropriate attention must be given to the possible effects that the apparatus may have on the true function of the phenomenon being investigated. For example, if means are employed to measure a factor of a phenomenon, other arrangements must be made to detect and measure any factors that are brought into the investigation simply by introducing detecting or measuring devices. Special regard must be given to those factors that arise from combinations of devices, since these factors cannot be detected by considering each piece of apparatus separately.

FROM PROBLEM TO HYPOTHESIS TO EXPERIMENT

Recall that episodes in the pursuit of science begin with the observation of selected parts of nature wherein a naturally occurring event or circumstance arouses enough curiosity to cause someone to seek to describe the phenomenon as accurately as possible. This description invariably associates the phenomenon with other and, usually, already familiar events and circumstances. It is the role of experimentation to establish these relationships.

Here arises what is probably the most significant stage or phase in the pursuit of science—significant because it is at this stage, more than at any other, that the eventual success or failure of an investigation is likely to be determined. Having settled upon a specific phenomenon to investigate, any aspect of the whole universe, for all that is known in advance, may be related to the phenomenon. *But in the framing of an hypothesis, the investigator is forced to establish boundaries to his investigation by declaring, at least tentatively, certain factors as being irrelevant and certain other factors as relevant.*

Obviously, no investigation will ever be successful if the "correct" answer was not included within the boundaries of the investigation. But it is the purpose of the investigation to determine this "correct" answer. The pursuit of science is very much like a hunter in pursuit of game, a rabbit, for example. When he sets out on a hunting expedition, he knows for sure what he hopes to find—a rabbit. He takes along a device to achieve his hopes—a gun. He goes to the woods and fields where his past experiences tell him rabbits are likely to be. But in doing so he has already begun to close the system in which his expedition will occur. He has declared city parks and lakes and streams, for example, as being out of bounds in his search for rabbits and fields and woods to be in bounds. Obviously, he has many good reasons for doing so, but suppose he finds no rabbit in the fields and woods. Is there not the remote possibility that all rabbits on the day of his hunting expedition had gone to the nearest city park or body of water?

And even if the decision to limit the expedition to fields and woods were the correct one, no hunter can cover a whole countryside at one time. Assuming that he wants to spend no more time than necessary, he must decide whether woods will be more likely than fields to produce his rabbit. Why does this become a more difficult decision? People who are familiar with the ways of rabbits know that woods and fields share a greater number of the factors that are related to where rabbits can be found than do city parks, lakes, and streams. The key phrase here is "people who are familiar with."

If the hunter, faced with the decision whether to hunt the woods or the fields, has been on other hunting expeditions, he will try to use what he learned from them as he continues to construct the boundaries of his new investigation. If, for example, he found rabbits in the woods on cold, rainy days and in the fields on warm, sunny days, he will base his decision on the prevailing weather conditions. But what will he do if he has never been hunting before under such weather conditions as prevail on the specific day of his current expedition? This requires him to theorize regarding the fundamental relationship between heat, humidity, sunlight and the other factors that combine to form the weather, and the physiological and ecological factors that determine where rabbits are likely to be.

The more the hunter knows about the ways of rabbits and their relationship to the geographical features of the countryside, the wiser can be not only his decision between woods and fields but also his choice of a specific wood or field. But remember always that even the wisest hunter will return empty-handed from his expedition if no rabbit existed in the system around which his carefully devised boundaries were constructed.

The scientific fraternity experiences no greater loss than the lives of the thousands of its members who persist in hunting with increasingly painstaking efforts for rabbits that had not been included within the boundaries of their investigations. Students who are beginning their pursuit of science must learn to make their observations with a specific hypothesis in mind but with at least a part of one eye open lest a glimpse can be caught of fleeting clues to the object of their search—even though these glimpses appear outside the prescribed boundaries of their investigations.

SIMPLE DESIGNS
FOR EXPERIMENTS

If the hypothesis under consideration is a simple generalization, it may be sufficient to test it by looking for more examples, seeing whether or not the generalization holds for them. For example, an investigator may be entertaining the hypothesis: If young people are given direct instruction in the tactics of the pursuit of science, then they will proceed more efficiently in the design and operation of their own experiments than will the contrasted category receiving no such instruction.

The investigator will very probably continue to compare the efficiency of the two categories of students included in the hypothesis. Unfavorable examples which violate the generalization may or may not lead to its rejection. If the generalization has any reasonable body of supporting data, the finding of new facts that do not fit usually leads to the refinement or elaboration of the original hypothesis rather than its complete rejection.

All too often, what appears to be only a naive generalization is the only kind of hypothesis that will enable the investigator to get started on the examination of exceedingly significant phenomena. One of the most difficult decisions facing young people in science is the choice between investing their time in a dimly defined hypothesis regarding what could be a very important phenomenon or in a sharply prescribed hypothesis concerning a phenomenon about which already enough is known to allow the investigator to frame an elegantly sophisticated hypothesis. The first of these choices holds special appeal for a variety of investigators, and they should be encouraged to make this choice if they are alert to every opportunity their preliminary efforts may yield whereby the refinement or elaboration of an ultimate hypothesis may be expedited.

Mill's Methods of Experimental Inquiry almost automatically suggest the designs of simple experiments. The first of these, the method of agreement, is simply a refinement of the procedure described in the preceding paragraphs. In general, this method assumes that if the circumstances leading up to a given event have in all cases had one factor in common, the factor may be the cause sought. This is especially true if it is the only factor in common.

The second of Mill's methods assumes that, if two sets of circumstances differ in only one factor and the set containing the factor leads to the event and the other set does not, this factor can be considered the cause of the event.

A third method assumes that if variation of the intensity of a factor results in a parallel variation of the effect, then this factor is a cause.

As pointed out in the discussion of their role in the creation of an hypothesis, Mill's Methods of Experimental Inquiry deserve adequate study by those who are beginning the pursuit of science. Science has, of course, become much more sophisticated during the century or so since Mill first framed these methods. But the beginners in science should not be expected to enter the pursuit thereof at its maximum level of sophistication.

Actually, Mill framed five methods of experimental inquiry, but the other two can be deduced from the three cited here. Although students who have yet to converse in the language of logic find it awkward at first glance, Mill's own discussion of these methods should be examined. Once the strangeness is overcome, they are appreciated as instances of precise communication. Consider, as an example, the method of concomitant variations. In Mill's words: "Whatever phenomenon varies in any manner whenever another phenomenon varies in some particular manner, is either a cause or an effect of that phenomenon, or is connected with it through some fact of causation."

Much of modern-day criticism of Mill's methods very probably stems from the shift from emphasis on seeking *causes* to describing *relationships*. These methods are equally if not more effective in establishing relationships than in *proving* causes, and thus there is even greater reason for the student of the pursuit of science to be familiar with them. This familiarity must include knowing their limitations and developing adeptness at choosing the proper method or combination of methods for the design of any specific experiment.

Mechanical use of Mill's Methods of Experimental Inquiry invites inefficiency in the design, conduct, and interpretation of experiments because these methods do not provide adequate safeguards against (1) reciprocity of causes and effects, (2) the possibilities of unseen or unimagined factors, (3) the existence of intrinsic counteracting or catalytic factors, and (4) the composition or plurality of causes combining to produce a new intrinsic effect.

Mill's methods are recognized as being adequate only to set the investigator on the road to the pursuit of science. They afford a general design for inquiry and, in keeping with Mill's own concept of his methods, they are not foolproof and must be used with a great deal of intuition. They are principally effective for deductive data gathering, whereas corroboration and verification must be accomplished through the use of more sophisticated principles of experimental design.

FROM EXPERIMENT
TO CONCLUSION

Data gathered during and, especially, at the conclusion of experiments are often nothing more than raw material for the powers of the mind that must be exercised in the pursuit of science. These data must be examined in every conceivable manner if their full value is to be exploited. Obvious, subtle, and even absurd categories of classification should be explored in the search for intrinsic relationships that might lead to a consistent description of the phenomenon being investigated.

Data gathered from a series of experiments should be projected against data from related investigations in a way that will bring to light consistencies and inconsistencies. Sometimes charts, models, or other visual devices can be used to nurture the incubation process in which raw data are to be made to yield insight into new and unsuspected relationships. To sit and stare at the wall seems to be normal procedure, and it is often possible to place things on the wall that will nurture the intellectual phases of the process.

Experimental results that appear to be "too good" invite special questioning and examination. All investigators, being human, are subject to becoming victims of wishful thinking that can lead to self-deception. The traditions of the scientific endeavor require the investigator to expose his data to evaluation and criticism by fellow scientists. This process is usually an adequate safeguard against self-deception and should be cherished as such.

Conclusions drawn from experiments reach their final fruition in the elaboration of new or more precise descriptions of phenomena. These descriptions, in turn, are fashioned into either explanations of these phenomena, revised beliefs, or technological inventions designed to predict or manage phenomena toward the increased knowledge, comfort, and welfare of mankind.

For Discussion and Further Study

1. Is it the process of experimentation that makes science a unique human endeavor?

2. Are there a few assumptions that are basic to the validity of the whole process of experimentation?

3. Is there a relationship between the general concept of randomness as it applies to the occurrence of natural events and to the concept of a random statistical sample?

4. Is the success of an investigator's project determined more by the finesse of his experimentation or by the wisdom of his hypothesis?

5. Can laboratory exercises be arranged that will give students overt instruction in the design of experiments? In determining the validity of experimentally derived data?

6. Defend or refute the argument that inasmuch as Mill's methods were conceived during the adolescence of science, they hold special significance to teachers who are introducing students to the pursuit of science.

7. Is it pedantic semantics to insist that school laboratory exercises be identified as *exercises* rather than as experiments?

8. Can Gore's lament for the misinterpreted experimental result be communicated to students, or is this something only the practicing scientist can know?

References

1. Leonardo da Vinci, *Notebooks,* Circa, 1500. Quoted by the Rand Corporation, *Scientific American,* **199** (October 1958), p. 1.

2. G. Gore. *The Art of Scientific Discovery*. London: Longmans, Green & Company, 1878, p. 109.
3. E. Bright Wilson, Jr. *An Introduction to Scientific Research*. New York: McGraw-Hill, 1952, p. 257. Used by permission of McGraw-Hill Book Company.
4. Claude Bernard, *L'introduction a l'etude de la medicine experimentale*. Quoted in Herbert Fiegl and May Brodbeck, *Readings in The Philosophy of Science*. New York: Appleton-Century-Crofts, 1953, p. 236.
5. Jean Baptiste Fourier. *Theorie analytique de la chaleur,* 1822. Quoted by the Rand Corporation, *Scientific American,* **201** (December 1959), p. 54.

10

The End Products
of Science

The greatest invention of the nineteenth century was the invention of the method of invention.[1]

Alfred North Whitehead   1925

In Greek science the desire to explain everything as arising out of a purpose was so strong that they read "purpose" into inaminate nature. . . . Their explanations always amounted to saying that something took place because it was in agreement with the purpose of the universe. . . . The twentieth-century version of this type of explanation is to say that a certain event took place because God willed it. . . . The interesting feature of both the Greek and the religious explanation is that they do not serve as scientific explanations unless we know what the purpose of the universe or the will of God is.[2]

John G. Kemeny   1959

Medieval science derived all observable phenomena from the principle that they are somehow analogous to the well-known phenomena in a living organism. . . . Seventeenth- and eighteenth-century science, in turn, preferred the analogy to simple mechanisms which are familiar to us from our everyday life experiences.[3]

Philipp Frank   1949

In an age like our own, which is essentially an age of scientific inquiry, the prevalence of doubt and criticism ought not to be regarded with despair or as a sign of decadence. It is one of the safeguards of progress;—la critique est la vie de la science, I must again repeat. One of the most fatal (and not so impossible) futures for science would be the institution of a scientific hierarchy which would brand as heretical all doubt as to its conclusions, all criticism of its results.[4]

Karl Pearson   1892

There is much criticism of scientists today for their alleged indifference to the uses to which their discoveries may be put. Scientists are blamed by many, for example, for contributing to the horrors of modern war. The fact is that the same people who now condemn scientists as soulless and amoral for their wartime work would have been the first to cry "Treason!" if any had refused to assist their country during the war. Nevertheless, the scientist has to consider moral factors before undertaking a new problem. . . . It is practically impossible for the pure scientist to predict the moral consequences of his choice of a problem, however much he may wish to do so. . . . But scientists are, and correctly so, under tremendous moral pressure to work incessantly for the proper utilization of their work by society.[5]

E. Bright Wilson, Jr.   1952

Does science leave no mystery? On the contrary, it proclaims mystery where others profess knowledge. There is mystery enough in the universe of sensation and in its capacity for containing those little corners of consciousness which project their own products, of order and law and reason, into an unknown and unknowable world. There is mystery enough here, only let us clearly distinguish it from ignorance within the field of possible knowledge. The one is impenetrable, the other we are daily subduing.[6]

Karl Pearson   1892

100

Explanations consist of accurate objective descriptions of antecedent conditions and specifications of the immediate influences between the observable antecedent conditions and the observable subsequent phenomena.[7]

Sheldon J. Lachman   1956

Even if it were true that science is concerned with means only, it would not follow that science ignores the intrinsic worth of man. For the values of human life cannot be achieved within a physical vacuum; they require for their fulfillment the existence of material conditions. To the extent that classical civilization failed to mitigate the evils of poverty, disease, squalor, and a generally low level of living among the masses, to that extent it failed to liberate man. Conversely, to the extent that science, especially in its medical and technological applications, has succeeded in dealing with these evils it has contributed to the realization of human values. Thus science has implemented the human-ism which classicism and Christianity have proclaimed.[8]

The Harvard Committee   1945

The search for truth should be the goal of our activities; it is the sole end worthy of them. Doubtless we should lend our efforts to assuage human suffering, but why? Not to suffer is a negative ideal more surely attained by annihilation of the world. If we wish more and more to free man from material cares, it is that he may be able to employ the liberty obtained in the study and contemplation of truth.[9]

Henri Poincaré   1905

SCIENCE IN THE HUMAN ENDEAVOR

The pursuit of science permeates so many areas of modern society that it is truly difficult for an observer to detach himself from the effects of its impact and examine without bias the end products of science. It is difficult to imagine, for example, how two societies would differ, the one a society in which science flourishes and the other a society in which science would appear to languish. To what degree, for example, might the differences between an isolated, self-contained Eskimo village and a specimen Ohio community be correlated with the relative dimensions of the scientific enterprise in the two communities?

In a spirit more in keeping with this book, contemplation regarding the end products of science can be provided by imagining two separate societies existing twenty or so years in the future. In one of these societies the education of its people included, but in the other failed to include instruction in the pursuit of science. What differences would there be between the two societies, and to what degree would today's science teachers be justified in assuming the responsibilities for these differences?

These questions do nothing more than suggest metaphorical vantage points from which to ponder the end products of the pursuit of science. And although one may never achieve a true and accurate grasp of the unique contribution of science to society, to ponder the question remains one of the essential elements in the training of those people who teach the pursuit of science.

The end products of science are revealed in (1) the explanations of natural phenomena that are embraced by the members of a society and reflected in their beliefs, and (2) in the solutions to technological problems within the society. The immediate end products of science are increasingly accurate descriptions of naturally occurring events and circumstances, but these descriptions almost immediately become inextricably entangled with art, business, ethics, industry, commerce, music, literature, religion, politics, and all other human endeavors. Thus, to accurately determine the unique end products of science requires one to determine the point at which other human endeavors begin to modify what was originally truly an end product of science. The intent is not to shun technology, ethics, the humanities, the rights and responsibilities of citizenship, but to examine and, hopefully, expand the contribution that teaching the pursuit of science can make to these other human endeavors.

PATTERNS IN THE EVOLUTION OF EXPLANATIONS

It is characteristic of man to demand or create explanations of natural phenomena, especially those that threaten or are vitally concerned with his continued welfare and comfort. Even the most primitive society quickly derives a satisfactory explanation of any puzzling event or object that appears within the society. Thus, evidence of the degree to which science flourishes in a society cannot be gained simply by determining whether or not the society possesses satisfactory explanations of its natural phenomena. This evidence must come from examining the dominant pattern within these explanations. To pursue this examination, consider first the proposition that mankind's concept of what shall be a satisfactory explanation has evolved through five reasonably clear-cut stages. Each is described and illustrated very briefly in the paragraphs that follow.

1. Primitive peoples tend to interpret events and circumstances that they observe in nature very much as though all things possessed animal feelings and were capable of animal behavior. Perhaps it is because the affairs of primitive people center around animals that they see clouds, carrots, calories, and everything else, animate and inanimate, as being alive and behaving as men and animals.

2. Somewhat less primitive people believe not only that things in nature act and behave, but that some things possess supernatural power. To these people, nature is personified, and both animate and inanimate events are looked on as rewards for good or punishments for bad behavior.

3. More recent is the invention of the idea of fate, fortune, or some other version of lady luck. Explanations that reflect this concept contain no logical antecedents to the event being explained. Events follow the will of fate. Things are just that way. Accidents simply happen. The affairs of the universe were set into motion many years ago and what occurs in any one event or circumstance is merely a part of a master plan controlled by fate.

4. A fourth pattern appearing in mankind's evolving explanations of natural phenomena seems to be linked with his ingenuity in fashioning tools and machines to aid him in solving his daily problems. Machines became such an omnipresent part of his environment that man began to "see" watchwork mechanism in the motions of the heavenly bodies, telephone switchboards in cerebral tissue, molecules as hard little balls, heat and electricity as fluids, in fact, mechanistic explanations became quite the vogue. All phenomena were looked upon as having locked-in causes which could be guaranteed to produce invariable results.

5. A fifth pattern that has evolved in the quest for satisfactory explanations of natural phenomena features the interpretation of any one event or circumstance only in terms of whatever other events are most likely to precede or accompany. Explanations strive for increasingly precise and complete descriptions of phenomena, descriptions which tend to be catalogues of those events that have calculated probabilities of being related to the phenomena.

These exceedingly sketchy descriptions of five patterns of explanation, assuming they do exist, are subject to much conflicting interpretation. Contributing to the conflict is the tendency for vestiges of each pattern to persist long after the pattern has ceased to be dominant.

However, to trace the explanation of a phenomenon, especially one of the smashingly obtrusive ones that even the most primitive people could not fail to observe, reveals the kind of evidence upon which the existence of these patterns is hypothesized.

Consider, for example, the phenomenon of earthquakes. Primitive explanations often invent an animal, such as the buffalo, that carries the earth on its back; earthquakes occur when the animal, tired by its immense burden, shifts the weight from one foot to another. Other instances of earthquakes were explained as reflecting heaven's dissatisfaction with worldly affairs, and Roman writers embodied fate in a wind or very great force of air, either from without or arising within the earth itself, that throws itself violently into the hollow places of the earth. The appearance of steam engines and the violent exhibitions of the explosive force of pent-up steam are reflected in the explanation that assumed that if large quantities of water were let upon the subterraneous fires deep within the earth, vapors would be produced whose quantity and explosive force would be more than adequate to cause the earth to quake. A modern explanation is likely to identify those processes that tend to accumulate the terrible energy released at the time of an earthquake, the actual mechanism by which the energy is released, and finally, the trigger forces that determine the probability that an earthquake that is about to occur will happen today rather than tomorrow, at this particular site rather than another.

CRITERIA OF THE "GOOD" EXPLANATION

If it is true that the explanations that arise from the end products of the pursuit of science are evolutionary in character and do not represent revelation of ultimate and eternal truths, how can the science teacher determine whether or not he is putting his students in touch with "good" explanations? To invoke a line of reasoning no more sophisticated than to argue that the more recent pattern or type of explanation is likely to be better than those patterns from which it has evolved, identifies the descriptive explanation as the most desirable. But to many people, sheer description is neither clarification, elucidation, nor understanding. Although they gain increased comprehension by relating the more complex and less familiar to the simpler and more familiar, many people fail to be satisfied by a purely descriptive explanation but retain an uneasy longing for a flow of forces from cause to effects within an explanation of any natural phenomenon. The minds of men, and to a lesser degree of children, are not content with naming, classifying, or otherwise only describing the environment: they crave explanation.

But many scientists have become increasingly wary of claiming to have recognized a flow of forces that can be guaranteed to cause a prescribed effect. Men have had to learn by sometimes humiliating experiences to curb their appetite for certain varieties of explanation. So eager to explain anything and everything immediately without completing the painstaking task of careful description, they have rushed to set up broad, cosmic reasons that seemed to be adequate explanations for all phenomena. The reactions against all explanation of this sort were so strong when modern science discredited many of its conclusions that, in keeping with the spirit of this book, teachers will be wise to move increasingly away from any explanation that retains animalistic, fatalistic, or mechanistic characteristics.

Assuming that the user knows what he is doing, it can be argued that the "good" explanation of a natural phenomenon is the one that accomplishes best what the user wants it to accomplish. For example, if the purpose at hand is to arouse interests in and nurture curiosity about stars and snowstorms, clouds and crustaceans, tornadoes or turtles, and the audience is so young as to be approachable only through personified fairy tales, explanations heavily laced with animalistic tendencies might be used. Similarly, an author should be permitted to add color or character to the people of his prose or poetry by endowing them with the powers of a personified nature or an advertising-copy writer should be permitted to capture a greater audience by describing a "mechanical brain" rather than by simply referring to an elaborate array of interconnected electrical circuits. All manner of mechanical models can be constructed to facilitate clarification of the description of a phenomenon, whether or not the phenomenon is in any way mechanical. But mark the key phrase in the opening sentence of this paragraph—"assuming that the user knows what he is doing."

When a proposed explanation is to be elevated to the status of a belief and, as such, is to be used to predict the consequence of further action, a totally different concept of "goodness" becomes involved. From this point of view, the explanation must be clear and unmistakably unambiguous. It must be consistent with facts that have come from extensive and accurate observation. There is a presumption against any explanation that conflicts with explanations of closely related phenomena. Finally, other things being equal, that explanation is likely to be the best that makes the fewest assumptions and requires the least complex interaction of causes.

SCIENCE AND THE "GOOD LIFE"

There is a saying that among the very young and the very old, there is an inescapable urge to contemplate the probability of whether and, if probable, the manner in which the pursuit of science influences and is influenced by man's inherent tendency to spiritualize. Such contemplations become literally soul-searchingly difficult to communicate, especially in a book with the title *Teaching the Pursuit of Science*. Perhaps it is timidity on the part of the authors, but they are inclined to borrow some words from Sir Arthur Eddington,[10] words not used by him to describe specifically the relationship between science and "the good life" but seemingly peculiarly fitting for such a purpose. When attempting to answer the question "What is real?" he admits that such an attempt "is likely to lead to a floundering among vain words and high-sounding epithets." And then he writes:

We all know that there are regions of the human spirit untrammelled by the world of physics. In the mystic sense of the creation around us, in the expression of art, in a yearning towards God, the soul grows upward and finds the fulfilment of something implanted in its nature. The sanction for this development is within us, a striving born with our consciousness or an Inner Light proceeding from a greater power than ours. Science can scarcely question this sanction, for the pursuit of science springs from a striving which the mind is impelled to follow, a questioning that will not be suppressed. Whether in the intellectual pursuits of science or in the mystical pursuits of the spirit, the light beckons ahead and the purpose surging in our nature responds. Can we not leave it at that?

For Discussion and Further Study

1. Select two societies, one untouched by and the other deeply influenced by the impact of a vigorous scientific endeavor. What differences between the two societies can be related to the differences in the vigor of their pursuit of science?

2. In the same spirit as Question 1, how would the technological development of the two societies differ?

3. Is the end product of the pursuit of science explanation or description of nature? Is it the interpretation of nature?

4. What does a student really desire when he asks to have a natural phenomenon *explained* to him?

5. Is it valid to infer from Alfred North Whitehead's quotation that there is a method whereby inventions can be achieved?

6. Is it realistic to expect the young person who is preparing to enter the teaching profession to contemplate and gain an operational concept of the end products of the pursuit of science?

7. Can it be that there is a kind of "ontogeny recapitulating phylogeny" in

the evolution of an explanation of any natural phenomenon? Does the development of explanation of phenomena first identified in the twentieth century tend to retrace earlier patterns of explanation?

8. Is the proper role of scientists in social and political endeavors to "be on *tap* but not on *top*"?

9. What should a teacher do if he senses that his students prefer and find greatest satisfaction in explanations that are mechanistic?

References

1. Alfred North Whitehead. *Science and the Modern World.* New York: The Macmillan Company, 1925, p. 141.
2. John G. Kemeny. *A Philosopher Looks at Science.* Princeton, N. J.: D. Van Nostrand Company, 1959, p. 170.
3. Philipp Frank. *Modern Science and Its Philosophy.* Cambridge, Mass.: Harvard University Press, 1949, p. 288.
4. Karl Pearson. *The Grammar of Science.* New York: Meridian Books, 1957, pp. 54–55. First published in 1892; revised in 1900; and published in final edition in 1911.
5. E. Bright Wilson, Jr. *An Introduction to Scientific Research.* New York: McGraw-Hill, 1952, p. 9. Used by permission of McGraw-Hill Book Company.
6. Karl Pearson. *The Grammar of Science.* New York: Meridian Books, 1957, p. 54. First published in 1892; revised in 1900; and published in final edition in 1911.
7. Sheldon J. Lachman. *The Foundations of Modern Science.* Detroit: The Hamilton Press, 1956, p. 27.
8. The Harvard Committee, *General Education in a Free Society.* Cambridge, Mass.: Harvard University Press, 1945, p. 49.
9. Henri Poincaré. *The Value of Science,* authorized translation by G. B. Halstead. New York: Dover Publications, 1958, p. 23. Originally published 1905.
10. Sir Arthur Eddington. *The Nature of the Physical World.* Ann Arbor, Mich.: University of Michigan Press, 1958, pp. 327–28. First published 1928.

11

On the Educational
Value of Science

*Science and its applications comprise an essential part of
the foundation for our economy, our defense, our material
welfare and comfort and our physical well-being. Science
is now completely interlocked with social and political questions so that wise national decisions cannot be made without
sound scientific bases.*[1]

Warren Weaver 1960

*In the conditions of modern life, the rule is absolute, the
race which does not value trained intelligence is doomed.
Not all your heroism, not all of your social charm, not all
your wit, not all your victories on land or at sea, can move
back the finger of fate. Today we maintain ourselves. Tomorrow science will have moved forward yet one more step
and there will be no appeal from the judgment which will
then be pronounced on the uneducated.*[2]

Alfred North Whitehead 1929

*There is a need for a voting and supporting republic of
non-scientists who understand the work scientists do. The
need of this group is for a valid image of research and of*

scientific knowledge . . . we need to imbue our courses and our exposition with the color of science as inquiry to give the student an effective glimpse of the vicissitudes of research.[3]

Joseph J. Schwab 1961

To accept the conclusions of science without a thorough familiarity with its method of warranting them is to remain ignorant of the critical spirit that is the life of science. Not every claim to knowledge is a valid claim; and without a clear grasp of the standards that evidence for a conclusion must meet, the risk is large of becoming a slave to every rhetorical appeal, to every plausible though specious argument, and to every intellectual fashion.[4]

Ernest Nagel 1959

The schools must nurture intelligence in persons in order that men thus well-nurtured may build an increasingly human, rational society, in order that increasingly sensitive, rational men may have freedom, scope, and mutual challenge further to create, and in creating to rejoice in and honor the beauty and power of man's mind. . . . For all the folklore of educational psychology about the improbability of the transfer of learning, one who has learned well the uses of the mind in the major disciplines of thought finds it a ready and delightful servant in all the exigencies of life, both the inward life and life among men, present and past. . . . There may be other things which schools could or should do, but they could or should do these things only after they have, as well as they can and as hard as they can and as patiently and persistently as they can, taught the use of that unique instrument of their humanity, the restless, questing mind. . . . Whenever a boy or girl in this country receives a less challenging, less appropriate, less worthy education than he or she mentally and morally deserves, there is a diminishing of the person, an impoverishing of a life, possibly a great loss to the nation, and a defeat suffered in the sector of the engagement of the mind of man with the mystery and wonder of the universe.[5]

William H. Cornog 1963

If men of science owe anything to us, we may learn much from them that is essential. For they can show how to test proof, how to secure fullness and soundness in induction,

how to restrain and to employ with safety hypothesis and analogy. It is they who hold the secret of the mysterious property of the mind by which error ministers to truth, and truth slowly but irrevocably prevails. Theirs is the logic of discovery, the demonstration of the advance of knowledge and the development of ideas, which as the earthly wants and passions of men remain almost unchanged, are the charter of progress, and the vital spark of history.[6]

Lord Acton 1895

An entirely new character has been given to the whole of our modern civilization, not only by our astounding theoretical progress in sound knowledge of Nature, but also by the remarkably fertile practical application of that knowledge in technical science, industry, commerce, and so forth. On the other hand, however, we have made little or no progress in moral and social life, in comparison with earlier centuries; at times there has been serious reaction. And from this obvious conflict there have arisen, not only an uneasy sense of dismemberment and falseness, but even the danger of grave catastrophes in the political and social world. It is, then, not merely the right, but the sacred duty, of every honorable and humanitarian thinker to devote himself conscientiously to the settlement of that conflict, and to warding off the dangers that it brings in its train.[7]

Ernst Heinrich Haeckel 1900

Humanity, surely, needs practical men who make the best of their work for the sake of their own interests, without forgetting the general interest. But it also needs dreamers, for whom the unselfish following of a purpose is so imperative that it becomes impossible for them to devote much attention to their own material benefit.[8]

Marie Curie 1923

PROCESSES OF SCIENTIFIC THOUGHT

Education in science equips an individual to absorb the mental nourishment to be gained from comprehending the great and rapidly flowing stream of thought that is the scientific endeavor. It is in the pursuit of science that scholars can find instances of the mind of man working in a spectacularly inventive and creative manner. Many episodes of science reveal examples of the use of the human senses to observe, with ever-increasing accuracy, a segment of nature. These observations, in turn, are examined by the processes of abstract thought, and often these processes are accomplished with supreme adroitness. When the mind of a scientist weaves these observations into a framework that enables him to establish a new concept of how a segment of nature fits into the total scheme of things, the maximum dimensions of human creativity and inventiveness are often exhibited. Thus, when students appreciate the scope of the great and rapidly flowing stream of thought that is the scientific endeavor, they may grasp a bit of that subtle urge to exercise their own intellects.

The total universe of man's activities during any phase of civilization is sharply influenced by the pursuit of science—not only during that phase, but also and often even more so by the roles science played during past phases of the evolution of civilization. In one or another sense, science has influenced and been influenced by man's moral, social, political, artistic, and technological enterprises. Comprehension of the scientific endeavor is an essential part of the comprehension of these and all other human endeavors.

FORM, TIME, AND SPACE

Education in science can give the individual a dynamic awareness of his environment. The rapid pace of living in the modern world militates against providing those pauses that enable one to experience in depth. One must be "taught" to observe and appreciate the rare beauty that is everywhere in the colors and symmetry of nature. Appreciation in depth implies understanding and association, and is motivated by wonder and curiosity. Appreciation is linked with creativity and the aesthetic with orderliness. As the pursuit of science takes mankind ever deeper into the nature of matter and energy, the structure of the universe, and the mystery of life itself, intricacies of form and design and magnitudes of time and space are being revealed that can awaken deep emotional responses. To have these responses awakened is the right of young people in a civilized society.

The career potential inherent within the scientific endeavor is so obvious as to need but to be noted. Science can lead an individual toward many interesting and rewarding hobbies. Although the day of the glorious amateur may never return insofar as the professional pursuit of science is concerned, the satisfactions reaped by those seventeenth and eighteenth century scientists await always the hobby scientist.

Whether or not the logic and discipline of the thought processes that are unique to the pursuit of science can be transferred to help mankind solve problems in other endeavors is highly debatable. Doubtlessly, the hypothesized transfer is a matter of degree. Surely people who have even dabbled in the kind of thinking that is exercised in the pursuit of science must be less easily influenced by folkways and superstitions than would be those people who have never come into contact with this kind of thinking.

In many ways, education in science provides an introduction for the individual to many facets of his natural and social environment. When the introduction is properly negotiated, a kind of familiarity is generated that, in contrast to the usual proverb of breeding contempt, breeds more familiarity. Whole new dimensions of interests are aroused, and these new interests add a new dimension to the sphere of activity that becomes the life of the individual. At a time when so many people seem to be encompassed by self-centered, self-limited, and otherwise reduced spheres of interest, exceedingly significant values may accrue from any aspect of education that turns one's thoughts toward his environment and away from himself.

For Discussion and Further Study

1. Defend or refute the statement that one of the primary values of instruction in science is to provide an introduction to one's natural environment, an introduction without which people tend to be denied the pleasures that accrue from appreciation of the beauty and orderliness of nature.

2. Can instruction in science add a new dimension to one's appreciation of art, music, literature, and the fruits of other human endeavors?

3. What is the significance of the number of people who associate school science with smelly chemistry laboratories or messy biological dissections?

4. Is Alfred North Whitehead's prediction of doom justified? How does his viewpoint differ from or reinforce the prediction of Bertrand Russell?

5. Is it true that facility in the processes of science protects a person from becoming a victim of specious persuasive tactics and strategy?

6. Is William H. Cornog's reference to the improbability of transfer of learning as being folklore a valid inference?

7. Does Cornog's plea for maximum education apply equally to all young people? Should it apply to the science prone and specially talented only?

8. What is the significance of the very small number of scientists who are elected to serve in state and national legislative bodies?

References

1. Warren Weaver. *A Great Age for Science.* New York: Alfred P. Sloan Foundation, 1960, p. 1.
2. Alfred North Whitehead. *The Aims of Education and Other Essays.* New York: The Macmillan Company, 1929, p. 22.
3. Joseph J. Schwab. "Some Reflections on Science Education," BSCS *Newsletter* No. 9 (September 1961). Based on "Inquiry, the Science Teacher, and the Educator," *School Review* (Summer 1960), pp. 184, 185, 186.
4. Ernest Nagel. *Education in the Age of Science,* edited by Brand Blanshard. New York: Basic Books, 1959, p. 192.
5. William H. Cornog. Paper presented at public meeting of the Council for Basic Education, Washington, D.C., October 25, 1963.
6. Lord Acton. *Lectures on the Study of History,* 1895. Quoted by the Rand Corporation, *Scientific American,* **204** (April 1961), p. 46.
7. Ernst Heinrich Haeckel. *Riddle of the Universe,* 1900. Quoted by the Rand Corporation, *Scientific American,* **203** (September 1960), p. 2.
8. Marie Curie, 1923. Quoted by the Rand Corporation, *Scientific American,* **203** (November 1960), p. 62.

II

GETTING THE FEEL
OF WORKING
IN SCIENCE

The history, philosophy, and logic of science provide a vantage point from which to view the whole of science, the interrelation of its parts, the patterns in its methods, and its fundamental significance. To convert theoretical and idealistic concepts of the pursuit of science into practical and realistic knowledge, many students will find it especially valuable to seek or select problems for their own investigations, frame their own hypotheses, identify their basic assumptions, plan and conduct their own experiments, interpret their own data, and arrive at whatever conclusions are warranted by the evidence obtained.

To launch one's own episode in science is, admittedly, highly individualistic with the choice of topic depending on the interests of the individual and the manner of pursuing the topic dependent on the facilities that are available. Guidance may be gained, however, by examining recorded observations of other people's initial excursions in science.

This experience can be eminently rewarding, either to the new teacher just entering teaching or to the teacher of experience. It can provide the rare experience of following the onset of wonder and curiosity about a real problem and the actual use of the processes of inquiry employed by the scientist in his pursuit. It can illustrate the elations and frustrations of scientific endeavor and thus give a teacher an opportunity for the clearer understanding of these intangibles and the insights into their nature that are so important if the teacher is to be able to instill them in the experiences of his pupils.

12

Finding or Selecting
a Problem

*The freedom to choose his own problem is often the
scientist's most precious possession.*[1]

Barry Commoner   1963

*A genuine problem for a student exists when something,
no matter how slight or commonplace in character, puzzles
or perplexes him; when something appears to him as unexpected, strange, or disconcerting. It may be "practical"
or not. . . . The teacher acts either in creating the situation
which arouses a doubtful state of mind, which, in turn, leads
to recognition of a problem, or in sensitizing students to
such doubtful states of mind.*[2]

Lester C. Mills and Peter M. Dean   1960

*Whilst one scientific man expends his time upon com-
paratively trifling matters, another slowly and persistently
works out a great idea. . . . The difficulty [of avoiding*

trifling and selecting worthwhile topics] is usually overcome by selecting from a stock of hypothetical suggestions and questions those which appear to have the greatest degrees of importance, probability, and ripeness, and adopting the most suitable one.[3]

G. Gore 1878

The difficulties encountered in selecting projects for research, resemble in a great many respects, the problems of a military commander. Long before his major military engagements he must collect information and evaluate the resistance to be encountered; he must choose that particular method of attack which will make the resistance most vulnerable; he must see to it that he has the right type of troops and fighting equipment; last, but not least, the esprit de corps *must be high and the attack must be precisely timed.*[4]

C. C. Harrell 1948

Inquiry starts only when something is unsatisfactory, when traditional beliefs are inadequate or in question, when the facts necessary to resolve one's uncertainties are not known, when the likely relevant hypotheses are not even imagined.[5]

F. S. C. Northrop 1948

. . . No fact is so simple that it is not harder to believe than to doubt at the first presentation. Equally, there is nothing so mighty or so marvellous that the wonder it evokes does not tend to diminish in time. . . . So has satiety blunted the appetite of our eyes. Desist, therefore, from thrusting out reasoning from your mind because of its disconcerting novelty. Weigh it, rather, with discerning judgment. Then, if it seems to you true, give in. If it is false, gird yourself to oppose it.[6]

Lucretius, first century B.C.

The scientist is a practical man and his are practical aims. He does not seek the ultimate *but the* proximate. *He does not speak of the last analysis but rather of the next approximation.*[7]

Gilbert Lewis 1926

SOME FIRST APPROXIMATIONS

Topics for their own investigations are likely to be found by people who (1) are actively aware of and remain sensitive to curiosity, and wonder about the things that exist or happen in their environment, (2) are adept at recognizing problems and in realizing what is known and what remains to be known about the topics considered in a course, (3) have access to an environment that reveals clues to natural phenomena, and (4) possess enough confidence to believe they can successfully plan and conduct at least a partially self-initiated investigation.

People who encounter difficulty in finding or selecting topics for their own investigations reflect the converse of the above characteristics, and also seem to (1) feel that their modest efforts hold little chance to add anything worthwhile to what is already known about everything, (2) feel that science has become so specialized and requires such expensive apparatus that it is hopeless for people without well-equipped laboratories to ponder topics in science, (3) look down on anyone who spends time and energy to find out something for himself rather than to know the right person to ask for the answer because "after all, I am sure that topic has already been investigated," and (4) have more confidence in answers reported to four decimal places in an austere journal than in results observed in their own all-too-often makeshift laboratories.

Delay in finding or selecting a problem may be due to simple tendencies to put off things. When this condition prevails, straightforward discipline, either self-imposed or otherwise, may be what is needed rather than to wrack one's brain seeking an environment more likely to inspire and nourish the characteristics of the scientist. After having spent a reasonable number of weeks prospecting for a topic, it may be necessary for the potential investigator to say to himself: "Although it may not be exactly what I want to investigate, if a better idea does not shape up within the next sixty days, I am going ahead with topic X."

After doing some first-hand browsing through one's environment and reflecting on tentative interests, help in settling on a topic may be gained from reviewing some topics that have aroused the interests of other people who were beginning the pursuit of science. Some have been interested in:

1. Discovering why the radii from the common center of the annual rings in a tree stump are of different lengths.
2. Explaining the iridescence of jellyfish observed in the tributaries of Chesapeake Bay.

3. Determining the causes of variations in color occurring in the mineral quartz.

4. Determining the effects of various soil conditions on the types of organisms living in the soil.

5. Explaining why an ordinary drinking glass, when dropped from table height, appears to break not on the first but on a second or subsequent bounce.

6. Determining the best metal or alloy to use as contact points on automobile voltage regulators.

7. What effect, if any, laughing gas has on honeybees (does it put them to sleep, kill them if given an overdose, make them lose their sense of direction, etc.).

8. Whether monozygotic and dizygotic mammal twins differ in acceptance of grafts between individuals of genetic diversity.

9. Determining whether the feeding habits of birds can be restructured, particularly with reference to the control of Japanese beetles.

10. Determining whether the firefly would exhibit a periodicity in flashing if never exposed to the diurnal light cycle.

11. After grass has turned brown during dry weather, whether the renewal of green color is due to growth of new leaves or to the return of chlorophyll to the brown leaves.

12. Finding whether 2×2 color slides can be used to clarify color addition and subtraction.

13. Determining the cause of the difference in physical properties of calcite and marble being quarried within a few yards of each other.

14. Explaining heteromorphosis—for example, that the regenerating capacity of an earthworm is higher at the anterior than the posterior end.

15. What the effect of gibberellic acid is on fresh-water algae.

16. Finding to what factors the red through blue colors of hydrangeas are related.

17. Discovering whether there is a dormancy period for zinnia seeds and, if so, whether it can be shortened.

18. Determining if the color exhibited by the ions of a substance in solution is the same as in the solid crystal and whether this is related to crystal system.

19. In a conventional Daniell cell, whether ions migrate through the porous cup and, if so, whether it is due to diffusion or electrical transfer.

20. What factors are related to the hardness of a particular batch of plaster of Paris.

21. Finding whether human hair color is related to the strength and thickness of the hair.

22. Discovering the factor or factors that cause or influence double monster production of frogs' legs.

23. How the tent caterpillar can be exterminated.

24. What factors in the physical environment are related to the formation of coral reefs.
25. Whether an object of specific gravity greater than but very close to unity sinks to the bottom of the ocean at its deepest points.
26. What factors are related to the fantastically rapid erosion at Myrtle Beach, South Carolina.
27. Why quantities of salt adequate to kill other plants do not kill asparagus.
28. To what extent the light energy from the sun can be concentrated by a hollow hemispherical reflector.
29. How fish can survive in water that is colder than the freezing temperature of fish blood.
30. Discovering whether, keeping in mind the probability of their biological significance, alpha, beta, gamma, or other high energy radiations can be detected by simple animals.
31. Finding, if flower color is controlled by one or more pairs of "blending" alleles, whether the pigments produced by each allele can be separated from a blended-color flower.
32. Why, in a cross between homozygous white-eyed and red-eyed drosophilae, the proportion of white-eyed flies in the offspring should depart significantly from the proportion predicted by Mendelian ratios.
33. Why a specific weed should be found repeatedly growing close to cultivated beds of zinnias.
34. What factors are related to the tendency of gnats to hover persistently in the vicinity of people's eyes.
35. Why white pine trees growing in a site south of the buildings of a producer of antibiotics in Groton, Connecticut, appear to be singularly unaffected by the white pine weevil.

These examples verify that topics for small-dimension excursions in science, and none may lead to earth-shaking discoveries; but the pur-puzzling events and circumstances that appear in almost any environment. Furthermore, what one reads and the conversations one has with other people often suggest problems that are worthy of study. Among the examples above, many topics are scarcely within the domain of science can be found or identified simply by being sensitive to the suit of their investigation may serve as training exercises. The completion of this training serves to convert a theoretical concept of the pursuit of science into practical and realistic comprehension.

SHAPING THE PROBLEM STATEMENT

How promptly an investigation gets under way and how smoothly it proceeds toward completion can depend very much on whether or not the investigator has a properly worded statement of the problem underlying the investigation. This is true even when the originator and would-be solver of a problem are the same person. The function of a problem statement seems to be not only to provide communication but also to accomplish an ordering process which, once it has been achieved, puts the investigator in better position to continue the investigation.

The raw material from which a problem statement is fabricated consists of the conditions and circumstances that the investigator recognized as being involved in the problem. To prune away any of these conditions that may be significantly connected with the investigator's interest in the problem, if done simply to achieve a concise problem statement, is a hazard to the continued interest of the investigator in the problem.

A problem statement must anticipate, to a degree, the skills of the investigator and the materials and equipment he will need during the early stages of the investigation. If the attack on the central problem cannot be launched until skills are acquired or supplies obtained, the problem statement can be improved by including secondary or supporting problems that can be attacked immediately.

The initial versions of a problem statement should sort and order the observations that gave rise to the problem in a way that will reveal whether or not there is a real and, as yet, unsolved problem. These observations may be supplemented with suggestions for ways to solve the problem, why it is important, or what uses are to be made of the solution when and if one is obtained.

To illustrate how problem statements materialize, several examples follow. The first example involves the question: If maple trees manufacture sugar during the summer and this sugar appears in sap in early spring, where is it during the winter months? Among the conditions and circumstances associated with the student's identification with this problem were (1) enrollment in a course in which selection of a topic for investigation was required, (2) presentation by the instructor of an array of topics to be considered by the student, (3) prior introduction to and appreciation of the photosynthetic process in plants, (4) enjoyment of maple sugar and maple syrup, (5) the availability of maple trees, (6) the possibility that maple sugar trees could be "tapped" at additional seasons of the year or that an enzyme or other factor could be isolated that would convert an intermediate carbohydrate to sugar or serve as a flavor for making artificial maple sugar, and (7) realization that sugars can be quantitatively determined and that different plant tissues can be identified.

Several preliminary efforts to convert these conditions and circumstances into a problem statement evolved into:

Knowing that maple trees manufacture sugar during the summer months and that these sugars appear in the sap of these trees during early spring, a problem exists in attempting to determine the condition and location of these sugars during the autumn and winter months. Preliminary problems that must be solved include (1) developing accurate methods for identifying, both qualitatively and quantitatively, stored sugars in whatever carbohydrate form they may be; (2) developing accurate methods for identifying different plant tissues, and (3) establishing efficient methods for extracting and purifying sugar and sugar conversion products.

A second example began with a student's interest in the substances that produce the distinct odors and flavors of certain plants. The student was aware of the obvious relationship between compounds and their properties. The pronounced fragrances of flowers and the flavors of fruits and spices are adequate to catch attention. After mastering the established methods for extracting, purifying, and identifying the various components of these substances, there is always the challenge of finding or synthesizing a compound that has peculiarly interesting or valuable properties.

After preliminary exploration of the occurrence, extraction, and identification of these compounds, the statement of this student's problem became:

Realizing that many plants produce compounds, the essential oils, that have pronounced and often pleasant odors and that these compounds represent only a small fraction of the total make-up of the plant that produces them, a problem exists in attempting to extract, purify, and identify these compounds. Preliminary to successful solution of this ultimate problem, it will be necessary to (1) identify sources of plants or raw plant products containing these essential oils, (2) develop efficient methods for extracting and purifying these compounds, and (3) develop accurate methods for identifying or verifying the presence of representative organic groups in the molecules of the purified extracts.

The spectacularly successful results obtained from modern antibiotics may have been one of the factors that aroused or contributed to the interest of a student in a third topic. The student knew the relation between microorganisms and the incidence of decay and decomposition of plant and animal tissues. His prior instruction had encouraged him to note special cases of disconformity within his environment, since these often become the clues to yet-to-be-identified phenomena. The sharp resistance to decay of fence posts cut from locust wood is one such disconformity. Curiosity aroused by this disconformity led to the problem statement:

Having observed that locust posts resist decay much more pronouncedly than do posts cut from trees of other species, a problem exists in attempting to extract an antibiotic substance from locust wood. Preliminary to solving this basic problem it will be necessary to solve such problems as (1) demonstrating measurable differences in the rate of decay of wood from different species of trees, (2) establishing pure cultures of those organisms most regularly associated with the decay of wood, (3) development of various extraction procedures whereby substances having antibiotic properties, if present, would be extracted from locust wood, and (4) practicing biological assay procedures adequate to demonstrate the antibiotic nature of these extracts.

A fourth topic to serve to illustrate the evolution of a problem statement has its origin in the explanation usually provided in introductory high-school biology courses for one type of genetic transmission of flower color. The color of flowers is often described as being controlled by one or more pairs of "blending" genes. This explanation, if not examined too closely provides a clear and simple explanation for pink, orange, purple or other shades of flowers that appear along with red, yellow, blue, or other pure colors. In some cases these flower colors can be duplicated nicely by mixing paint pigments. But not in all cases, especially where blues and yellows are involved. Curiosity aroused by discrepant observations such as this led to the problem statement:

Accepting the belief that flower color can be inherited by the transmission of one or more pairs of blending alleles, a problem exists in determining whether each allele operates independently or in combination with accompanying alleles. For example, does an orange-colored flower result from blending within the flower tissue of red and yellow pigments produced independently, or do alleles for red and yellow, when present in the chromosomes of the same individual, interact to produce an orange pigment? Preliminary problems must be solved such as (1) determining how to extract flower pigments uniformly without allowing the extraction process to decompose or combine individual pigments, (2) establishing a probable pattern of gene action that will suggest or be consistent with observed incidence of pigments, and (3) establishing methods that will identify differences in gene dosage within a flower, e.g., to determine whether there is more red pigment in a red than in a pink flower of the same species.

A fifth example further emphasizes the role played by the unusual or disconforming observation in the identification of possible topics for investigation. This topic produced the problem statement:

Having observed that the feet of water striders cast unduly large shadows, a problem exists in describing accurately the effects of the feet of this insect on a liquid surface and the correlation of these effects with peculiarities in the structure and function of the insect's feet. This description may need to touch on the behavior of light as it enters and passes through water, the phenomena that are peculiar to the surface of a liquid, and any peculiarities in the structure of the insect's feet. The description should be as quantitative as possible.

Although the changing colors of leaves that accompanies the arrival of autumn in many parts of the world is obviously related to changes in the pigments within the leaves, curiosity is aroused by apparent discrepancies in the way a single tree or a single branch on a tree changes color. Such curiosity is expressed in the problem statement:

Noting that all trees of the same species or that all branches, twigs, or leaves of an individual tree do not follow the same schedule or pattern of changing colors even though they share a common physical environment, a problem exists in attempting to correlate peculiarities in the discrepant instances with generally accepted knowledge regarding plant physiology, especially those aspects of metabolism that might affect leaf pigments.

These six instances of problem statements have been selected to represent a variety of phenomena and to reflect some of the basic patterns that seem to recur where science is being pursued. The first two examples, involving as they do the properties, occurrence, and preparation of substances, are quite simple in their origins and move easily into the mechanics and procedures of their investigation. The problem involving the isolation of an antibiotic from locust wood, although similar to the first two, is more difficult in that it is a search for a substance that may or may not exist and may or may not have the hypothesized property.

The fourth example, which involves a chemical approach to the elaboration or verification of a genetic pattern, is somewhat characteristic of those problems that are suggested by questioning the consistency of a published description of a phenomenon or by attempting to improve the accuracy of an established description of an event or circumstance.

The fifth example was chosen to represent that category of investigations in which nothing more than idle curiosity provoked the problem. The shadows cast by the feet of water striders seem to be far removed from the practical interests of mankind. A description of this phenomenon holds no apparent promise of contributing anything to the comfort and welfare of the investigator or his fellow men. If there are satisfactions to be gained from the successful completion of investigations of purely nonpragmatic problems, these satisfactions might accrue from an attempt to describe accurately the water strider and its shadows.

The sixth example, by departing from the patterns of investigations which require the experimental derivation of new facts, is selected to represent that type of investigation which features a search for new relationships among already established facts. Much is known about the chemistry of the pigments that are found in plant leaves and the changes whereby one pigment can be converted to another. Similarly, much is known about basic plant physiology. Rather than turning to test tubes and microscopes to extend the accuracy of this already established information, the problem here takes on more of the character of correlation or the so-called "arm-chair" research.

Whether problem statements should be followed immediately by the elaboration of hypotheses or by a period of more or less undirected data gathering remains an unresolved issue among the scholars who describe their concepts of the pursuit of science. Having acknowledged the question as being unresolved, the discussion here leads directly into the tactics and strategy of hypothesis elaboration.

For Discussion and Further Study

1. List a dozen or so things a person can do that will increase the probability that he will come up with a problem worth investigating.

2. Would students who need stimulus toward finding problems worth investigating be assisted by the list prepared in reply to Question 1?

3. Prepare a statement on the necessity and hazards of stating problems in such a way as will facilitate moving ahead with their investigation.

4. Assume that you are in a situation in which it becomes necessary for you to identify yourself with an investigation and have it under way within a six months period. Prepare your plan of attack and assign dates for the completion of each phase.

5. Keeping the spirit of science in mind, is it appropriate for science teachers to keep a file of problems they would like some day to investigate or to have their students investigate?

6. Are there valid substitutes for actual experience in the pursuit of science to which a person might turn if he is asked to teach science and cannot take on his own investigation?

7. Do the usual laboratory exercises that accompany college and university course work in science provide experience in the pursuit of science?

8. How far should teachers go in using the supplies and equipment of their school laboratories for their own investigations?

References

1. Barry Commoner. "Is Science Getting Out of Hand?," *The Science Teacher,* **30** (October 1963), pp. 11–16.
2. Lester C. Mills and Peter M. Dean. *Problem-Solving Methods in Science Teaching.* New York: Science Manpower Project Monographs, Teachers College, Columbia University, 1960, pp. 3, 9. Copyright © 1960 by Teachers College, Columbia University. Reprinted by permission of the Bureau of Publications, Teachers College, Columbia University. All rights reserved.
3. G. Gore. *The Art of Scientific Discovery.* London: Longmans, Green & Company, 1878, p. 376.
4. C. C. Harrell. In C. P. Haskins *Research in Industry,* edited by C. C. Furnas. Princeton, N.J.: D. Van Nostrand Company, 1948, p. 106.

5. F. S. C. Northrop. *The Logic of the Sciences and the Humanities.* New York: The Macmillan Company, 1948, p. 17.
6. Lucretius, 1st Century B.C. Quoted by the Rand Corporation, *Scientific American,* **199** (August 1958), p. 26.
7. Gilbert Lewis. *The Anatomy of Science,* 1926. Quoted by the Rand Corporation, *Scientific American,* **202** (May 1960), p. 60.

13

Framing a Working Hypothesis

We cannot take a single step forward in any inquiry unless we begin with a suggested explanation or solution of the difficulty which originated it. Such tentative explanations are suggested to us by something in the subject matter and our previous knowledge. When they are formulated as propositions, they are called hypotheses. . . . The function of a hypothesis is to direct our search for order among facts. The suggestions formulated in the hypothesis may be solutions to the problem. Whether they are, is the task of the inquiry.[1]

F. S. C. Northrop 1948

Young men, young men, have confidence in those safe and powerful methods, of which we know only the first secrets. And, whatever your career may be, do not let yourselves become affected by a denigrating and barren skepticism, do not let yourselves be discouraged by the sorrows of certain hours which pass over a nation. Live in the serene peace of laboratories and libraries. Say to yourselves first, "What have I done for my education?" and as you gradually advance,

"What have I done for my country?" until perhaps you may have the immense happiness of thinking that you have contributed in some way to the progress and to the good of humanity. But whether or not our efforts bear fruit, let us be able to say, when we come near the great goal, "I have done what I could."[2]

Louis Pasteur 1892

From the beginning until now men have begun to philosophize because of wondering. At first, they wondered about the extraordinary things near at hand, then they moved on from little things near at hand to raise questions regarding greater happenings. . . . The man who is puzzled and is wondering is aware of his ignorance.[3]

Aristotle c. 330 B.C.

THE WORDING OF HYPOTHESES

Arriving at a good wording of an hypothesis is quite likely to be a try-and-try-again process. Initial efforts invariably need to be remodeled as the investigation proceeds. During this remodeling and revising, time can be saved by prompt attention to the criteria of the "good" hypothesis.

Initial wordings of an hypothesis tend to reflect "usefulness" more than "truthfulness." For example, consider the following initial hypothesis framed by a science teacher who was also associated with an enterprise that rented hives of bees to orchardists during the flowering season. "If honeybees are knocked out with laughing gas sufficiently to let them be handled, will the bees upon recovery still be able to find their way back to their hives after going on nectar-gathering excursions?"

Compare this initial effort with: "Can honeybees retain or recover their direction-finding abilities after being rendered inactive by laughing gas?" This rewording loses nothing of value and expands the scope of the investigation. The expanded scope, in turn, promises greater predictive power from the investigation if successfully completed.

In general, hypotheses in question form lead less directly into the design of an experiment or investigation than do statements of probability. In this connection, continuing to follow the evolution of the honeybee hypothesis, consider this wording: "Exposure of honeybees to laughing gas erases prior direction-finding experiences but does not destroy the ability to establish new patterns of direction-finding."

The wording of an hypothesis often creates conflict between the criteria of simplicity, testability, and clarity. One investigator might prefer such a wording as: "What effect, if any, does laughing gas have on honeybees?" This is a clear question and testable in several ways. But which way? Contrast the absence of structuring in this streamlined statement with: "If honeybees of proved ability to find and remember directions are rendered inactive by laughing gas, then they will have lost, upon recovery, prior direction-finding experiences, but will retain the ability to establish new patterns of direction finding."

An investigation based upon this hypothesis as finally worded should move smoothly into the design of an appropriate series of experiments. The hypothesis meets fairly well the criteria of hypotheses, with the possible exception of adequacy of depth. To really comprehend the effects of laughing gas on the direction-finding abilities of honeybees would require the hypothesis to probe into the physiological processes and anatomical structures related to the direction-finding process and the effects of laughing gas thereon.

There is no assurance that a basically unsophisticated problem will not require effort to produce a carefully thought out and worded hypothesis. In contrast to the fairly complex honeybee direction-finding problem, consider a problem that arose from observations of marked eccentricity in the shapes of annual rings of tree stumps. Again, a science teacher with special interests in forestry used a try-and-try-again method to establish an effectively stated hypothesis.

An initial statement was: "Why should the lengths of the radii of a black oak tree stump be different?" A little more thought revealed the lack of clarity and prompted an effort to improve the wording. One effort yielded: "Why should more wood accumulate on one than another side of a black oak tree stump?" And still the statement is not clear. Further effort to add clarity yielded: "Using the center of the annual rings as the center of a stump, why should opposite sectors have markedly different length radii?" A simpler statement with even more clarity would be: "Why should the centers of the annual rings be markedly displaced from the geometrical center of the stump?"

Recall, however, that clarity alone cannot produce the good hypothesis. It is obvious that no help in designing an investigation can be gained from the statement as worded. But hypothesis formation is only another instance proving the adage that getting out is possible only by putting in. The putting in, in this case, is background knowledge. A step in this direction would be: "What factors are related to the distance between any two annual rings in a tree stump?" Another step employing more knowledge would be: "Is unequal accumulation of wood in opposite sectors of a tree stump correlated with unequal exposure to food, light, water and/or space?"

This could be an appropriately stated hypothesis. However, the advantage of using "connectives" is shown by: "If wood has accumulated unequally in opposite sectors of a tree stump (using the centers of the annual rings as indication of accumulation), then the tree has received more light, water, food, and/or space on the side of greater accumulation." This hypothesis can still be criticized as lacking depth but, as will be shown later, an investigation needs not be limited in depth by the wording of its hypothesis.

PRELIMINARY HYPOTHESES

During their early stages, many investigations do not trigger an hypothesis in which the investigator has enough confidence to move ahead with the experiment or investigation that it prompts. The investigator may want to elaborate several before following up any one hypothesis. The problem that follows is intended to illustrate this.

How can fish survive in water that is colder than the freezing point of fish blood? Faced with a problem such as this, the investigator may raise a variety of not necessarily interrelated questions: Does the blood continue to circulate? Does the temperature of the fish's blood reach the same low temperature as the water it exists in? Can a fish survive without circulation of its blood? Is this a phenomenon that can exist for only a very short period of time? Assuming that the blood of a fish has congealed, must its functions in exchanging materials cease? Can we be sure that the freezing point of blood removed from a fish will be the same as for blood yet within the blood vessels of the fish? Could it be that by changing the concentration of dissolved materials in the blood, the freezing temperature of fish blood is locked into the fish's changing temperature?

Although only rarely is such an assumption justified, assume that the investigator feels that to pursue any one of these questions is no more likely than any other to advance him most rapidly along his investigation. What should he do? It is at least logical to begin with those questions most easily converted into working hypothesis. He knows, for example, that no great investment of time or resources would be required to explore the hypothesis: "Capillary blood flow will continue in the thin, transparent tail tissues of a minnow that has been frozen in a thin wedge of ice." Having established or refuted this hypothesis, the investigator then can move ahead to the more elaborate studies involving blood concentrations and fluid-exchange mechanisms.

To illustrate further the approach to problems that do not suggest immediately an hypothesis, consider an additional example. In this case, the investigator was seeking an adequate description of the iridescence of certain Chesapeake Bay jellyfish. This investigation involves a physical phenomenon occurring in a biological situation, and thus may be approached by way of both physical and biological hypotheses.

Basically physical hypotheses can determine whether the iridescence is a refraction, fluorescence, phosphorescence, or bio-oxidation phenomenon. Basically biological hypotheses can establish the anatomical structures and physiological processes most closely related to the iridescence. Approaching the problem in piece-meal fashion allows the investigation to get under way, and no great problem will be encountered in rejoining the elements into the pattern in which they actually exist. Some examples of such preliminary hypotheses are:

If the iridescence of these jellyfish is more intense under ultraviolet light, then it is a fluorescent phenomenon.

If the iridescence continues after the ultraviolet light is extinguished, then it is a phosphorescent phenomenon.

If the iridescence continues after the organisms are dead, then it is more likely to be refraction than a bio-oxidation phenomenon.

If the phenomenon is strictly one of physical refraction, then there must be organs or tissues present capable of diffracting white light.

If the observation is due to bio-oxidation, then there must be certain organs in which this physiological process takes place.

WHEN TO PROCEED

From the practical point of view of getting on with an investigation, the investigator is torn between two decisions. He can decide to move along with whatever hypothesis is at hand, or he can delay in the hope of coming on a more promising hypothesis. Although the mechanical consistency of an hypothesis can be assayed, and there are things that can be done to improve how well an hypothesis will lead into an experiment, it is with much less confidence that one can predict that the fruitful hypothesis is likely to evolve from a maximum number of observed events and circumstances. Hypotheses that are consistent with closely related proved relationships are, obviously, more likely to gain confirmation, but the truly great strides in man's pursuit of science could never have occurred if men were forever unwilling to venture forth on hypotheses that were not only inconsistent but down right contradictory to widely accepted relations among similar events and circumstances.

The important thing seems to be to settle upon an hypothesis early enough to ensure that the pursuit of the investigation does not die aborning but not so prematurely as to fritter away one's time and resources on a half-baked and totally fruitless hypothesis.

The following examples may further clarify the wording of hypotheses and, hopefully, encourage the reader to move ahead with the design of experiments or other appropriate investigations.

1. If gardenia flower petals are touched, with or without transfer of oily substances to the petal, then brown discoloration will be due to mechanical damage to the cells of the touched petal.

2. If, in a laboratory cross between homozygous white-eyed and red-eyed drosophilae, the proportion of white-eyed flies from the cross is less than the proportion predicted by Mendel's theories, then an ecological factor is acting against the survival of white-eyed flies.

3. Assuming the presence of temperature inversions in the ocean depths, and that a ship might sink under conditions that cause its gross density to be almost equal to but slightly greater than the density of sea water, then the ship would remain submerged at some point between the surface and the floor of the ocean.

4. If ions actually migrate through the porous membrane during the operation of a conventional Daniell cell, then copper will be present in the zinc-sulfate solution and zinc in the copper-sulfate solution after the cell has operated for a period of time.

For Discussion and Further Study

1. Select several problem topics from the preceding chapter more or less at random. Join a group of colleagues or students in a "brainstorming" session to see the kinds of hypotheses generated when it is decreed that all and sundry hypotheses are to receive enthusiastic acceptance.

2. Identify several of the major unsolved problems of science and follow the suggestion in Question 1.

3. How far should a teacher go in imposing the "if . . . then" format on students who are being introduced to the process of elaborating and stating hypotheses?

4. Under what circumstances might an assumption be converted to an hypothesis?

5. Published reports of many episodes in science suggest that the investigators entertained only one hypothesis, the one that led them to the re-

ported discovery or invention. What evidence can be obtained to verify or refute this inference?

6. What are the hazards that accompany the practice of beginning an investigation with a dimly seen hypothesis, hoping to sharpen its focus and clarify its boundaries as the investigation proceeds?

7. Is it possible to accumulate data that bear on an investigation in advance of deriving at least one hypothesis?

8. What are the advantages versus disadvantages associated with an investigator keeping several hypotheses under investigation in concurrent but separate investigations? Should one person keep several problems under investigation concurrently?

References

1. F. S. C. Northrop. *The Logic of the Sciences and the Humanities.* New York: The Macmillan Company, 1948, p. 11.
2. Louis Pasteur, 1892. Quoted by the Rand Corporation, *Scientific American,* **203** (October 1960), p. 2.
3. Aristotle. *Metaphysica,* c. 330 B.C. Quoted by the Rand Corporation, *Scientific American,* **205** (December 1961), p. 44.

14

Planning the Investigation

The researcher should have the skill of spelling out the value of his work to others—both with written and oral reports. Presentation to a group for discussion and evaluation is a valuable technique to use in science laboratory activities. . . . Modern processes deal with such minute and exact tolerances that more emphasis should be placed upon training in cleanliness, precision, and meticulous attention to detail in scientific laboratories. . . . The Edisonian, or "trial and error," method of approach to a problem is far from dead in today's research laboratories. After all logical approaches have been explored it still may be necessary to encourage students to "try it and see if it works." . . . Selection of school laboratory facilities should be made with an idea of flexibility, mobility, and replacement due to obsolescence. . . . The school administration should provide and science teachers should use a specified period for preparing, repairing, and storing laboratory materials and equipment.[1]

N.S.T.A. Staff Report 1955

*Though the solution of a problem may flash into the mind
of a person without his knowing how it arose, nevertheless
he has always done a good bit of thinking, puzzling, wondering about it before the flash occurs.*[2]

George Boas 1959

*The main business of natural philosophy is to argue from
phenomena without feigning hypotheses, and to deduce
causes from effects, till we come to the very first cause,
which certainly is not mechanical; and not only to unfold
the mechanism of the world, but chiefly to resolve these
and such like questions: What is there in places almost
empty of matter, and whence is it that the sun and planets
gravitate towards one another, without dense matter between them? Whence is it that nature doth nothing in vain;
and whence arises all that order and beauty which we see
in the world?*[3]

Sir Isaac Newton 1704

*I have tried to think what characteristics seemed to be out-
standing in the successful pursuit of research. . . . There
are two areas that have repeatedly come to my attention . . .
(1) Ability to cut through a maze of information to see
what the fundamental problem actually is; to see what
parameters are involved and what data or avenues of research are needed to supply the basis for further appraisal. . . . (2) Ability to identify the many relevant
variables in a problem and to make reasonable estimates of
how each may affect the conclusion.*[4]

Gordon M. Dunning 1956

*Laboratory notebooks should be permanently and strongly
bound. . . . Loose-leaf pages or separate sheets are too easily
lost. . . . Data should be entered directly into the notebook
at the time of the observation. . . . It should be possible to
take each scientific paper and show just where every figure,
description, or statement in it is backed up by original
observations in the laboratory notebook. . . . Some statement
of the purpose of each experiment and a summary of the
conclusions reached make the notebook vastly more useful.
Sketches, drawings, and diagrams are essential. Since so
much observation is visual, it is important to record what is
actually seen, including things not fully understood at the*

time. Bad or unpromising experiments, even those deemed failures, should be fully recorded. . . . Data should always be entered in their most primary form, not after recalculation or transformation.[5]

E. Bright Wilson, Jr. 1952

Facts are the air of science. Without them the man of science can never rise. Without them your theories are vain surmises. But while you are studying, experimenting, observing, do not remain content with the surface of things. Do not become a mere recorder of facts, but try to penetrate the mystery of their origin, seek persistently for all laws that govern them. And then—modesty. Never think you know all. Though others may flatter you, retain the courage to say, "I am ignorant." Never be proud. . . . Pride will make you lose objectivity. . . . And lastly, science must be your passion. Remember that science claims a man's whole life. If you had two lives they would not suffice. Science demands an undivided allegiance from its followers. Your work and your research must always be your passion.[6]

Pavlov 1936

COURTESY OF THE RAND CORPORATION

We ought either not to pretend to scientific forms or we ought to study all the determining agencies equally, and endeavor, as far as can be done, to include all of them within the pale of the science; else we shall infallibly bestow a disproportionate attention upon those which our theory takes into account, while we misestimate the rest and probably underrate their importance.[7]

John Stuart Mill 1843

COURTESY OF THE RAND CORPORATION

Having selected the specific question or problem on which his attention is to be focused, and having elaborated one or more promising hypotheses, an investigator advances to the stage of inquiry in which he plans and designs experiments that, it is hoped, will provide an answer to the question, a solution to the problem, or, at best, suggest more promising hypotheses.

DESIGNING AN EXPERIMENT

The examples of simple experiments and investigations that are discussed here are intended to illustrate and clarify the theoretical analysis of experimentation as presented in Chapter 9. Consider, first, the hypothesis: If honeybees of proved ability to find and remember directions are rendered inactive by laughing gas, then they will have lost, upon recovery, prior direction-finding experiences, but will retain the ability to establish new patterns of direction finding. An experiment can be designed to "accumulate, bit by bit, evidence for or against" the probability inferred in the hypothesis. The validity of this evidence will depend on how many "extraneous factors are eliminated or their probable influence taken into account." The validity of generalizations projected beyond the immediate results of the experiment, in turn, will be tested by how consistently "a determined set of antecedent or accompanying events or circumstances occur" under the conditions specified by this one experiment.

To continue this illustration, assume that the investigator is familiar with the general skills of beekeeping, that he has a supply of bees, and facilities for setting up an experiment. The variable of greatest concern is whether or not the experimental organisms have or have not been subjected to partial anesthesia by nitrous oxide. The constant factor is the ability to learn and remember directions to and from sources of food. To be a valid experiment, its design must ensure that no factor other than anesthesis by nitrous oxide be permitted to influence the direction-finding ability of the experimental honeybees. Does the following design provide this validity?

A hive of bees is taken into an area where no natural food sources exist. Using sugar water, the investigator establishes feeding sites north (A) and east (B) of the hive: one hundred bees are trapped at site A and each bee is marked with a spot of red enamel; a similar number of bees trapped at feeding site B are marked with spots of green enamel; upon observing these marked bees make repeated trips between the hive and the feeding sites, the investigator argued that he now had 200 bees of proved ability to determine and remember directions. The 200 marked bees were trapped at the hive and partially anesthetized with nitrous oxide and taken to new feeding sites south (C) and west (D) of the hive. If the marked bees, after recovering from the anesthesia and being returned to the hive, are observed repeatedly visiting the new feeding sites and returning to the hive, argued the investigator, the original hypothesis would be proved to be in error.

One technique for improving the design of an experiment requires the investigator to detach himself from his role of creator or designer and assume the role of skeptical critic. In this role, he anticipates attack and defense of the conclusions that the experiment is expected to yield, and must honestly inspect the design of the experiment and identify, if at all possible, any unsuspected variables that may have been overlooked or might be introduced during the completion of the experiment. In other words, much can be gained, in advance of investing time and other resources in actually conducting an experiment, by asking oneself such questions as: Will I really be willing to believe the results from my experiment? Will these results actually yield an answer to my question, or a solution to my problem, or at least a worthwhile portion of it? Is the event or circumstance around which I have constructed my experiment exactly the same event or circumstance that first aroused my curiosity?

Returning to the honeybee anesthesia problem, would the proposed experiment answer such questions as: Are bees better able to determine and remember directions on sunny days than on cloudy days? Does marking bees with red or green enamel affect their direction-finding abilities? Can bees that possess the direction finding and remembering ability "instruct" bees that have had this ability destroyed?

For additional discussion of improved experimental design, consider the hypothesis: If wood has accumulated unequally in opposite sectors of a tree stem, then the tree has received more light, water, food and/or space on the side of greater accumulation. There are ways to "accumulate, bit by bit, evidence for or against" this hypothesis. But what kind of evidence is really worth the trouble to devise an experiment to accumulate? Is not enough already known about plant physiology to put one's mind at ease about this hypothesis? This depends upon what it takes to put the individual investigator's mind at ease. Some investigators want the satisfaction of deriving evidence for themselves by experimentation even though equally sound evidence is available in the literature. Other investigators will want to design experiments that will extend or strengthen the perspective of available evidence, especially as it applies to the specific instance in which their curiosity was aroused. This type of investigator may say: "Granted that unequal light, water, food, or space will influence the rate of growth of new wood in a tree stem, but does the structure of plant stems prohibit horizontal circulation or transfer of the elements that are involved in nutrition and growth?" By asking this second-level question, the investigator is ready to elaborate an hypothesis that, for this investigator, is worthy of the investment of time and resources required to design and conduct an experiment.

Assuming that the thinking that one does during the initiation of an investigation is likely to follow a pattern similar to the thinking that another investigator may do, the following report of plans for an investigation will be of interest:

The puzzling event that I propose to investigate is one I have noticed several times during recent years. I have observed that people's moods seem to change without apparent reason when thunderstorms are imminent. After some reflection, I decided this could be related to the excess of either positive or negative charges that tend to build up before thunderstorms. How the charges are formed, where they come from, and similar questions, did not interest me so much as the possible effect such concentrations of charges may have on a person. After more deliberation, I concluded that the problem could be divided into (1) psychological effects and (2) physiological effects—with full realization that the two effects are highly interrelated.

Having decided to investigate this phenomenon, I needed to select experimental subjects. Convenience suggested the white rat. At this point my thinking seemed to be sufficiently organized to enable me to gather my deliberations together into a problem statement. One question remained: How to incorporate both psychological and physiological effects in a single problem statement? Or, for that matter, how to be sure that the psychological effects observed are not caused by physiological changes and vice versa. One way around this impasse was to select one set of changes for immediate study, with the understanding that I would return to the other set after gaining additional information.

After some thought on this, I selected the psychological effects to try to observe, because they seemed to be associated with the fewer variables. However, in doing so I recognized that psychological effects or changes in behavior may well have physiological causes produced by my experiment. Variables that might have been introduced by my experiment included diet, changes in feeding habits, or surroundings. At this point a tentative statement of my problem became: What psychological effect does the concentration of positive or negative charges in the air have upon rats?

Immediately we see the need for clarification of some terms. First, what do I mean by psychological changes—how can they be recognized? Troubles arise from choosing psychological events to study since they cannot be handled with the same objectivity ordinarily associated with purely physical phenomena. In other words, I must be content to classify psychological changes as any changes that seem to be out of the ordinary. To decide what is ordinary implies prolonged observation of rats under normal circumstances. For example, suppose we place a rat in a white box, the bottom of which has been wired so as to give an electric shock when touched. One sees behavior out of the ordinary when the rat feels the electric shock. Furthermore, if the process of placing the rat in the same box is repeated several times we will soon be able to eliminate the electrical shock and still notice behavior which can scarcely be called normal. The rat will run about the box frantically searching for a way out; behaving not at all like an ordinary rat put for the first time in an ordinary box.

This experimental rat has had a state of anxiety created in him that he associates with the wired box not so much because it was wired but because of the general appearances of the box. That such is the case can be further demonstrated by attaching a box with black walls and a glass top to the wired white walled box. Add a doorway between the boxes through which the rat can pass only after he has learned to operate a lever to open the door. In his frantic search about the box the rat by chance may trip the lever and find his way to the haven of the black box. While searching through the black box, if the rat by chance again trips the lever, thus re-opening the door, it will not return to the white box. Ordinary rats under usual circumstances would be expected to spend equal time in either box, but our conditioned rat, if again placed in the white box, will trip the lever and move to the black box.

I have now clarified, at least sufficiently for an experiment, what I mean by psychological effects or changes. Returning to the tentative problem statement, the term "concentration" requires explication. The problem of measuring the concentration of positive and negative charges in the air poses problems. First, I need a way to place these charges in the air in reproducible quantities. I cannot simply create ions in the air because that hazards changing the chemical nature of the air. Suppose I introduce some minute dust particles, each carrying a charge. If I have dust in a box and introduce electrodes that are charged positively with high-voltage direct current, say 20,000 volts, all of the dust particles become charged positively in a short time. This procedure seems satisfactory for my investigation, providing I can establish quantitative methods.

It has been found that about 90 per cent of the dust particles present in a system are likely to become charged under the above circumstances. This suggests I can control the concentration of ions within a box by simply controlling the amount of dust introduced into the box. This assumes that each dust particle carries a single charge, an assumption justified by the repulsion properties of like charges. Admittedly the dust introduces a new variable into our experimental system, but its effects, if any, can be isolated by a separate control system.

Having now clarified the terms in my problem statement, I was ready to move along to the formation of an hypothesis. What factors must I consider in formulating an hypothesis? First, the answer proposed by the hypothesis must be within the boundaries of my investigation. It must be precise enough to belong to the specific problem at hand and yet broad enough to cover all aspects of the problem. It must provide a clear preview of the end product of the investigation and be logically consistent. Finally, I must avoid ambiguities and tacit assumptions and, as a general rule, seek the simplest hypothesis possible.

A tentative statement of an hypothesis is: If the air breathed by rats contains an excess of either positive or negative ions, then observable psychological changes will occur and be evident in changed behavior of the rats.

I will now proceed toward the design of an experiment to test this hypothesis. I must ask myself what results I wish to obtain, how I expect to go about attaining them, and try to anticipate every variable that might affect my procedure. Basically, I desire to observe a change in the behavior of rats that I can define as being a psychological response to the presence of excess ions in the air breathed by the rats. I recognize that my plans have also introduced an experimental variable—the dust. Thus, I seem to have these situations to observe: (1) rats in dust-charged air wherein the charge is due to negative ions, (2) rats in air with positive-charged dust particles present, and (3) rats in uncharged-dust-filled air. Furthermore, I must parallel these observations with rats in uncharged air containing only the ordinary amount of dust.

Equipment for my investigation will consist of two identical glass-topped boxes, identical except that one has white inside walls and the other black. Three holes are drilled in the glass tops; one through which electrodes may be introduced and the other a larger one through which the rat may be introduced. A tube fits over the hole for the electrode, through which air may flow into the box. The third hole is for an air gauge to permit equalization of pressure within and outside the box. A small hole in one corner of each box permits drawing air from the boxes through needle valves. The intent of these designs is to insure that air can be caused to flow in, through, and from the box at constant, measured rate.

The boxes are connected by a door that is operated by a lever; when the lever is pressed, the door opens for five seconds and then closes. On the white-box side of the door is a small wire that is connected to a low-voltage source of direct current. By maintaining this wire at the same charge as the air in the white box, it will repel those dust particles that might flow into the black box when the door is opened.

A high voltage, about 20,000 volts, will maintain the charge on the electrodes in the white box. Two air pumps permit controlling the air flow into the two boxes and one of the entry tubes must be fitted with a port enabling dust to be added to the air. Last but not least, I will need several healthy, normal rats.

To conduct an observation, I will set up the boxes and ensure that the air in them is at atmospheric pressure. I will introduce a rat into the white box, taking care to seal the cover afterwards, and observe its behavior for one hour. My observations should include the amount of time spent in each box and how long it takes the rat to learn to open the door between the boxes. I will then remove the rat, flush the air from the boxes and again introduce the same rat into the white box. This is to see if he has learned anything about the situation which it applies in case it prefers one box to the other. After recording observations for a second hour, I will remove the rat and proceed to the next phase.

I will now measure 1 mg. of fine dust, introduce it into the white box, and maintain a negative charge in the box. The same rat will be introduced into the white box and observed again for one hour. After removing the rat, the boxes will be again flushed and the rat introduced once more into the white box but this time there will be no charge added to the air. This is intended to give evidence of any states of anxiety which may have been created due to the negative air formerly in the box. The rat will be removed. The same quantity of dust will again be introduced into the white box, and this time charged positively. Again, the rat will be introduced as before. Finally, the same amount of dust will be introduced into the white box, but this time no charge is added; the procedure with the rat will be repeated. As the final control check, I will reintroduce the rat into the white box when only fresh, clean air is present.

The order in this procedure is: clean air, negatively charged air, positively charged air, dust-filled air, clean air. This whole procedure should be repeated with random changing of the steps of the procedure and with as many different rats as possible or, at least, until a definite pattern in the response of the rats becomes evident even though this pattern is actually a lack of a pattern. Ultimately, the amount of dust to be added to the air should be increased in 1-mg. quantities as a further check, using the concomitant-variation concept.

When all this has been completed, my investigation will be virtually over and I will need only to organize and interpret results to see if my hypothesis is verified or refuted.

The preceding plans were prepared by a person with an under-graduate major and one-half year of graduate work in physics. With this background, many of the complications that are sure to arise in the course of an investigation could be predicted by the investigator and adequate precautions made to reconcile them. The anecdotal records that follow, on the other hand, are drawn from students who were only beginning their ventures into self-directed investigations. Furthermore, each of these students was carrying a full load of school and community responsibilities. The daily schedules of these students included one fifty-minute period that could be used to pursue their investigations. In actual practice, this time was often spent in completing laboratory-assistant chores, preparing other lessons, or helping out with various school activities. Because these records show how small-scale excursions in science are likely to proceed under the conditions prescribed by full-time enrollment in secondary school programs, they are of special value in alerting other students to the trials and tribulations of spare-time research.

The records were prepared either from the students' notes or were re-constructed during conferences with the instructor. The first of these records reports the experience of a high-school-senior boy. He had com-pleted the usual introductory biology and chemistry courses, and was enrolled in the physics course during the year in which he was observed to provide the information in this report.

September 15. Met with chemistry teacher and discussed a variety of ideas for possible investigation. Settled for the water-strider-shadow idea "for lack of something better to do and, after all, my curiosity is aroused by wondering how needlelike feet such as these insects have can cast such large shadows." Planned to capture a supply of the insects to bring into the laboratory so the phenomenon could be observed more conveniently and accurately.

October 1. Still putting off catching insects. Know where to find them. Not particularly embarrassed to be seen waving an insect net. Just can't seem to get around to it.

October 16. Observed phenomenon using insects brought to the laboratory by instructor. More than a little entranced by the insects' feet when viewed under the microscope and the discrepancy between their size and the size of the shadows cast by the point where the feet touch the water. Noticed odd structure protruding beyond hairy portion of "feet."

October 17. Observed insects on water from as many angles as possible. Sketched apparent distortion of water surface at point of contact.

October 18. Attempted to "photograph" shadows by arranging to have them fall directly on photographic printing paper in a dark room. Found that if the lights were left on for about six seconds using Kodak Velox paper, the exposure gave reasonably satisfactory results.

October 20. Made some exploratory experiments on the effects of adding detergent to the water. Found that the smallest weighable quantity of detergent seemed to be more than needed to at least partially scuttle the bugs. Decided that a surface tension phenomenon was quite likely to be involved but did not see how to proceed toward gaining an accurate measurement or description of the phenomenon.

November 8. Collected a new supply of striders. Realized that they wouldn't be available during the winter months so decided to mount several specimens in as near lifelike condition as possible. Also realized that bugs would lose weight in dry condition and, lest weight of the bugs might be a significant factor, weighed several freshly killed specimens and compared weights before and after drying. Found that dry weight is about 25 per cent of live weight.

November 17. During conference with teacher agreed that scarcely satisfactory progress was being made. Admitted that the basic problem was not turning out to be too exciting and was not very sophisticated. Delays, however, were more often due to the lack of a clear-cut hypothesis and definite plan of attack. Agreed that the structure of the insects' feet, weight of the insects, anything that might be secreted or otherwise accumulate on the feet, and any factor affecting surface tension or other liquid-surface phenomena would need to be included in the development of a satisfactory working hypothesis. Phenomena involved in the entrance into and passage of light through a liquid were recognized as being related to the original shadow problem. Agreed to work on the formulation of a good hypothesis and the development of a definite plan to investigate any or all of its features.

November 20. Read the following papers that were prepared by two college students who had been asked to think about the water-strider-shadow problem.

AN EXPERIMENT DESIGNED TO DETERMINE WHAT FACTORS ARE RESPONSIBLE FOR THE LARGE SHADOWS CAST BY WATER BUGS

Water striders, members of the family Gerridae, are thought to be supported on the water by surface tension. A number of writers including chemists and biologists have stated that these insects "skate" along the surface of water, being supported by surface tension. When one observes these insects he may note that the shadows cast by the insects' feet appear quite large and that there are bright bands of light outlining the shadows.

W. S. Blatchley, in *Heteroptera of Eastern North America*,[8] describes the depressions in the water, caused by the feet, as "saucer-shaped." Since the insect is supported by surface tension, this must be a factor in producing the concavity that cradles the foot of the insect. To test this hypothesis, experiments must determine to what degree light rays be altered by the pressure of the insects' feet on the surface of the water.

The rays of light from the sun, because of the great distance between the earth and the sun, are parallel, thus, parallel rays should be used in any experimental situation. It is true that when light rays travel from one medium to another in which the speed of transmission is different, the direction of the rays will change. Light moving from air into water is bent toward the normal, a relationship expressed as $\frac{sin\ i}{sin\ r} = n$ where i is the angle of incidence and r is the angle of refraction and n a constant known as the index of refraction.

A kind of experiment might place a thread or any fiber that will be supported by surface tension on the surface of a container of water. If, when a beam of light is cast on the object, there is formed a large shadow with accompanying light bands, it can be argued that surface tension rather than simply buoyancy is involved. Additional information can be gained by supporting the thread or fiber immediately above the surface or definitely submerged beneath the surface.

For a second experiment, cut a two-inch square of cellophane. Remove all fingerprints or other smudges. Place on the surface of water, allowing no air bubbles to form underneath. The result should be a floating object that casts a slight, if perceptible at all, shadow around the edges. Apply pressure to the center of the square and note that the shadows around the cellophane square become darker and that they are surrounded by bright bands. Now add water a drop at a time to the center of the square and note that as the amount of water increases, dark shadows and bands are produced by the edge of the water and a bright spot is produced coinciding with the center of the water. If one edge of the square is pushed below the surface of the water, additional peculiar shadows will appear—shadows similar to those formed by the feet of water striders.

In all cases in this experiment, the shadows were formed where the edge of the object was at the surface. In the case of the cellophane, the shadows were not due to the object being opaque. The surface of the water was depressed at the edge of all the objects and this depression is the result of surface tension. The shadows produced by the cellophane coincided with the depressions, thus it can be generalized that the shadows produced by the feet of water striders are at least partly dependent upon surface-tension phenomena.

"TRACKS" OF WATER STRIDERS AND THEIR SHADOWS

It has been observed that water striders can walk on water and the shadows cast by their "tracks" are large and elliptical in shape. A problem exists in attempting to identify the properties or arrangement of properties of the water and the water strider that are responsible for the size and shape of these shadows. As a working hypothesis, it may be that the water is unable to "wet" the legs of the water strider and the surface tension of the water exceeds the weight of the insect. The elliptical shape of the tracks results from the angle at which the leg of the strider intersects the water.

The first part of this hypothesis can be tested by adding a substance to the water that reduces surface tension, a detergent, for example. Prepare detergent solutions of various concentrations. Measure the surface tension of each concentration by the capillary rise method. Place a water strider on each solution and establish the maximum concentration of a solution which permits the insect to walk securely. Note any changes in the size and shapes of shadows cast by the insect's feet while on each of the solutions.

Carefully remove one leg from a strider. Measure the diameter of the foot with a precision micrometer or a microscope. Suspend the leg from a sensitive laboratory balance into a dish of water. Balance the scale first with the foot out of the water and, second, with the foot just touching the water. The difference between the two scale readings should be the force of surface tension. From the equation, $F = r^2 \gamma \cos \theta$, where F is the force of surface tension, r is the radius of the foot, and γ is the accepted value for the surface tension of water, the contact angle θ can be calculated. Repeat these measurements with the detergent solutions and data will be at hand regarding the contact of the insect's feet on the surface of water.

Additional significant information can be obtained by photographing the insect while it is walking on normal (no-detergent) water. If a vertical photograph is available, measure the major axis (a) and the minor axis (b) of the elliptical shadows. From a horizontal photograph, measure the angle (B) between the leg and the normal. Be certain when taking the horizontal photo that the line of action of the camera is perpendicular to the plane of the water strider's leg. By applying simple geometric considerations, mathematical relationships between the variables in these relationships may be established.

If the leg is at the center of the ellipse, then the relationship $\dfrac{b}{a} = \cos B$, exists. If the leg is at one focus, then the relationship would be: $\dfrac{\tan (A - B)}{\tan (A + B)} = \dfrac{a - \sqrt{a^2 - b^2}}{a + \sqrt{a^2 - b^2}}$ where $A = 180 - \theta$. If either of these relationships is proved to exist, the relationship between the elliptical pattern of the "tracks" and the angle at which the leg of the strider intersects the water will be proved.

Contrary to expectations, these procedures when suggested to the student failed to arouse sufficient interest to cause him to see them through. Several sporadic efforts were initiated but by the end of the semester, the student was investing his time in other interests.

The second report of the experiences of a young person setting out on his own investigations involves the work of a boy who had completed the usual biology and chemistry courses and was currently enrolled in high-school physics.

During 1960–61 School Year. First became involved with individual investigations during chemistry course because "I thought the idea of individual project work as presented in the course would be tied in with grades. Stayed with the idea, however, and applied for chemistry laboratory assistantship because of general interest in chemistry. Had done science fair projects in seventh, eighth, and ninth grades. These projects dealt with bacteria, electrostatic generators, and regeneration of planaria. Can't say I really drove any of these ideas far enough to really get the results I would liked to have gotten."

Chose idea of attempting to extract an antibiotic material from locust wood because it was one of a dozen or so ideas suggested by chemistry teacher. "I, too, had noticed that fence posts cut from locust wood would last far longer than would much thicker posts cut from nearly any other kind of tree." Obtained some locust wood. A woodworking student helped reduce it to chips. Steam distilled these chips, but the distillate gave no positive results when tried on the kinds of molds and bacteria that appeared on culture media left around the laboratory. Discouraged still more when molds appeared on the locust chips that had been left in the distilling flask.

September 15, 1961. During conference with teacher, agreed to continue work on locust-wood antibiotic.

September 19. Prepared culture media and made some preliminary experiments to see if the locust wood or anything extracted from it would inhibit the growth of molds or bacteria. No positive results.

September 25. Changed culture media and collected new growths of molds and bacteria. Again tried various locust extracts but found no indication of any antibiotic effect.

September 29. Teacher suggested that thin slices of as many different kinds of wood as are readily available be obtained and placed in warm, moist soil. These test specimens to be examined periodically to see if the locust specimen is any less inhabited by molds and bacteria. Organisms found growing on decaying wood specimens to be transferred and grown as pure cultures. Locust extracts then to be tried, one at a time, for antibiotic effect on these pure cultures.

October 11. Having difficulty obtaining wood specimens. Practicing pure-culture techniques but running into sterilization problems.

November 28. Admitting to almost complete conviction that no antibiotic material can be extracted from locust wood and that the hypothesis was ill-founded from the beginning, decided to abandon the problem. On the alert for a new idea.

December 4. Discussed with teacher the possibility of designing a system of gears that would illustrate the principles of machine computation. This interest grew from enrollment in an optional honors course dealing with computer theory and practice. Idea was questioned from point of view of relationship between principles of machine computation and electronic computer theory.

December 6. Expressed interest in any kind of investigation that combines engineering, mathematical, and scientific principles. Agreed to try to construct a demonstration apparatus that is described in a textbook in "experimental philosophy" written near the middle of the eighteenth century. The apparatus promised to be quite useful in demonstrating several of Newton's ideas regarding the motion of satellites and involved some clever engineering theory.

December 8. Began sketching plans for the ellipse device.

December 15. Abandoned the ellipse device. Couldn't see any purpose in simply demonstrating something already proved or merely converting a set of plans into a mechanical device. Because of a coin-collecting hobby was quite interested in rumors of a solution of unknown composition that restores the date after it has been worn away on five-cent pieces. Deterred by chemistry teacher's skepticism but did order a bottle of the solution.

December 20. Impressed by how effectively the solution made legible the dates on worn five-cent pieces. Set out to prepare a solution that would do the same for worn twenty-five cent pieces. Realized that to develop such a solution it would be helpful to understand how the commercially available date-restoring solution works.

January 5. Upon learning that a nearby agency had a method for restoring the serial numbers on guns, requested interview. Deterred until the agency was convinced of sincere and legal interest.

January 8. Visited technicians at gun-serial-number-restoring agency who explained metal-etching processes and the effects of minting or other impact processes on etching patterns. Suggested differential-etching susceptibility as an appropriate hypothesis for the date-restoring action. Hesitated to advise use of cyanide in a proposed silver-coin-date-restoring solution because of poison hazard.

January 11. Admitted to two highly probable hypotheses regarding basic nature of action of date-restoring solutions. Either the date becomes legible because of differential etching or because metals plate from the solution onto the coin at different rates where the date was originally stamped. Decided against the plating hypothesis because a coin left in the original solution for several days grew much thinner rather than thicker.

January 15. Set out to prove presence or absence of ions, in the date-restoring solution, that are customarily associated with the etching of metals. Became diverted to a general qualitative analysis of the solution checking in one way or another for such ions as CN, Fe, Cu, Ag, NO_3, etc.

January 22. Performed many spot tests based either on self-conceived strategy or in suggested short-cut analytical manuals. Obtained no results that could be held as entirely dependable.

February 25. Observed another student "playing with" action of nitric acid on pennies. Tried nitric acid as a date restorer for one-cent pieces and gained positive results.

March 19. Agreed to attempt a disciplined qualitative analysis of the original date-restoring solution as soon as a new supply could be obtained.

March 22. Added two new hypotheses concerning ways to restore dates on worn coins. Perhaps the deforming of metal crystal structure during minting will change the heat conductivity of the coin sufficiently to cause a visible effect if the coin is heated in contact with heat-sensitive copy paper. Similarly, the deformed crystal structure may show changed magnetic properties and a sensitive probe may be used to "map" the surface of the coin.

April 3. Planned a series of experiments to see if one or more metals would be replaced from the date-restoring solution by metals of different activity.

April 15. Brought work on this investigation to a stopping point. Had exhausted several bottles of the date-restoring solution. Found that tests for many ions gave positive results, but was continually puzzled and confused by conflicting results from what should have been confirming tests. In retrospect, decided he did learn some chemistry but believed strongly that a student should not undertake an investigation such as this until he had gone through formal courses in qualitative and quantitative analysis.

To contemplate what could have been done to cause this student to proceed more efficiently in his work raises several questions. Several things point to his lack of confidence and security while attempting to chart his own way through procedures he had not yet been taught. His attitude in this respect was in sharp contrast to the student whose work with essential oils will be discussed later and who seemed to like nothing better than to bump into something that required him to explore new references or otherwise learn how to proceed.

There is the question of whether the boy was permitted to drop his original topic too soon. True, he was quite discouraged by his initial efforts to isolate an antibiotic from locust wood. His belief that there were no reports in the literature of similar efforts, although not followed up at the time, suggests that he had yet to learn how to do literature search. It is interesting to contemplate what direction his work would have taken had he had access to such references as:

Baxter, D. V. *Pathology in Forest Practice*. New York: John Wiley, 1945. Contains material on "extractives" believed to be toxins that keep locust wood from rapid decay.

Yoskii, Tominago, and Mariaka. "Inactivating Effect of Plant Juices on Tobacco Mosaic Virus," *Ann. Phytopathol Soc. Jap.*, **19** (1955), pp. 8–25.

Waterman, Alma M. "Locust Woods," *Tropical Woods*, **88** (1946), pp. 1–11. Black-locust water-soluble extractions are toxic to growth of two wood-decaying fungi.

Kershbaum, Amiel and Bernard Arret. "Assaying the Commonly Used Antibiotics," *Antibiotics and Chemotherapy*, 9 (1959), pp. 613–17.

Frendenberg, Harmann. "Constituents from *Robinia Pseudoacacia* Inhibit the Growth of Wood-Destroying Fungi," *Naturwissenschaften*, **40** (1953), p. 413.

The third report of a student's first small-scale excursion in science is that of a junior girl who had completed the usual high-school courses in biology and chemistry and was enrolled in a second-year biology course.

During 1960–61 School Year. Thought about taking on a project as optional work in chemistry course but no appropriate idea came along. Decided to do some special browsing during summer months.

Summer, 1961. Visited library at National Institute of Health, Bethesda, Maryland, several times and read five or six books hoping to find an idea worthy of extended study. Embraced temporarily such ideas as chromosome abnormalities, oak-leaf gall formation, and various cytology problems, each of which seemed to involve tissue culture. Abandoned all tissue-culture problems because of sophisticated equipment and experimental conditions. After reading report of successful artificial synthesis of the lichen relationship, transferred interest to lichens in general and their digestive secretions in particular. Interest partially traceable to the rather exotic nature of these organisms and having lived in Colorado where extensive lichen flora abound. Further reading led to the specific question: Are the pigments that mark many varieties of lichens produced by the fungus or the alga member of the system? This question, however, was answered through additional reading.

Found many questions that seemed to be worth pursuing "if only I had the time and facilities." Many references available beginning with typical encyclopedia treatments and including periodical articles such as:

Hale, M. C. "Ultraviolet Spectra of Lichen Depsides and Depsidones," *Science,* 123 (April 20, 1956), p. 671.

Ahmadjian, V., and J. T. Reynolds. "Production of Biologically Active Compounds in Isolated Lichenized Fungi," *Science* 133 (March 10, 1960), p. 700.

These references are typical of the many that appear in *Readers Guide to Periodical Literature.* Each reference includes interesting ideas but each is likely to include an "almost bewildering" vocabulary.

September 15. After conference with chemistry teacher agreed to continue on lichen topic.

September 29. "Even after all my poking around with the lichen topic, decided to abandon it because of the difficulties to be expected in attempting to culture the organisms, especially the long time it takes to attain reasonable growth." Having no other idea to turn to, accepted teacher's suggestion to look into discrepancies in autumn leaf coloration to see if correlations existed between these discrepancies and identifiable environmental conditions.

October 5. Began to sense a relationship between original interest in lichens, especially their pigmented metabolic products, and leaf pigments. Further interest sparked by concurrent consideration of basic plant physiological processes in advanced biology course.

October 6. Gained a bit of a boost from a *New York Times* article that related sugar metabolism to abnormalities in leaf coloration.

October 8. With help of teacher, began collecting color photos or sketches of specific abnormalities in autumn leaf coloration.

October 10. Beginning with basic encyclopedia treatments of leaf pigments and their chemistry, took on rather extensive readings regarding the carotenoids, xanthophylls, and related compounds. Representative references are:

Fieser, L., and M. Fieser. *Organic Chemistry.* Boston: D. C. Heath Co., 1960.

Biddulph, S., and O. Biddulph. "The Circulating System of Plants," *Scientific American,* February 1959.

Muir, R. M., and R. E. Yager. "Abscission," *Natural History,* 67 (November 1958), pp. 498–501.

October 12. Gained quite a little inspiration from visits with Dr. Otani and Dr. May at National Institute of Health. Impressed by the usefulness of chromatographic techniques and the great promises inherent in efforts to redesign complex organic molecules.

October 16. Problem statement clearly in mind. (See page 125.)

November 1. Realized that two hypotheses might be developed: If there is a degradation of transport efficiency within the tissues of a pigment-prone leaf, then the abnormal concentrations of metabolates lead to abnormal pigment changes. Abnormal concentrations of metabolic products in leaf tissues will be accompanied by abnormal pigment changes. This latter hypothesis, being less structured, is more likely to survive proof but is less suggestive of the experiment by which such proof can be gained.

November 15. Decided to limit investigation to the following six instances of abnormalities in autumn leaf coloration·

1. On some trees the leaves first to undergo autumn color change are those that are closest to the stem whereas on other trees, maples for example, the leaves farthest from the stem are first to lose their green color and to take on shades of yellow and red. In the case of sumac, the leaflets closest to the base of the petiole may be a dark purple with the leaflets farther out showing a range of colors from red through orange, yellow, yellow-green, and green.

2. Leaves on twigs or limbs that have been injured or are diseased tend to color in advance of those on uninjured and healthy limbs. Leaves that are sharply creased may color earlier in those portions that are exterior to the crease.

3. The leaves on trees that have had soil added around the stem may color earlier in the fall than do other trees of the same species. Trees showing this discrepancy may die during the dormant season.

4. The leaves on twigs that carry fruiting bodies, the horse chestnut for example, may color well in advance of twigs on the same tree that carry no fruit.

5. The leaves on trees close to street lights or other illumination beyond the usual daylight hours may remain green for several weeks after other trees not so affected have changed to yellows or reds.

6. Leaves on the limbs of a tree above a constricting wire twisted around the stem may change colors well in advance of the leaves on twigs below the point of constriction.

January 3. Having continued extensive reading about the chemistry of plant pigments and related plant physiology, became somewhat swamped by a large mass of often conflicting information. Teacher suggested converting reading notes to a series of index cards, with each card limited to a single fact or concept. Hopefully, to display these cards on a large table would permit associating all the facts they represent with one or more of the observed discrepancies in leaf coloration. From these associations may come working hypotheses that will lend themselves to experimental verification.

January 20. Cards not yet prepared. Questioned the immediate value or advantage to be gained. Felt that so many notes had been taken, especially during the preliminary phases of the project, that turned out to be nothing more than "dead wood" and, thus, were practically worthless.

February 9. Resumed work after devoting all spare time to semester examinations. Put together an hypothesis that seemed to be logical and adequate for one discrepancy, namely: Continued functioning of the tissues in a leaf builds up in the cells a substance that, when its concentration reaches a critical limit, the leaf and nearby tissues show symptoms of senescence, one symptom being coloration. It was suggested that she try to extract this hypothesized substance and inject it into younger leaves as an experimental test of this hypothesis.

Since a discussion of the work of this student appears in Chapter 29 of this book, the anecdotal record is interrupted here. A term paper was required in her second-year biology course, and it seemed to be logical to use her investigation of abnormalities in autumn leaf coloration to meet this requirement. Her decision was something more than one of convenience. It was becoming increasingly evident that the nature of her investigation justified spending far more than the one school year in its pursuit. Furthermore, the biological calendar demands that many experiments dealing with this topic evolve autumn by autumn. Thus, a term paper became an almost ideal format for summary of background reading.

The summer months also provided an opportunity to make a more leisurely search of the literature. How extensive a chore this can become is suggested by listing some of the new references uncovered during the summer.

Pandele, Juliana. "Correlations Between the Chlorophyll Content of the Leaves and the Intensity of the Biochemical Activity in the Course of the Active Growth Period of Fruit Trees," *Acad. Rep. Populare Romano, Stuci cercetari biol. Seria Biol. Veg.,* 11 (1959), pp. 165–79.

Zimmermann, M. H. "Movement of Organic Substances in Trees," *Science,* 133 (Jan. 13, 1961), pp. 73–79.

Mitchell J. W., *et. al.* "Translocation of Particles within Plants," *Science,* 131 (June 24, 1960), pp. 1863–70.

Tukey, H. W., *et. al.* "Leaching Carbohydrates from Plant Foliage as Related to Light Intensity," *Science,* 136 (July 19, 1957), pp. 120–21.

The fourth example traces a senior boy's interest in the extraction, identification, and related study of a class of chemical substances. This boy had no specialized training or experience, but he had completed quite successfully the usual high-school chemistry course.

During 1960–61 School Year. Encouraged to take on a small-scale investigation as optional work in the chemistry course. Having no better idea, followed teacher's suggestion to see if the substance that is responsible for the characteristic odor of sassafras could be extracted, purified, and its molecular structure verified. Instructor provided roots and suggested water-distillation extraction. No great success. Procedure evolved into steam distillation. Fairly

successful if accompanied by differential solubility separation techniques.
Began visiting National Institute of Health library and reading general
chemistry of the essential oils, especially the multivolume series on essential
oils by Guenther.

Visited with a practicing chemist who discussed several analytical procedures that might be used to prove the presence of various portions of the
saffrole molecule, this compound being responsible for about 85 per cent
of the composition of sassafras oil. Blocked out general procedure for testing for double bonds, OH groups, methoxy groups, etc. Many of the needed
reagents were not available in school laboratory so could not practice these
identifications.

September 15, 1961. Agreed in conference with chemistry teacher to continue work on the sassafras-oil problem and, possibly, to expand to include
other essential oils.

September 20. Checked references to obtain physical and chemical properties of mint, clove, cinnamon, and a few other easily obtainable essential
oils.

September 29. Tried extracting mint oil by steam distillation of mint that
was brought to laboratory by other students. Not much success, which "I
could have predicted from its physical properties." Attempted but unable
to solve apparatus problems of high-pressure steam distillation.

October 2. Tried steam distillation on a particularly smelly weed. Obtained
an oil but in no great quantity.

October 12. Visited Dr. May at NIH, who discussed the general strategy of
remodeling organic molecules and his specific attack on the synthesis of a
new and highly promising pain-relieving drug.

October 16. Noted similarity between structure of eugenol (clove oil)
and saffrole molecules. Began considering possibility of converting sassafras
oil to clove oil.

November 20. Rather long periods of nothing much accomplished, brought
on by increasing pressure from other school subjects, lack of reagents for
qualitative analysis work, difficulty in accumulating a sample of sassafras
oil large enough to work with and, most important of all, lack of a clear-
cut plan of attack.

November 21. During conference with teacher, agreed to invest time available between now and February 1 in effort to (1) prove the structure of the
saffrole molecule, (2) prove presence or absence of other types of organic
compounds in raw sassafras oil, and (3) convert sassafras to clove oil.
Willing to have whole episode of the semester's work as a laboratory assistant
judged on progress made on these efforts.

December 1. Examined textbooks that describe qualitative tests for organic
groups. Accumulated specific procedures for phenols, carbonyl, aldehydes,
methyl ketones, aromic aldehydes, carbonic acids, esters, halogens, nitrogen,
primary and secondary alcohols, and nitro and nitroso compounds.

December 5. Listed all reagents needed for above tests and prepared an
order for the twenty or so reagents not in the school laboratory supply
room.

December 8. While awaiting delivery of needed reagents, provided help for another student who wanted to compare the strontium-90 of teeth formed prior, during, and after extensive atom bomb tests.

March 1. First shipment of reagents arrived. Began making up solutions.

March 20. Finished preparing solutions; ready to practice tests using known compounds.

At this point, the teacher decided to assign an honor student from the current year's chemistry class to serve as an assistant or co-investigator of the saffrole-eugenol problem. The young man who was selected wrote himself into the 90-plus percentile scores that had been established by year-end students on the ACS-NSTA Chemistry Achievement Examination. On this basis, the teacher was reasonably confident that he had mastered the usual high-school chemistry course and could well invest the remaining twelve weeks of the school year on a small-scale excursion into chemistry. In addition, the original investigator had accumulated valuable knowledge and skill, and it was hoped that the new "assistant" would serve as a vehicle to pass this resource along to a coming generation of students. The new team worked fairly well. There was an obvious difference in the attitudes with which each boy pursued the work. Although the older lad was especially cooperative and a gentleman in all respects, there were repeated instances in which his instructions to the new person were so superficial as to suggest: "You get your know-how the way I got mine."

Other differences between the two boys might also shed light on the influence of grades on this kind of pedagogical activity. In contrast to having no grade recorded for his work, as was the case with the original investigator, the new lad knew that he was still enrolled in a course for which the final grade was yet to be recorded. Both boys were exceptionally able to read, comprehend, remember, and apply chemical knowledge. Neither was highly communicative, but for different reasons. Each was inclined to slug things through for himself and especially so when they realized they were exploring ideas not yet explored by their teacher. On one or two occasions this led to air-pollution problems and minor explosions that, although never really dangerous, kept everyone concerned aware of the need to apply fundamental knowledge as well as common sense.

As the work of the two boys progressed, their hypothesis became increasingly elusive and a slight change was made. Vanillin replaced eugenol as the desired end product. They were successful, at least reasonably so, in effecting the hoped-for transitions and proving the presence of the new derivative at each step. The characteristic odors of sassafras oil and its derivatives constitute one element in the strategy of selecting this substance for student investigation. Labeled samples of the initial, intermediate, and final compounds can be purchased and "nose tests" permit keeping partial track of the reactions. Although the pleasant odors serve effective motivation purposes, confirmatory tests followed established procedures.

On the negative side, the vanillin synthesis is admittedly complicated, economically infeasible, and contradicts the usual pattern of going from simple to more complex molecules. These features need not, however, detract from its value as a learning exercise. Students who would like to extend or duplicate this small-scale excursion into chemistry should begin with the following references:

Ernest Guenther. *The Essential Oils.* New York: Van Nostrand, 1950.
Frances S. Sterrett. "The Nature of the Essential Oils," *Journal of Chemical Education,* **39** (April and May 1962), pp. 203–05, 246–50.

The fifth illustration of events and circumstances likely to accompany a person's first excursions into science also involves the work of a high-school senior girl. Her work followed an interest in the genetic "blending" of flower pigments. See page 124 for a development of the problem statement. The conditions under which her work evolved were quite similar to the preceding five examples. Her anecdotal record will not, therefore, be presented; only those features are cited that make a unique contribution.

Recognizing that chromatography, primarily paper, promised to be an effective procedure whereby this hypothesis could be explored, the student was encouraged to develop basic skills in this procedure. Willingly but not too patiently, she practiced the usual training exercises using food colorings, inks, and other highly pigmented substances easily separated by common solvents. She became reasonably adept in several versions of ascending paper-strip and cylinder separations, and at least recognized the potential of two-dimensional techniques.

Since she used quite a little time to track down, interpret, and modify the procedures that appear in the literature, the teacher suggested that she might want to work her notes into the form of a modest manual for students who would be taking up chromatography for the first time. Repeated inquiries, intended to discover why this suggestion appealed not at all to the student, brought such replies as: "Everything I have done is so simple." "Things didn't turn out well enough to justify recording them." "Why not let other students use the 'try and see' approach?" Although her reasons were inconsistent, her reaction proved quite consistently that the teacher's suggestion was not an adequate solution to the problem of causing the student to keep complete and meaningful notes.

As with the lad investigating the sassafras oil problem, this girl also received a co-worker near the end of the school year. He was a senior boy and his reaction paralleled that of the other "assistant." When he joined the team, work speeded up noticeably. The refinement of equilibrating the paper was added, and, by the end of the school year, the two students were able to present to the teacher reasonably valid separations of the pigments in several species of flowers.

The solvents found to be effective were formix (15 parts formic acid, 15 parts water and 70 parts butyl alcohol); the supersaturated layer from 40 parts butanol, 10 parts glacial acetic acid, 50 parts of water; the butanol layer of a 1:1 butanol 2N hydrochloric acid mixture; and 45 parts petroleum ether, 5 parts acetone, and 1 part benzene.

The results gained from this investigation suggest strongly that certain genes for flower color can function independently even when appearing in a plant in contrasting forms. In the case of four-o'clocks, for example, the chromatogram from orange flowers appears to be exactly the sum of the chromatograms from red and yellow specimens. Other species, petunia for example, show migration without separation of what would appear to be complex blended pigments.

Again, students or teachers who want to extend this investigation may find the following references of value:

Schutte, H. R., W. Langenbeck and H. Bohme. "2-D Paper Chromatography using BuOH: AcOH: Water (4:1:5) and 2% AcOH to Separate Pigments of Snapdragon Mutants," *Naturwissenschaften*, 44 (1953), p. 63.

Karlis, Lesins, and Irma Karlis. "Some Improvements in Paper Chromatography Technique for Soluble Plant Pigments," *Proc. Genet. Soc. Can.*, 3 (1958), pp. 44–46.

Thompson, J. F., *et al.* "Partition Chromatography and Its Use in the Plant Sciences," *Botan. Rev.* 25 (1969), pp. 1–263.

Dayton, T. O. "The Inheritance of Flower Pigments," *Jr. Genetics*, 54 (1956), pp. 249–60.

Williams, J., and H. Kirby. "Hollow Cylinder Paper Chromatography System," *Science*, 107 (1948), p. 481.

The sixth and final illustration of how students may be expected to approach their first excursions in science is provided by the work of a high-school senior girl who was noted for maintaining a very high overall grade record. She had completed the usual biology and chemistry cources and was enrolled in physics.

September 15. During conference with chemistry teacher, discussed a variety of possible topics for investigation. Tentatively settled for a topic dealing with maple sugar. Interested in nutrition and nutrition-related careers. In biology class, had been impressed by the photosynthetic process.

September 18. Read general encyclopedia discussions of sugars. Dealt primarily with industrial processing of sugars. Little information on chemistry of sugars.

October 2. Rather long interlude of no visible progress but unable to do anything about it. Have no well-laid-out plan of work.

October 3. Teacher provided a supply of Testtape, a commercial material used to prove the presence of sugars. Found Testtape would work with sucrose if the sample was either first boiled with hydrochloric acid or partially reacted with yeast. Ran out of Testtape "just about the time I began to gain confidence in this analytical technique."

October 13. In conference with teacher, developed problem statement. (See page 122.)

October 20. Still seeking a way to prove presence of sugar quantitatively. Neither a polariscope nor a commercial saccharimeter available.

October 22. Tried to use Benedict's solution to compare concentration of sugar in solutions made up to contain different concentrations. Worked fairly well.

October 26. Gained additional interest in problem because "during a visit with my grandfather, I learned that his business includes a process in which he grows yeast for commercial sales by buying cellulose by-products and using them in a carbohydrate conversion process. He was quite glad to learn that I was studying the chemistry of maple sugar."

November 2. Began looking for a good place to collect maple-tree buds, twigs, bark, and roots. Decided the best solution to this problem was to dig up a whole young maple tree. One unpleasant encounter with poison ivy.

November 9–13. Having located a source of young maple trees, attempted to compare sugar content in buds, twigs, and wood using Benedict's reagent. "I placed about 2 grams of maple buds in a test tube and added some HCl. A few minutes later I added the Benedict's solution. After foaming briskly, a deep-green, thick precipitate formed even without heating. About the same amount of shredded bark was placed in a test tube with HCl. After a few minutes, some of the liquid was transferred to another test tube. When Benedict's solution was added, foaming resulted and the color changed from deep blue-green to colorless. After boiling, a dark red precipitate settled out. When a sample of shredded wood was given similar treatment, nothing happened to suggest there was any sugar in the wood."

November 18. Despite gaining increased interest from seeing that different concentrations of sugar in maple buds, bark, and wood can be demonstrated, was disturbed because "I am beginning to realize that I have practically no knowledge of the chemistry of sugars beyond the very fundamental information provided by my introductory biology and chemistry courses. Decided I would have to overcome this handicap before I could make any real progress on my investigation."

December 3. Copied the structural formulas of sucrose, d-glucose, and d-fructose from a reference source. Recognized that sucrose can be broken into a mixture of dextrose and levulose, invert sugar. Also learned that complex sugars are hydrolyzed by dilute acids or enzymes into simpler sugars.

December 5. Could not find much information dealing specifically with sugar metabolism in maple trees. One reference reported that the maple flavor does not exist in the sap but is developed by heating. The intensity of the flavor can be increased four or five times by heating to about 120°C. The compounds responsible for the flavor make up only a very small per cent of the maple sugar.

December 8. Began spending less and less time on this investigation. "My mind was pretty much on getting admitted to a college and my Saturday morning computer class was becoming more and more interesting. Also, the teacher in this class asked each of us to do a computer project and I began thinking about that."

January 25. A rather long period of inactivity was broken when the teacher called attention to an adaptation of the Benedict's test for sugars, an adaptation that yields quantitative data.

At this point there developed a somewhat awkward period that extended through several weeks. The student would make sporadic efforts to pick up the thread of the investigation, but more and more of her time was being directed to other interests. Communication between the student and the teacher was not so good as it might have been, primarily because neither seemed to be particularly disturbed by the transition in interest. Several newspaper articles described the advanced work the student was doing in the computer class, and this, together with her academic reputation, was more than adequate to assure her teacher that her talents were being adequately exercised.

May 6. Inasmuch as the chemistry teacher realized that interest in a computer project had taken priority over interest in a chemistry investigation, he interviewed the student regarding the origins, evolution, and transfer of her interests. Portions of the transcribed interview follow:

Carrying five major subjects: English, Far Eastern History, Latin III, senior mathematics, and physics. Scored in the 700's on College Board examinations. Seemed to follow her mother's interest in scientific fields. Although interested in many things, nudged more and more toward mathematics because of consistently high grades. Found could do mathematics most easily and enjoyed it most.

Upon being introduced to calculus in senior mathematics, was quite intrigued by it and followed teacher's suggestion that those who were interested could go further than simple differentiation. Also introduced to descriptive statistics.

Quite captured by a Saturday morning course in computer principles. Realized that to put a problem for computer function, the problem must be broken down to its most fundamental mathematical operations. Believed that computers hold almost unlimited potential for solving problems. That they were much more than instruments for projecting data against hypothetical relationships dreamed up by the operator. Seemed to be confused by such phrases as "man versus computer," "computer language versus man language," etc.

After a false start or two, set out on a project in which, in effect, she "hoped to use Boolean functions to design a computer that would simplify Boolean functions." In other words, "to set up domain A and domain B and attempt to describe a set of possible-impossible relationships based on permutation ideas." During the interview, the student, after being repeatedly questioned about the origin of her interest in this computer project, suddenly shifted her total manner to one of informality and said, "There I was, talking on the phone to my girl friend, the only one of my classmates who had applied to Wellesley and two other colleges. I hadn't applied to the other colleges. We knew our letters were to come the next day. Suddenly we began to predict how many possible combinations of "yes" and "no" replies we could receive from six colleges. Suddenly we were into Boolean Algebra."

Another question during the interview involved the satisfactions to be gained from projects in science compared with projects in computer analysis. "In the computer thing, I knew what was coming off and if I made a mistake, I knew I could go back and correct it. In the chemistry lab, I was never sure whether I was doing things right or whether I had poured things together too fast. There were too many chances to make a mistake. With the computer, you can sit down at home and do it over and over until it comes out. In the lab, you can't be sure you will ever get it to come out the way it should. Take that time last year when I tried to burn charcoal in pure oxygen. Always there was a little water left in the collecting bottle and maybe the charcoal would get wet. True, you could come in after school and keep at an exercise, but even then you were never really sure things would come out right. Maybe it was that sort of thing that made it easy for me to divert my time and energy from chemistry to the computer project."

There are great and obvious differences between actual and vicarious experience in science. It is equally obvious that no pedagogical strategy can reconcile these differences. However, the descriptions of the six small-scale excursions into science that are described in the preceding pages bring into focus many of the kinds of problems that teachers may encounter when attempting this kind of teaching. One very obvious problem involves obtaining the specialized apparatus, supplies, and reference sources when they are needed. The usual school science laboratories are stocked with only those items that are needed to conduct the standard array of laboratory exercises and lecture demonstrations. Almost any hypothesis selected by a student for extended investigation takes him quickly beyond the domain of these standard exercises and, therefore, confronts the students with the need for reagents that are not on the shelf or for apparatus not in the storage cabinets. Similarly, he will need repeatedly to examine first-hand the original papers of related research, and seldom do school libraries maintain bound volumes of research journals.

Traditionally, those science teachers who are motivated to provide laboratory and library facilities for their students above and beyond the traditional program for laboratory exercises are expected to rely on adapting, borrowing, begging or otherwise scrounging what their students need. The students, in turn, are often encouraged to employ similar means to solve their own supply problems. Although this solution can be effective, and its practice can develop some skills that are needed in many of the laboratories in which practicing scientists find themselves, reliance on scrounging for needed supplies and references has obvious limitations.

In a modified version of this solution, the student identifies himself with a practicing scientist or scientific organization. In a role of "assistant" or "apprentice," the student then gains access to the facilities of his associates. Along with the advantages in this solution, there are limitations, one of the more subtle ones being the tendency to promote the student too rapidly toward identifying himself with highly sophisticated investigations in advance of preliminary work adequate to ensure that he can sense their significance and the perspective in which the investigations fit. When the student returns to the classroom, and his science teachers attempt to help him put his "advanced" work into its perspective, there is the hazard that the teacher will resent the student's superficial sophistication, and the student, in turn, will wonder if the teacher is as well trained as he might be.

In general, fewer problems arise when teachers consistently interpose themselves in their students' efforts to scrounge supplies, apparatus, references, and consultant services. For one reason, teachers are ultimately responsible for their students, and to abandon this responsibility or to allow the responsibility to range into situations with which the teacher cannot hope to stay in contact, is to invite sometimes serious criticism.

A much more promising solution to the supplies, apparatus, and reference problem consists of establishing a fund and granting the teacher the privilege of buying, without further requisitioning procedures, what he and his students need as and when they need it— obviously, within the limits of funds available. Many teachers are willing to effect a reduction in their established budgets for standard supplies and equipment in order to create such a fund. Sometimes boards of education can be prevailed upon to add such a fund to the established budget of the science department. When all else fails, science teachers who are sufficiently dedicated to the values inherent in small-scale excursions into science for themselves and their students will resort to raising the money for such a fund by approaching parent associations or local scientific societies, by charging student laboratory fees, or by selling refreshments at sports activities, or by various other money-raising activities. Unfortunately, the time a teacher and his students spend raising money to finance their investigations must be subtracted from the all-too-few hours most teachers and students can devote to actually pursuing science.

There are several problems that teachers will meet when they attempt to send their students on small-scale excursions into science that, although possibly more subtle than the problem of providing supplies and apparatus, are even more crucial. These problems appear repeatedly in the records of the six examples referred to previously. Note first how many interests compete intensely for the time and attention of the high-school science student. Both within the school program and in community enterprises outside the school there are many, many activities that provide opportunities for the gifted or dedicated student to gain valuable recognition in return for an investment of a portion of his time and talent. Quite often the knowledge and skills to be gained by the student who takes advantage of these opportunities are fully as potentially valuable as what he could hope to gain from a small-scale excursion into science. Furthermore, the success and, consequently, the continuity of these activities all too often hinges on engaging the participation of the best students and motivating them to become "winners" or to rise to a level of achievement adequate to merit public recognition.

Note, as a second subtle problem, how fragile is the thread of interest that ties a student to a problem. Although a student may be strongly interested in investigating something—anything—the tie that binds him to the pursuit or verification of a specific hypothesis may be much less strong. Nor is there assurance that a pursuit spawned by a student's own needs and interests is any less likely to abort than is a pursuit transmitted to a student by the interest and enthusiasm of the teacher. Circumstances leading to a student's abandonment or abortion of a topic may differ significantly from those leading to stagnation. Not always, for example, does abandonment result from emergence in the student's mind of a more intriguing problem. There are students, apparently, for whom the satisfactions to be gained from the pursuit of science are simply not worth what they cost. To salvage these students and ensure they do not prematurely and irreversibly turn their backs on the scientific endeavor, the teacher must either maneuver the student into position to better enjoy the satisfactions gained from, or reduce the cost of, his continued pursuit of science. Usually, either of these approaches is possible, but the teacher must decide when he should invest his time to salvage a student. Equally dependent upon the wisdom and pedagogical finesse of the teacher is the decision to invoke self-discipline or other extrinsic pressure to cause a student to stick with or get on with an investigation.

A third problem identified in these six sets of anecdotal records involves the matching or congruency of the teacher's suggestions with the students' concepts of what they think they need to do in order to advance their work effectively. In the case of this teacher and his six students, this problem reached almost critical dimensions in connection with the need to keep adequate records during an excursion into science. Too often the students seemed to interpret suggestions to this end as being simply the same kind of busy work they had come to associate with "writing-up" traditional laboratory exercises. Things read or noted that were "really important" they would remember, and the teacher was constantly taken aback by their abilities to remember the formulas of reagents, the requisite conditions of a reaction, and similar factual information. When the need arose, however, to return to a reference for verification, the lack of adequate records caused much time-consuming and rapport-threatening delay.

As could be expected, the six students differed sharply in their interpretations of the value of and, consequently, acceptance or rejection of the teacher's suggestions. If the teacher suggested that a background of familiarity with qualitative tests should precede an attempt to apply a specific test, for example, one student would laboriously check himself out in a wide array of qualitative organic chemical analyses, whereas a second student would persistently limit his work to whatever analytical test seemed to be needed at the time. Another student almost drowned herself in notes from her readings on basic plant anatomy and physiology, whereas another would only reluctantly practice a chromatographic separation process using known materials in advance of moving directly toward applying the chromatographic process in a situation involving many unknowns. Again, it is a matter of pedagogical finesse (it is assumed this includes becoming well-acquainted with his students) for the teacher to decide when and how to help a student balance his available time between gaining background and moving ahead to new investigations or experiments.

SATISFACTIONS IN SMALL-SCALE EXCURSIONS

Despite the problems and frustrations that show through the records of these six students, there are even more indications of the satisfactions teachers and their students gain from their combined efforts to take small-scale excursions into science. To see, for example, the look of discouragement be replaced by hopeful anticipation when a student finds a helpful reference, or to share his enthusiasm when he presents a chromatogram in which the solvent did actually separate the pigments in a flower, or to see the light in a student's eyes when she senses a relationship between what seemed to be two widely divergent instances of abnormal autumn leaf coloration, does more than can be easily worded to cause a teacher to have a really great day in his classroom or laboratory.

Ideally, teachers best gain comprehension and appreciation of the tactics and strategy of science through their own pursuit thereof. What is probably the second-best approach is to guide students on their small-scale excursions in science. The discussion of the individual project (page 448) as one of the lesson formats available to science teachers provides additional illustrations of how students react to this activity. In practice, seldom do teachers work as closely with students on their individual projects as they do when engaging in a mutual excursion into science. This need not be so. Just as many teachers expect their students to gain vicarious experiences from the teacher's training and ventures in science, teachers can use the efforts of their students to grasp the spirit of science, to clarify the methods used in the pursuit of science, and to appreciate its function as a vital part of the human scene.

For Discussion and Further Study

1. Analyze the anecdotal reports of student investigations reported in this chapter and suggest what a teacher might have done to have caused the investigators to have achieved greater progress.

2. What would have been the proper action on the part of the teacher at the point where the student investigator asked to shift from the locust-wood-antibiotic to the coin-date-restoring project?

3. What are the advantages versus hazards of teachers talking about their own investigations to their students? Their colleagues? To practicing scientists in the community?

4. Should investigators be encouraged to repeat the work of closely related research as a "holding" procedure while the investigator is shaping up his major attack on a problem?

5. Set up a tentative experimental investigation of a problem, actual or contrived, and then subject the design of the investigation to the kind of attack that would be launched by a totally unsympathetic critic.

6. What are the advantages versus hazards of taking on a problem that involves seasonal changes or other long-term features that force the investigator to keep the investigation running for several years?

7. Discuss the ethics that become involved when a teacher allows his students to work on investigations of primary interest to the teacher.

8. What community resources hold promise of encouraging and assisting teachers to conduct personal investigations?

References

1. N.S.T.A. Staff Report. "New Ideas for School Science Laboratory Activities," *The Science Teacher,* 22 (February 1955) pp. 26-40.
2. George Boas. *The Inquiring Mind.* La Salle, Illinois; The Open Court Publishing Company, 1959, p. 397.
3. Sir Isaac Newton. *Opticks.* 1704. Quoted by the Rand Corporation, *Scientific American,* 200 (May 1959), p. 44.
4. Gordon M. Dunning. "Critical Thinking and Research," *Science Education,* 40 (March 1956), pp. 83-86.
5. E. Bright Wilson, Jr. *An Introduction to Scientific Research.* New York: McGraw-Hill, 1952, pp. 130–32. Used by permission of McGraw-Hill Book Company.
6. Ivan Petrovich Pavlov. *Testament to the Academic Youth of His Country,* 1936. Quoted by the Rand Corporation, *Scientific American,* 202 (April 1960), p. 54.
7. John Stuart Mill. *Logic,* 1843. Quoted by the Rand Corporation, *Scientific American* 204 (February 1961), p. 40.
8. W. S. Blatchley. *Heteroptera of Eastern North America.* Indianapolis: Nature Publishing Company, 1926, pp. 967–1002.

III

PURSUIT OF SCIENCE
IN CLASSROOM
AND
TEACHING
LABORATORY

Teachers direct their instruction in classroom and laboratory toward achieving several purposes. One goal is to develop within the minds of students increased appreciation of the knowledge of science, its inventions and discoveries. A second goal is to nurture the modes of thought and abilities of the mind that seem to be exercised in the acquisition of knowledge and the execution of inventions and discoveries. A third goal is to foster increased appreciation of the general spirit and procedures of inquiry that accompany the pursuit of science. Obviously, each of these goals is inextricably interwoven with the others.

The success of lessons in the pursuit of science must be measured, ultimately, by the behavior they produce in students. Ideally, a textbook dealing with teaching the pursuit of science should specify the kinds of lessons that advance students most rapidly toward the desired goals. This idealism, however, ignores the complexity of factors that cause established teachers to make almost imperceptible but gradual changes in their accustomed lesson formats. Another equally complex set of factors causes beginning teachers to try out many kinds of lessons, and to taste the satisfactions that derive from emphasizing various educational objectives before they settle on a working repertory of lesson formats.

The two types of material in this section are intended to provide perspective and guidance for teachers who seek to extend, adapt, or evolve their collections of types of science lessons. First, the historical growth of science curricula is reviewed. Second, the types of lessons that are most often used are described briefly and illustrated with teacher's actual working papers and representative student responses.

15

The Evolution of
School Curricula and
Science Courses
of Study

Most science curricula were developed in a highly uncertain manner and have come down to us in a fashion hardly calculated to build confidence in American education. The courses grew by adding new scientific information and theory without eliminating any of the old. The emphasis was typically on science as a static body of knowledge. . . . The result of all this is that many science courses consist of massive doses of facts without conceptual order, without unity, without a knowledge of how facts were developed, and without a feeling for the intellectual method that won them from nature. Only the mere skeleton of science has been presented. The facts are divorced from anything that might be called the process of inquiry; they are sterilized of their beauty and are left dangling without a place in the scheme of things.[1]

J. Stanley Marshall 1962

The treatment of science as enquiry is not achieved by talk about science or scientific method apart from the content of science. On the contrary, treatment of science as

167

enquiry consists of a treatment of scientific knowledge in terms of its origins in the united activities of the human mind and hand which produce it; it is a means for clarifying and illuminating scientific knowledge.[2]

Joseph J. Schwab   1962

We believe now that young people, and old as well, learn only that for which they feel a need. A person cannot successfully be directed to do an assigned task unless the task is accepted by him as important. Education cannot be given. It must be gained. Motives are not given. They are discovered. Motives are intrinsic.[3]

Samuel R. Powers   1952

Emphasis on the scientific attitudes, like that on scientific principles is not out-moded. The scientific attitudes have now been defined by enough investigators so that we know what they are. It is discouragingly difficult to inculcate them in boys and girls to the extent that the latters' subsequent behaviors will reflect them. But there is no hope if we assume a defeatist attitude toward attempts at such inculcation.[4]

Francis D. Curtis   1952

The teaching of science is just as much a human endeavor as is the total scientific enterprise. Teaching science is also one of the things men and women do, and how science is taught is the product of the gradual interaction between teachers and their students, an interaction that is reflected in the school curricula and courses of study in science. This interaction produces an evolutionary process. What science teaching is at any one period of history is determined by the points of view and pedagogical practices passed along through many generations of teachers. Similarly, what science teaching is in any one part of the world is determined not only by the local interests, customs, and traditions, but also by beliefs and practices developed elsewhere and adopted or adapted to local conditions. How much the teaching of science in one country or locality is influenced by outside practices depends more often on the effectiveness of communication than on inherent differences in the subject matter or the students ω whom it is being taught.

The teaching profession, and its science segment is no exception, has been teased much for the publicity it gives to "new" movements and schools of thought, which sweep through the profession with almost seasonal regularity. In reality, the evolution of curricula and courses of study seems to proceed at a measured pace. When ideas first appear in professional literature, no greater reaction may be aroused than to attract the interest of that small fraction of teachers who are always discontented with status quo. Decades may pass until a mysterious combination of social, political, and who knows what other forces combine to pluck the new idea from its obscurity and bring it forth to become a widely heralded answer to the profession's problems. Invariably, the heralds of the new become the "progressives" and the defenders of established practices the "traditionalists," and battles between the two are joined on editors' desks and conference platforms. It is stimulating to participate in these battles and, if one has an adequate perspective, this participation can do much to give a teacher confidence in his own comprehension of the role and function of the teaching of science.

THE EARLY HIGH SCHOOLS

To gain perspective for viewing the development of science courses, consider briefly the general historical evolution of this segment of school curricula. In the Latin Grammar schools of Colonial America, there is no evidence that science was a part of the curriculum. Between 1750 and 1850, the public academy developed as a school to enroll the non-college-bound student. In contrast to the narrow restrictions of the earlier Latin grammar Schools, the curriculum of these schools was more practical. Natural philosophy, a forerunner of physics, was a part of the curriculum of the academies.

The free public high school grew out of the academy movement. The first of these was the English High School, which was established in Boston about 1821. The science curriculum of the early public high schools was influenced by the academies and the offerings consisted for the most part of natural philosophy, natural history (largely biological science), and chemistry. Each of these subjects was in the curriculum of the English High School in Boston. The nature of these offerings will be considered in greater detail at a later point.

Science, in the first fifty years of the public high school movement, was taught largely for its informational and practical values. There was a very limited amount of demonstration and practically no laboratory work. Emphasis was placed on the memorizing of factual material. Judged by the few reports on enrollments, the courses appear to have been popular, and were taken largely by those pupils not going to college. While some of the textbooks were written from an inductive point of view, most of the instruction was by lecture and recitation.

STANDARDIZATION
OF THE CURRICULUM

In 1872, Harvard College announced that work in physics and other high school sciences would be accepted for college entrance. Within a few years, most of the colleges had followed the lead of Harvard, and the offerings in high school science showed increasing effects of college influence. Courses of study were prepared by college teachers of science, and many of the textbooks were written by them. High school science became a simplified and condensed college course, and its value was determined almost entirely by how well it prepared the student for college-level work.

The most influential of the written standards and requirements prepared by colleges was the Harvard Descriptive List, issued in 1887, a listing of forty-six experiments in physics acceptable for college entrance. In 1893 the National Education Association's Committee of Ten published a report of standards that was widely referred to, and reports were published in 1896 and 1899 by the N.E.A.'s Committee on College Entrance Requirements. In 1900, the College Entrance Board was organized.

The reports of the N.E.A. committees had a far-reaching effect on the teaching of high school subjects, particularly high school science. Prior to these reports, schools had been offering short-term courses in many sciences, such as physics, chemistry, astronomy, geology, botany, zoology, and physiology. The Committee of Ten and later the Committee on College Entrance Requirements, condemned the practice of short courses and recommended full-year courses in fewer sciences. As a result of the work of these commitees, the first recommendation of a science sequence for high schools came about. The courses proposed were: first year, physical geography; second year, biology; third year, physics; and fourth year, chemistry.

C. R. Mann[5] points out that:

The influence of the Descriptive List on the development of physics teaching in America has been tremendous. It appeared at the psychological moment when demand for object teaching had reached its full force. It exalted this demand for object teaching into a requirement of quantitative laboratory work. It showed teachers and school boards how a laboratory of teaching could be introduced into the work in physics with the use of materials at hand and with a small outlay for equipment. As a result of this movement the American public high schools now have laboratories while France and Germany are just beginning to secure them.

G. R. Twiss[6] sums up the effects of the period of college domination of high school science as follows:

As far as science is concerned the results have been both good and bad. Among the good results are the establishments of the principles (1) that high school teachers should have adequate collegiate training for their work, (2) that laboratory work, field excursions, and some reference book work should be carried on in connection with each of the sciences, (3) that schools should be adequately equipped with laboratories, apparatus, and libraries for such work, (4) that double laboratory periods should be provided in the time schedules for the laboratory exercises, (5) that laboratory notes should be systematically entered in suitable books by the students, (6) that pupils should be taught not merely to memorize but to think. Among the bad results have been (1) the tendency to cast all instruction in one mold in the attempts to meet the specifications of syllabi and examinations, (2) over-emphasis on the assimilation of subject matter, and the consequent undervaluation of the scientific method of study, by means of which the subject matter of science is best acquired, and (3) worst of all discouragement of initiative on the part of school teachers and administrators because of the burdensome amounts of subject matter that were called for by these authoritative syllabi.

CURRICULUM EXPANSION
AND READJUSTMENT, 1920–30

In the closing years of the last century, a rapid increase began, both in the number of high schools and in the high school population. This movement gathered force in the first decade of this century and reached a peak between 1910 and 1920. The tremendous influx of students into the high schools created some problems and exacerbated others, but most important among the problems was the narrowness of purpose of the college-prescribed curriculum.

The demands for types of curricula more in keeping with a student body composed of an increasingly large fraction of the total population led to the junior high school movement. In the older scheme, schools had been organized almost universally on a plan that comprised eight years of elementary school training, and four years of high school training. Between 1900 and 1910, some schools began to organize to give six years of elementary training, three years of junior high school, and three years of senior high school training.

Concurrently, and for similar reasons, the science offerings in the high school changed. Perhaps the most significant change was the introduction of general science to replace physical geography as the first-year subject of the four-year science sequence. This change was made in order to provide a terminal course in science for students not going to college and also to provide an exploratory course for the later, specialized sciences.

In some of the newer junior high schools, the science offerings were pushed down into the seventh and eighth years. This had the effect of increasing the opportunities for science teaching over a longer period of schooling. In the course of a few years, general science largely replaced physical geography in the science program, and enrolled a larger percentage of the total high school population than any of the older and more specialized sciences.

Changes to meet more adequately the new demands on the high school came slowly, but the pace was considerably accelerated by the reports of the Commission on the Reorganization of Secondary Education[7] of the National Education Association. A report on the reorganization of science in the secondary schools was issued by a subcommittee of this commission.[8] This report was the first comprehensive document to deal exclusively with the teaching of science, and, although it was limited to science in the secondary school, it constituted one of the landmarks of science teaching in American schools.

The report sought to show how science instruction could contribute to the cardinal principles of secondary education. Objectives stated by the commission emphasized bringing order to the science offerings of the high school; the report also offered help on the selection and organization of materials, and on the general problems of teaching high school science. The report gave impetus to an emerging science sequence in the high schools and pointed science instruction toward larger social goals than had been encompassed previously. Some critics believe that the report tended to overemphasize immediate and practical goals at the expense of giving adequate attention to the larger influences that the accumulation of science knowledge has on civilization.

A committee of the American Association for the Advancement of Science in 1927 issued a report entitled "On The Place of Science in Education."[9] This report emphasized the importance of scientific thinking as an objective of science teaching, recommended that studies of a national scope on science teaching be set up, and urged that a field secretary be provided to assist teachers of science in the study of their problems.

THE PERIOD 1930–50

This period in the history of science teaching in America witnessed the beginning of what might be called the "modern influences," which have come to shape the curriculum developments of the 1950's and the 1960's. In 1932 the *Thirty-first Yearbook* of the National Society for the Study of Education carried an influential report titled: *A Program for Teaching Science*.[10] This report advocated, for the first time, a twelve-year science sequence beginning in the elementary school and extending through the high school. It also advocated that science instruction on all school levels be organized around certain broad concepts or generalizations. The report stated thirty-eight such principles as guides in the selection of specific objectives for science teaching. The influence of this report has been far reaching: it has given impetus to the introduction of science into the elementary school, and has gone a long way toward promoting the organization of science courses in terms of larger principles.

As a part of the National Survey of Secondary Education, in 1932, a bulletin entitled *Instruction in Science*[11] was published. This report was based on observations in fourteen cities over the country and on evidence obtained from the analysis of a large number of courses of study in each of the four high school sciences. The investigation indicated a great lack of agreement among the science educators and teachers of science regarding aims, content, and methods. The investigation also revealed that general science and biology were well established in the high school curriculum and were more forward looking, both in aims and methods, than the older sciences of physics and chemistry.

In 1938 the Commission on Secondary School Curriculum of the Progressive Education Association issued a report entitled *Science in General Education*.[12] This report advocated that science in the secondary school be taught around broad areas of living such as (1) personal living, (2) immediate personal-social relationships, (3) social-civic relationships, (4) economic relationships, and (5) the disposition and ability to use reflective thinking in the solution of problems. The report traced the implications for science teaching in each of these proposed areas of living.

The National Committee on Science Teaching of the Department of Science of the National Education Association, after a three-year period of study, issued a series of reports in 1942. Two of these reports had to do with the changed emphasis in the teaching of science in America. These were entitled *Science Teaching for Better Living*[13] and *Redirecting Science Teaching in the Light of Personal-Social Needs*.[14] These reports were significant because they were prepared by committees of science teachers and reflected the opinions of many other science teachers over the country. The reports advocated and extended the same point of view as that of the Progressive Education Association report. The trend of teaching science for purposes of general education was further emphasized by a report published by the Educational Policies Commission in 1944 entitled *Education for All American Youth*[15] and a report published by Harvard in 1945 entitled *General Education in a Free Society*.[16]

The recommendations of these two reports as they relate to science were well summarized in 1947 in the *Forty-Sixth Yearbook* of the National Society for the Study of Education[17] as follows:

(a) Science instruction should begin early in the experience of the child.

(b) All education in science at the elementary and secondary levels should be general. Even for students going to college, general courses in biological science and in physical science (according to the Harvard report) "should make a greater contribution to the student's general education and his preparation for future study than a separate one-year course in physics and chemistry." The document of the Educational Policies Commission goes even further in its recommendations for reorganization of high school science courses.

(c) The development of competence in use of the scientific method of problem solving and the inculcation of scientific attitudes transcend in importance other objectives in science instruction.

The *Forty-Sixth Yearbook* stressed the importance of science taught for its functional value in aiding the adjustment of individuals. It recognized and endorsed the present science sequence through the elementary and high schools. It urged support for the growing tendency to offer physical science in the high school for those pupils not going further in the study of science.

During the last part of the decade 1950-60 and the beginning of the 1960's, several reports on the teaching of science were published by committees and organizations. While the recency of these documents precludes a valid judgment concerning their influences on the curriculum, the following ones should be mentioned:

1. *Rethinking Science Education*.[18]
2. *It's Time for Better Elementary School Science*.[19]
3. *Planning for Excellence in High School Science*.[20]

At the halfway point of the twentieth century, there appeared a new agency in the United States that rapidly added new dimensions to several of the forces that influence the design and administration of science courses in that country. The National Science Foundation Act passed by Congress in 1950 established the National Science Foundation "to promote the progress of science; to advance the national health, prosperity, and welfare; to secure the national defense; and for other purposes." For reasons that can be comprehended only by examining many deeply rooted and subtle sociological factors at work in the United States, the times seemed to be ripe for a federal agency to become actively involved in the construction of science courses and their administration.

Within ten years, the foundation accepted as one of its major functions the improvement of education in the sciences throughout the nation. The Division of Scientific Personnel and Education expanded rapidly into sections specializing in fellowships, institutes, special projects in science education, course content improvement, scientific personnel, and education studies. Congress appropriated relatively large sums of money for the administration of the various programs that were developed within these sections, and soon the responsibilities assumed by the National Science Foundation ranged through nearly all the things that promised to improve the training and function of teachers, especially science and mathematics teachers. The pattern of summer institutes that had been developed during the 1940's under sponsorship of several industrial organizations was adopted, and the subjects included multiplied. The late afternoon and evening "extension" programs of teacher training colleges and universities were extended, not only by freeing the enrollees of tuition costs, but also by providing reimbursement for travel and other expenses. There was a great expansion of the sums of money available for fellowships for approved study programs at all stages of the educational sequence—from programs for especially capable secondary school students through programs for post-doctoral study.

Among the foundation's most widely publicized efforts have been its comprehensive programs to improve content, and instructional materials for courses in mathematics and science in elementary and secondary schools. Outstanding scholars who sensed the need for this sort of thing developed proposals for new or modified courses of study. Upon receiving approval by the foundation, large sums of money were made available for the prompt execution of the proposals. The prevailing pattern of these projects begins with the initiation of a proposal by a relatively small group of scholars. Textbooks, teaching aids, and teacher re-education techniques that are needed to launch the new courses are then produced by this group, often supplemented by cooperating teachers during the summer months. Another unique feature of this pattern has been the use of subsidized pilot groups to whom the salient features of the new courses were presented. The teachers in these groups, in turn, were encouraged to report to the sponsors the strengths and weaknesses that became evident when the courses were presented to students.

In contrast to the traditional "play of the market place" concept of curriculum development and course construction, especially in connection with textbook publication and adoption, the pattern of course improvement introduced under the sponsorship of the National Science Foundation was markedly different. Comprehension of the ultimate impact of this new pattern on American science education becomes an essential goal of anyone who seeks to put the total evolution of the science teaching profession into its true perspective.

Tracing how those segments from the total domain of science were selected and molded into the specialized science courses and how a sequence of such courses came to be adopted as a science curriculum for elementary, junior, and senior high schools, is not only interesting but also essential background information. Highlights in the historical evolution of each of the specialized science courses appear in the following section. Each subject is presented in the order of its emergence in the total curriculum, this order being physics, chemistry, biology, general science, and elementary science.

PHYSICS IN THE SCHOOL CURRICULUM

The Period of Natural Philosophy, 1750–1870

Natural philosophy, the forerunner of physics was an offering in the public academies, the public schools of earliest record in America. It is not clear from early documents just when natural philosophy was made a part of school curricula. There is a record of its introduction in an academy at Northampton, England, as early as 1729. Many books were written on the subject during the early years, one written by James Ferguson was published in 1750. This book went through many editions and was published in America in 1806 by Robert Patterson, Professor of Natural Philosophy at the University of Pennsylvania. The following is taken from the introduction to one of the early editions of this book:

The chief object of Mr. Ferguson's labors was to give a familar view of physical science and to render it accessible to those who are not accustomed to mathematical investigation. To his labors we must attribute that general diffusion of scientific knowledge among the practical mechanics of this country, which has in a great measure, banished those antiquated prejudices and erroneous maxims of construction that perpetually mislead the unlettered artist.

As early as 1754, Rev. William Smith was teaching "natural and moral philosophy" in the "Publik Academy in the City of Philadelphia"[21] founded by Benjamin Franklin. Natural philosophy was offered in the earliest curriculum of the first public high school in America, the English High School, in Boston, from its beginning in 1821. This subject was also included in the course of study in the first high school in New York in 1825.[22]

The academies and the early public schools were established in part as a revolt against the rigid prescriptions of the earlier college preparatory courses. They were founded, in the words of one writer, "in order that pupils might learn those things that are likely to be most useful and most ornamental." Since natural philosophy was offered both in the early academies and in public schools, it must have been regarded as useful in meeting the needs of the people in their struggle for the common welfare.

Some Early Textbooks in Natural Philosophy

Ferguson's book on natural philosophy went through many editions between 1750 and 1825. The book enjoyed a wide popularity, as evidenced by the quotation from Sir David Brewster about 1805:[23]

No book upon the same subject has been so generally read, and so widely circulated among all ranks of the community. We perceive it in the workshop of every mechanic. We find it transferred into the different encyclopedias which this country has produced, and we may easily trace it in those country systems of philosophy which have lately appeared.

The usefulness of this book is explained in part by the fact that the span of its popularity was also the age of the steam engine, the steam boat, and the locomotive, the age when machinery was being brought into all branches of industry. Mann[24] notes that in Ferguson's book "sixty two pages were devoted to machines and forty pages to pumps."

It appears that natural philosophy met real, practical, and useful needs in the lives of people who were living in a world that was being overwhelmed by the first onslaughts of the technology that resulted from inventions of the period. This is further attested by the large number of books which were written on the subject and the many editions of most of them. Blair's[25] *A Grammar of Natural and Experimental Philosophy* had gone into twelve editions by 1822 when it appeared in its first American edition in Hartford, Connecticut. Parker's[26] *School Compendium of Experimental Philosophy*, 1837, went through twenty-two editions in its first twelve years. Comstock's[27] *System of Natural Philosophy* was in its seventy-third in 1846.

The title pages and prefaces of some of the early books give a bit of flavor regarding their authors and the point of view of science teaching of the day. The authors were men of broad interests. Ferguson was a self-educated man, a mechanic by trade who was later elected as a member of the Royal Society of London because he had a unique ability "to make abstract subjects clear." Blair was a clergyman, also the author of such works as *The Class Book, Universal Preceptor, English Grammar, Reading Exercises and Models of Letters.* Comstock was a physician who wrote, besides his *Natural Philosophy, Introduction to Mineralogy, The Elements of Chemistry, Introduction to Botany, Outlines of Geology, Outlines of Physiology, Natural History of Birds,* and other books.

The table of contents of Blair's *A Grammar of Natural and Experimental Philosophy,* 1822, contains the following topics: Physics, Dynamics, Mechanics, Hydrostatics, Hydraulics, Pneumatics, Acoustics, Optics, Astronomy, Electricity, Galvanism and Magnetism. From the Preface of this little book one may read:

> Every instructor of youth must be aware, that mere disquisition are of no use in the art of teaching; and that no science can be taught if the student does not *work* or perform operations in it: or answer *questions* which involve the consideration of its various details.
>
> He who only reads *about* a science, can be nothing more than a smatterer; whilst he who commits its terms and elementary principles to memory, and applies them by some act of his own mind to the various combinations of the science, soon becomes a master of it.

From the fifty-third edition of *A System of Natural Philosophy* by Comstock, 1840, one may read on the title page:

> The principles of Mechanics, Hydrostatics, Hydraulics, Pneumatics, Acoustics, Optics, Astronomy, Electricity, Magnetism, The Steam Engine, and Electro-magnetism, are familiarly explained and illustrated by more than two hundred engravings to which are added questions for the examination of pupils.

and from the preface:

> It is the chief object of the author to make himself understood by those who know nothing of mathematics, and who indeed had no previous knowledge of natural philosophy. The author has also endeavored to illustrate the subject as much as possible by means of common occurrences, or common things and in this manner to bring philosophical truths as much as possible within ordinary requirements.

The following quotation is from *The Elements of Natural Philosophy,* by A. W. Sprague, fifth edition, 1858. One may read in the Preface:

> The principles of Natural Philosophy are best comprehended by visible illustrations. But few minds obtain a clear understanding of the operations

of Nature's laws from mere written or oral descriptions; the eye must see the *modus operandi* before the mind can gain a full and just comprehension of the principle; an interest must be awakened by an *ocular demonstration* before the attention can, in most cases, be sufficiently secured to fix the idea. Hence, the importance which has come to be attached within a few years to the use of philosophical instruments for scientific illustrations and the rapid and general introductions of these into the various seminaries of the country.

The skill requisite for the successful and commercial use of a philosophical apparatus is far greater than is often supposed. For this reason many teachers and lecturers, thoroughly conversant with the theories of Natural Philosophy, fail sadly in their attempt at a practical illustration of its principles by means of instruments. No one familiar with the theories merely of steam or electro-magnetism, as learned from a general study of these subjects, could reasonably expect without some specific practical directions, to run a locomotive or operate successfully a telegraph; in either case such an attempt would likely result in a failure, if not in positive injury or destruction of the machine. . . . Textbooks of Natural Philosophy seldom contain any real serviceable directions for the inexperienced manipulator. In prescribing the more obvious rules, they too often pass over the real difficulties in the philosophical experimenting. . . .

In treating of the subjects contained in this work, it has been our aim to present such a practical view of each as the wants of a practical age demand; avoiding, however, those mathematical formulas and those specific details, ill-suited to a work designed merely as a textbook for schools and seminaries of learning.

Convinced by past experience that principles in philosophic science are much better comprehended and longer retained when accompanied with appropriate illustrations, we have endeavored to make such a selection of experiments as seemed best adapted for elucidating those principles and rendering them intelligible to the youthful mind. . . .

The subject of Astronomy, so generally introduced into textbooks of Natural Philosophy, has been omitted in this work; this, in the opinion of the author, being better learned from a separate treatise while Heat, which is often rejected as a subject exclusively within the province of Chemistry, has been retained as properly belonging either to this or Natural Philosophy.

A concise and practical description of the Magic Lantern, Oxyhydrogen Microscope and other articles of a philosophical apparatus now extensively used for popular exhibitions of science, has been added. . . .

. . . A cheaper class of instruments has not been described in the following pages, such being but little used, and, when used the manner of operating them may be learned equally well from a more perfect apparatus.

From these excerpts one gets the feeling that Natural Philosophy was a subject that was eminently practical and designed to meet the needs of people generally. Most young people who attended school in this period studied the subject. In the textbooks published before 1890 one can hardly find any mathematical formulas, and the illustrations are of real objects. There are real pumps and pulleys and levers, commonly with a hand where the force is applied.

Mann[28] sums up the case for natural philosophy as follows:

(1) That natural philosophy was introduced into the schools for a specific purpose—namely, to supply the common people with information about physical phenomena in those schools that were founded for the common good and supported by the public funds.

(2) That the natural philosophy so introduced and so taught did supply the desired information and did do its part in improving those schools.

(3) That natural philosophy had a very different origin from university physics, since the latter consists essentially in studying mathematical forms, in discovering interrelations among these forms, and in deducing and verifying their consequences.

The Period of College Domination, 1872–1900

Natural philosophy in its original format had about disappeared from the school curriculum by 1872 and had been replaced by physics. This change in science offering coincided with the rapid growth of the high schools and their gradual gravitation toward the colleges. This period began about 1872 and continued until nearly 1900.

THE NATURE OF THE EARLY PHYSICS COURSES.   As noted earlier, physics was offered in the Boston English High School as early as 1821. In 1823 the school announced a series of lectures in natural philosophy. Four years later the school purchased a small amount of equipment to "illustrate" the lectures. While no exact record is available, it is quite certain that no student laboratory work was done until many years later. The physics classes were very formal and consisted largely of lectures followed by recitations in which the students reproduced factual material from memory.

The teaching of physics in these early schools, while generally adequate from the point of view of purveying information, left much to be desired from the standpoint of method. The value of laboratory work was not sensed and was very slow in its acceptance. It was not until 1872 that laboratory work in physics was generally supported by educators, and even then it was actually practiced in only a few instances.

INFLUENCES TOWARD STANDARDIZATION.   As early as 1857 natural philosophy was required by law in Massachusetts. This law remained in effect almost to the close of the century. The U.S. Bureau of Education, now the U.S. Office of Education, was established by an Act of Congress in 1867. One of its earliest tasks was an attempt to bring some order out of the great educational chaos of the time. Physics was in a bad way, and a very good example of chaos. It was being taught in many ways and for periods of time ranging from a few weeks to a full year. There was very little agreement as to the selection of content, the aims, or the methods. Perhaps the first move toward some sort of standardization came in 1872, when physics had gained sufficient respectability as a curriculum offering to be made an entrance requirement for Harvard University. In 1873 Syracuse University followed Harvard in this respect. Soon the subject was required for entrance to a large number of colleges.

THE PHYSICS COURSE IN 1880.   In 1880 the U. S. Bureau of Education issued Bulletin No. 6, compiled by Frank W. Clarke, Professor of Physics at the University of Cincinnati. This study reports a summary of replies received from 175 public high schools and 433 private secondary schools to a questionnaire compiled and sent out by the Bureau of Education.

The findings from this study as reported were: (1) Four secondary schools over the country offered a full one-year course in physics with laboratory work by the pupils (the high schools at Pittsburgh, Pa., and Worcester, Mass., the Punchard Free School at Andover, Mass., and the Friends' Select School in Philadelphia). (2) Two public and seven private schools reported shorter courses with some laboratory work by pupils. (3) Thirty-eight public and twelve private schools reported a full-year course in physics with experiments by the teacher. (4) Fourteen public and ninety-five private schools reported one year or less of textbook work only. (5) Seven public and six private schools reported no physics at all.

Steel's *Fourteen Weeks in Physics* was in use by 34 public and 116 private schools. The next most popular textbook was Quackenbos' *Natural Philosophy,* in use in 15 public and 72 private schools. With Steel's *Fourteen Weeks in Physics* in use in a quarter of the schools, it seems quite evident that there was a great popularity in the short, informational type of course.

THE NATURE OF THE PHYSICS COURSE IN 1884.   In 1884 the U.S. Bureau of Education published a second bulletin, Bulletin No. 7, which was compiled by Charles K. Wead, Professor of Physics at the University of Michigan. This study reported returns from thirty-two secondary schools, seventeen normal schools, and twenty-one colleges. Some of the findings of this study, as reported by Mann,[29] follow:

There was general agreement that some sort of science should be taught in the grammar schools—not for information but "mental training and discipline which the pupils acquire through studying the methods whereby the conclusions of physical science have been established."

There was agreement that about 200 hours was the amount of time needed for the physics course and that the third year of high school was the best time. In regard to requiring physics for college entrance, the report says: ". . . the study of physics is fitted to give results in mental training that are of very high value and that cannot be given so well by other studies— . . . it will usually be better taught if the college has even slight supervision over the teaching that a requirement for admission would give, and so this requirement would react to the communities where these schools are situated."

About methods of teaching physics the report has some things to say that sound very familiar today—nearly 80 years later: "The weight of opinion is decidedly that the course should be inductive." It is inferred, as it is today, that inductive teaching would be difficult because

The teacher has probably known little or nothing of it in his own education and does not know how to begin. . . . Again, the progress of the student following the inductive method is so slow, if measured by the usual examination tests, as to discourage faint heart. . . . The common advocacy of scientific studies for the value of their information makes it more difficult to follow a method in which information is a subordinate end.

The report goes on to describe the inductive method:

. . . Following the scientific method we first observe the phenomena sharply, and then seek for a cause or for the law according to which the forces act. A dozen guesses may be made quickly, perhaps to be found insufficient. But if the guess is a definite one, definite conclusions (deductions) can be drawn from it which will lead to new observations or experiments. Perhaps our supposed law is immediately disproved; then we make a new guess, and so continue until one explanation remains which is consistent with all our knowledge and stands all tests we are able to apply; and now is the time for us to consult the published record of other men's experiments, and in this way learn those facts that are otherwise unattainable by us. If to reason accurately on physical facts be of any value to the student, is not a conclusive disproof of an hypothesis (provided he originated it) more valuable than the incomplete proof with which he must usually remain contented when he learns the accepted hypothesis?

The report summarizes the matter of teaching methods in the following manner:

[1] Because, consciously or not, we must use inductive methods all our lives in ways where we cannot avail ourselves of the principle of the division of labor, depending on others. The professional opinion of the physician and lawyer, all our judgments of men, and our opinions on common matters of life must be largely the result of inductive reasoning. . . . [2] Because in the

opinion of many teachers, more physics can be taught so as to be remembered in this way, than in any other.

The report indicates that "laboratory work was favored by the majority" of those replying, although it may be inferred that by laboratory work some implied only demonstration.

The report closes with a list of basic experiments which, it states, ". . . may be shown by the teacher, or some of them may be performed by the student in the laboratory."

Compare and measure lengths, volumes, and masses
Composition of forces
Inertia
Parallel forces
Center of gravity
Lever, inclined plane, &c.
Pendulum
Centrifugal action
Archimedes' principle
Density and specific gravity
Capillarity
Simple barometer
Boyle's law
Air pump experiments
Pumps and siphon
Expansion of liquids and gases
Bending of compound bar
Verify fixed points of thermometer.
Conduction of heat
Temperature of mixtures of water
Specific heat of a solid
Latent heat of ice, steam, vapors
Heat from friction
Useful forms of galvanic cells

Properties of permanent and temporary magnets
Magnetic curves
Simple galvanic cell
Effects of current on magnetic needle
Electro-magnets
Influence of resistance of conductors
Chemical effects of current
Heating effects of current
Induction
Telegraph and telephone
Frictional electricity; two states
Electrical machine; Leyden jar
Vibration and production of waves
Resonance
Interference of sound (fork and jar)
Monochord
Photometer
Reflection; plane and curved mirror
Refraction of light
Dispersion and spectrum
Total reflection
Lenses; construction of image
Combination of colors

In this list there is no mention made of work, atoms, molecules, kinetic theory, acceleration, falling bodies, units, conservation of matter, or Newton's laws of motion, and yet within these forty-seven topics it was regarded that there was sufficient material for a one-year course in high school physics.

It is interesting to note that over seventy-five years ago in this bulletin of the U.S. Bureau of Education many things were advocated that have been largely missing in science teaching over the years—inductive teaching, simple experiments in familiar units, and training in the scientific method of thinking—and now we are seeing a revival of the same point of view and some definite action in the new curriculum materials to really implement the point of view for the first time.

THE PUBLICATION OF THE HARVARD DESCRIPTIVE LIST. The year 1887 provided the next significant development in high school physics when Harvard University published its famous Harvard Descriptive List of forty-six experiments acceptable for entrance to that college. The point of view of this bulletin is expressed in the following quotation from the preface of a textbook of the period:[30]

The objects to be sought in the course of experimental physics . . . may be stated thus: *first* to train the young student by means of tangible problems requiring him to observe accurately, to attend strictly, and to think clearly; *second,* to give practice in the methods by which physical facts and laws are discovered; *third,* to give practical acquaintance with a considerable number of these facts and laws with a view to their utility in the thought and actions of educated men.

The Harvard Descriptive List had a profound effect on the teaching of physics especially as it influenced the spread of laboratory work in the schools. It was only a list of experiments, but it gave rather precise instructions for how these should be carried out. Coming at a time when there were only a few teachers of physics, and when laboratories in high schools were scarce, this type of specific guidance was a great boon in experimentation in the subject. There can be little doubt that the widespread use of laboratory work in physics courses can be traced directly to the influence of the Harvard Descriptive List.

THE COMMITTEE OF TEN AND ITS REPORT. In 1892, the National Education Association appointed a Committee of Ten to investigate the status of the high school curriculum. A subcommittee of this group was formed as the Conference on Physics, Chemistry and Astronomy. The report of this subcommittee[31] recommended that

. . . physics be pursued the last year of the high school course, in order that the pupils have as much mathematical knowledge as possible to enable them to deal satisfactorily with the subject . . . physics be required for admission to college; [that it be taught by] a combination of laboratory work, textbook work and thoroughly didactic instructor, [that the laboratory work should be largely quantitative and that the aim of teaching should be] to make a so-called rediscovery of the laws of physics.

Between 1887 and 1900, in addition to the Report of the Committee of Ten, there were several other forces such as the Report of the Committee on College Entrance Requirements, 1899, the National Physics Course, and State syllabi in physics, which tended to formalize the topics and the teaching into stereotypes. Thus, in this period there was a rapid gravitation of the course in high school physics toward college domination.

The Physics Course, 1900–50

Following nearly thirty years of college domination and an increasing formalism in high school physics, there developed a sharp reaction and a return to a more practical kind of course, with emphasis that was very similar to that in the heyday of natural philosophy. The following quotations from textbooks of the period are reported in Woodhull:[32]
Henderson and Woodhull, 1900:

Physics should be so taught as to be a desirable and even essential subject for every pupil in the secondary school.
The relations of physics on all sides to human life and human interests have been emphasized.
The laboratory deals with inductions and verifications and its chief purpose is to make knowledge real.
Both laboratory and classroom work are essential to a correct knowledge of elementary physics and they should correlate.
Portraits and brief sketches of men who by their researches have contributed much to our knowledge of physics, have been introduced.

Slate, 1902:

My experience proves beyond reasonable doubt that elementary instruction in physics suffers when contact with phenomena and with experimental methods is confined to a small group of quantitative experiments; the possibilities of the class (lecture) experiment have not been fully exploited.
Instead of feeding them with crumbs from the specialists' table, physics for the school must be treated in relation to the average boy and girl, approaching the threshold of active life.

Andrews and Howland, 1903:

We have sought to make prominent the practical bearings of physics. To those students at least whose schooling ends with high school, physics should be a connecting link between their study and their work. Except in special cases it bears more on the daily affairs of life than on any other subject.
The student should constantly keep in mind that the data of physics are much easier to remember if they are interpreted in terms of past experiences, everyday events, and that such interpretations are far more valuable than the mere acquisition of the data.

Mann and Twiss, 1905:

The aim has been to show the student that knowledge of physics enables him to answer many of the questions over which he has puzzled long in vain.

Beginning arguments with inventions or general observations of phenomena, may not be the logical order, but it is more nearly the order in which Nature herself teaches, and the result of the argument does not lose in definitions, clearness or accuracy, provided the laboratory is continually held up as the final court of appeal where all doubtful questions are settled.

The attempt is made (1) to interest the student in observing carefully and accurately first the familiar things about him and then the things in the laboratory; (2) to interest him in detecting analogies and similarities among the things observed; (3) to train him in keeping his mind free from bias and in drawing conclusions tentatively; (4) to make him see the value of verifying the conclusions and accepting the result whether it confirms or denies his inference.

We have tried deliberately to give the student the impression that science leads to no absolute results—that, at best, it is merely a question of the close approximation; of doing the best we can, and accepting the result tentatively, until we can do better. This attitude places the teacher also in the position of a learner and prohibits him from making use of didactic or dogmatic statements.—Science instruction that does not develop mental integrity, freedom of the personal judgment, and tolerance, fails in a vital spot.

References are given to books in which the biographies of the great men of science may be read and the student is urged to read them and report. The arguments used by some of the great thinkers have been briefly sketched, and the methods devised by them for reaching conclusions have been given. The attempt has been made to present them as they live in the ideas which they have handed down to us; to picture their mental processes and attitudes, and to show how one thing leads to another as the subject develops in the discoverers mind.

These quotations amply document the clear-cut nature of the break that occurred in the early years of this period with the college domination, which had persisted since 1872. There was a sharp trend toward teaching physics as an interpretation of environment in all of its practical aspects. Physics was deemed essential to the life of everyone. There was evidence of the beginning of a belief that physics should be taught as a humane pursuit, with the historical, biographical and philosophical sinew and tissue built back on the skeletal frame of fact and principle, and that the student could and should learn to apply the processes of inquiry used in physics to the solution of other problems. Coleman[33] wrote in 1906:

The subject matter has been selected with reference primarily to its value as a part of general education, and includes an unusual amount of information based upon the facts of our daily experience, introduced as illustrations and applications of physical principles.

Physics deals largely with natural phenomena and is therefore of special interest and profit as a part of a general education.

In this quotation we again see the intense desire to make physics useful and practical and a real part of a liberal education.

Millikan and Gale[34] wrote in their high school physics book in 1906:

The book attempts to give a simple and immediate presentation in language which the student already understands, of the hows and whys of the physical world in which he lives.

In the description and illustration of physical appliances the course has been made unusually complete because that is what the student is most eager to learn but cannot obtain from books because their language is too technical for him.

Hoadley,[35] in 1908, wrote: "Especial effort has been made to lay proper emphasis upon the applications of physics in everyday life."

Crew and Jones[36] had the following to say in their textbook published in 1909: "Appeal to the everyday experience not only of boys but also of girls—show them physics as a science of daily life—assist the pupil in explaining the material phenomena of the world about him."

As early as the middle of the second decade of the new century the trend toward extreme emphasis on technology had begun. In a 1924 edition of their widely used *Elementary Principles of Physics,* Fuller, Brownlee, and Baker[37] wrote: "Following the thirty two chapters covering the topics of the usual first course in Physics, there are additional chapters treating . . . such subjects as the Automobile, Radio, Engines, Radium and Radio-activity and Water Power."

In a 1934 edition of *New Practical Physics,* Black and Davis[38] commented:

. . . We are by no means unmindful of the very great activity of the theoretical physicists in the last ten years and of their far-reaching discoveries. It goes without saying that we believe these to be of the greatest interest and importance to the mature student. But for the beginner in physics with his limited experience, such matters are too remote from his own life to be of significance. We have therefore touched on them but lightly.

Furthermore, in the last decade an unparalleled number of able minds have been at work in our industrial-research laboratories with the consequent discovery of many new applications of fundamental principles.

Since the 1930's there appears to have been a steady gravitation away from the physics teaching of the early years of this century toward an almost complete emphasis on technology. The textbooks became encyclopedias of explanation about the applications of basic principles and the laboratory work became filled with routine experiments which did little to educate the student in the processes of inquiry and much to stultify and dull the intent in the course.

The Physical Science Study Committee[39]

The Physical Science Study Committee (P.S.S.C.) was first supported by the National Science Foundation in 1956. Although various reform efforts in mathematics and in some of the sciences had earlier beginnings, the P.S.S.C. physics project was the first of the major curriculum reforms to get under way on a large scale, and its work has helped to set the tone for the whole reform movement. For this reason, somewhat more detail will be included in the description of the work of the P.S.S.C. than for the other major secondary school projects which follow.

In the early stages, reformers found that the changes they wished to effect in high school physics were of such a fundmental nature that a fresh start was the only sensible strategy. A prime aim was to present physics as a system of inquiry rather than as a body of knowledge. To this end, they placed great emphasis on having the student first come to grips with a new phenomenon in the laboratory, rather than having him use the laboratory solely for verification. Through the laboratory (using text, problems, and films) the effort is to develop in the student, insofar as is practicable, a viewpoint and mode of attack consistent with that of the professional physicist in his approach to physical problems. Thus, for example, he is led to explore new situations from various directions and is encouraged to develop the tools necessary for this attack: that is, facility in thinking in terms of orders of magnitude so that different hypotheses can be tested quickly without the necessity for laborious calculations in each case. The gain here is not only in speed, but in the lowering of the barriers to those intuitive intellectual leaps that are an essential part of the creative process. The student is also led to make precise calculations, but only as precise as the available data warrant, and he is encouraged to value the best answer he can get with the tools at hand in a difficult situation as much, if not more, than a very precise answer in an easy situation.

The P.S.S.C. writers wish to convey to students an understanding not only of the way a physicist attacks a particular problem, but also of the cumulative effects of many attacks by many scientists over long periods of time—namely, complex models of the physical world and of a few general principles. They wish also to give students some sense of the seeming inexhaustibility of nature as a subject of study and an understanding of some of the great unanswered questions that physicists are grappling with at the moment.

A third desire is to provide students with knowledge and understanding that will serve them best in future years, whether they go on with technical studies or sever their formal connections with science. Thus the writers, not unwillingly, concentrated on relatively deep development of a limited number of principal physical themes especially relevant to contemporary physics, rather than on a general coverage of physics. The determination to have the students take as little as possible for granted is manifest from the start by a dicussion of the way in which we come in contact with the physical world—through the senses —and how we make measurements of time and space.

Matter is considered next and the student is led to understand through discussion, problems, experiments, and films how we are forced to the conclusion that matter, which is to first appearance continuous, is actually "grainy." The idea of a physical model as a mental construct useful in organizing our knowledge, in formulating new hypotheses, and in suggesting tests of such hypotheses, is introduced and developed in connection with the molecular model of a gas. The notion of a model is carried further in a discussion of light, in which the particle model is not presented as a quaint delusion of Isaac Newton's but as a model that is quite serviceable for many purposes. The situations in which it does not seem to work are attacked from another direction after a preliminaary discussion of the properties of waves in various media, in which very effective use is made of the ripple tank. It is shown that the wave model succeeds in all classical situations, including those where the particle model fails.

Next, attention is turned to the causes of motion. With use of the essentially frictionless dry-ice puck, other simple laboratory devices, and flash photography, the student is led to develop his intuition concerning the relationship of forces to motion and then the conservation of momentum and energy. After a treatment of electricity and magnetism, again approached through experimental observation, the student brings together his work in these subjects with his previous work on measurement, motion, the particle nature of matter, light, waves, forces, the conservation principles, and physical model-making to look more closely at the atom. Filmed experiments on scattering of alpha particles by a gold foil lead into a discussion of the Rutherford model of the atom with its highly concentrated, positively charged nucleus. The student is then led, here with liberal use of filmed experiments and demonstrations, to see how classical theory alone is unable to explain the frequency threshold of the photoelectric effect and how this phenomenon and others, such as the existence of discrete spectral lines and the diffraction of electrons, lead to a new model, which unifies our view of matter and radiation. The fundamental break in going from classical to quantum theory is made clear, but so too is the way physicists proceeded from one to the other and how much the language and models of one were carried over into the other.

The P.S.S.C. course now consists of a textbook, a set of films carefully integrated with the text, a series of paperback monographs, special laboratory experiments, inexpensive apparatus kits, a laboratory guide, special tests, and a rather comprehensive teacher's guide.

Through a separate monograph series, the P.S.S.C. encourages students to explore paths branching off from the main course. Thus, students who wish can pursue technological interests in such monographs as *The Physics of Television, The Origin of Radar,* and *Heat Engines.* Some thirty of these monographs are now in existence, and a like number of additional ones under consideration cover such topics as the telephone, the electron tube, and synthetic polymers. The present close relationship of technology to physics is such that subjects such as masers cannot be said to belong exclusively in either category. Discussions are being held at the present time that may lead to the formation of a new group or groups to develop alternative approaches to high school physics. One direction that has had some discussion is a course in which the student is led into good physics through modern technology rather than as in the P.S.S.C. course previously described.

The course materials prepared by this committee are now available from commercial sources, as is much of the equipment needed for the course. Despite the recency of the advent of this course in the school curriculum, it has made an impact on the high schools. Recently, it was estimated that about one-fourth of the students studying physics in the Nation were using the P.S.S.C. materials. Many teachers report an upsurge of interest among students who study the course. While the course was designed for the upper 10 or 15 per cent of the pupils, schools report that the course can be handled by students who are average and above if the pace is slowed. There has been some reaction to the removal of most of the technology from the course, but there are many who support it. The course materials have had an impact on other competing textbooks.

CHEMISTRY IN THE SCHOOL CURRICULUM

The history of physics in the school curriculum was developed in considerable detail to provide a general background of the various movements which affected early science teaching in America. The historical developments for the remaining sciences will be somewhat less in detail since they were affected by the same forces and movements.

The Period of the Academies

The early academies were organized as a revolt against the formal and unrealistic curricula of the Latin grammar schools. Records show that chemistry was offered in some of these academies. Powers states:[40]

The Academy first fostered the teaching of chemistry to adolescents. Reference to curricula and advertising material published by the earlier schools shows that there were at least 4 academies which gave instruction in Chemistry previous to 1820; at least 15 that began such instruction not later than the period of 1820–1829; and at least 14 that began not later than the period 1830–40.

A very practical kind of chemistry was taught. Much emphasis was placed on aspects of the course for which immediate application could be found in the home and in agriculture. The courses were largely presented by lecture, with very few demonstrations and pratcically no laboratory work.

Chemistry in the Early High Schools, 1821–30

As in the case of physics, chemistry was offered in the Boys' Classical School in Boston when it was first opened in 1821. No doubt its popularity as a practical course in the still-existing academies made it somewhat mandatory that this subject be a part of the curriculum of the new public high schools. It was also an offering in the Boston High School for Girls in 1826.

The course was mostly textbook-oriented, with the instructor performing a few standard demonstrations to illustrate his lectures. There is no record of student laboratory work in these early high schools. Although some of the early textbooks of the period state in the preface that the pupil will be trained in "mental discipline and habits of thought," there is little evidence to indicate that the course served much more than to purvey information about the subject.

Chemistry Teaching, 1830–60

Over the next three decades chemistry flourished and grew in popularity with the schools. Many textbooks appeared, and these went through several editions. Chemistry developed in somewhat the same manner as natural philosophy did during this period—as a practical subject, taught for its cultural and informational values. The course continued to be taught as a lecture-demonstration presentation, but the number and variety of demonstrations increased with each new edition of the textbooks.

Unlike the natural philosophy of the day, chemistry was somewhat handicapped by a persisting attitude among some people that it was something related to the "black art" and evil spirits. Among the extremely religious of these decades it is quite probable that chemistry as a subject was retarded by medieval ideas coming down through literature in stories such as "Faust."

Student-experimenting in the laboratory was still several years away. This important movement was retarded, no doubt, by the lack of laboratory facilities in the schools, the high cost and scarcity of apparatus and chemicals. Yet, in the late years of this period, chemistry came into its own as an offering in the high school curriculum. By 1854 its popularity had grown so that 26.6 per cent of all high school students in Ohio, for example, were reported as taking chemistry.

The Decade of 1860–70

In the years just following the Civil War, a very significant change came about in the teaching of chemistry in the colleges, normal schools and high schools. This was the introduction of laboratory work to accompany the lecture and textbook. Frank[41] notes,

By 1865 provision was made in many schools for laboratory instruction, though a few schools had rather poorly equipped laboratories as early as 1854. By 1870 the great number of students returning from the German Universities had brought about a general interest in laboratory instruction so that numerous schools equipped their laboratories in the decade that followed.

By 1885 every high school that offered chemistry tried to make provision for laboratory work.

The Period of College Domination in Chemistry, 1872–1900

The parallel between physics and chemistry is very close during this period. As was the case with high school physics, the colleges began to accept chemistry for entrance in 1872. This began a period in which the teaching of chemistry gradually gravitated to being under the domination of the college professors. They prepared many of the textbooks used in the high schools, which for the most part were merely condensed or "boiled down" versions of their college books.

The textbooks were organized around the logic of the subject and gave practically no attention to the psychology of learning. No doubt the chemistry teaching of this period was rigorous and demanding of students. Many earlier writers have condemned this as a rather barren period, and yet the popularity of the subject, as indicated by increasing enrollments, does not seem to bear this out completely. Probably, both good and bad influences come from college domination.

One is also impressed by the intent of the authors of textbooks written during this period. In 1872 Eliot and Storer, in the preface of their *Elementary Manual of Chemistry*,[42] wrote: "The authors' object is to facilitate the teaching of chemistry by the experimental and inductive method, to develop and discipline the observing faculties." Somewhat later in this period, Storer and Lindsley[43] wrote: "The student acquaints himself with facts and principles through attentive use of his own perceptive faculties."

Between 1873 and 1880 Steele's[44] *Fourteen Weeks in Physics* and *Fourteen Weeks in Chemistry* enjoyed considerable popularity. In the preface to these books the author wrote the following excerpts:

Unusual importance is given to that part of chemical knowledge which concerns our everyday life. . . . A closer relation between schoolroom, kitchen, farm and shop. . . . The author has used simple language and practical illustrations [and the student] is at once led out into real life. From the multitude of principles, only those have been selected which are essential to the information of every well-read person. . . . Aim to lead young to become lovers and interpreters of nature. . . . Simple experiments within the range of every pupil at home. . . . The textbook only introduces the student to a subject which he should seek every opportunity to pursue. . . . As far as possible every question should be submitted to nature for a direct answer by means of an experiment.

Woodhull[45] comments on the above: "And in no other books have I found the text fulfilling so completely the promise of the preface, as his." In 1881 Avery[46] said in his *Chemistry*, "As far as possible the experiments are to be performed by the pupil rather than for him." And in 1882 Gage,[47] a teacher and writer from the English High School in Boston said:

Laboratory practice and deductive study should go hand in hand, and divide the time with one another about equally. . . . So far as practicable, experiments should precede the statements of definitions and laws, and the latter are not given until the pupil is prepared by previous observation and discussion, to frame them for himself.

The above quotations from textbook authors of the period when colleges tended to dominate the curriculum in high school science indicate that, at least in aim, their intent was good, and the emphasis was not altogether to be condemned. Toward the end of this period, in the last decade of the century, there were some evidences of a developing formalism in the curriculum and a general distrust of the inductive method. Carhart and Chute,[48] authors of this decade, wrote:

A few years ago it seemed necessary to urge upon teachers the adoption of laboratory methods to illustrate the textbook; in not a few instances it would now seem almost necessary to urge the use of a textbook to render intelligible the chaotic work of the laboratory. . . . The pupil should be kept in his classwork well ahead of the subjects forming the basis of his laboratory experiments.

Avery[49] in 1895, wrote: "The classroom work must be kept ahead of the laboratory work; i.e., the pupil must come to the laboratory with some knowledge of the principles involved in the work that he is required to perform." From Cooley,[50] 1897: "The student should study the textbook before entering the laboratory." The order recommended is: "(1) Oral instruction—involving illustrative experiments. (2) The study of a textbook. (3) Laboratory work to practice experimental methods of reaching or testing truth." Hortvett[51] said in 1899: "It is found in practice that the purely inductive method fails at points where it is expected to do the greatest amount of good." Torrey,[52] 1899, said:

Chemistry has suffered from the inexpressible wave of laboratory madness which has swept over the whole educational world. . . . Nothing too severe can be said against the mechanical and demoralizing system of note-books with "operation," "observation," and "inference" headings. They are wholesale breeders of dishonest and superficial work.

An objective appraisal of this period would have to acknowledge certain gains in the early years. There was a very genuine attempt to upgrade the teaching of chemistry through the improvement of laboratory work. There was also considerable evidence to indicate that there was an emphasis placed on inductive teaching. However, in the closing years of the century the domination by the colleges slowly developed into a formalism that resulted largely in authoritarian teaching by deductive methods. Concurrently, interest in the subject waned, as evidenced by declining enrollments, which continued even into the first decade of the new century. The following table indicates this trend:

PERCENTAGE OF STUDENTS IN PUBLIC HIGH SCHOOLS OF THE UNITED STATES ENROLLED IN CHEMISTRY (1890–1928)

YEAR	PERCENTAGE OF TOTAL HIGH SCHOOL ENROLLMENT ENROLLED IN CHEMISTRY
1890	10.10
1895	9.15
1900	7.72
1905	6.76
1910	6.89
1915	7.38
1922	7.40
1928	7.07

Chemistry Teaching 1900–50

Beginning in the last decade of the nineteenth century, the development of the modern high school had a profound effect on each of the high school sciences including chemistry. The domination of the colleges was eased, if not broken, and thus new content and new methods of instruction began to appear. General science emerged as a Ninth Grade course, and biology became quite standard as the Tenth Grade science offering. It was about this time that chemistry was the usual Eleventh and physics the Twelfth Grade offering. The emergence of this course sequence improved the lot of the specialized sciences.

Following World War I, a war that brought much attention to chemistry, many chemical processes were taken over from Germany by American industries. There was a sharp rise in industrial chemistry over the nation. This proved to be a great influence on the course in high school chemistry. There was an increasing demand for "practical" and "applied" courses in the subject, and many textbooks appeared with one of those words in the title. In some of these texts, considerable emphasis was placed on the tests for commonly used products. The pupil learned such tricks as how to remove stains and test for adulteration in foods, but there was decreasing attention to the understanding of basic principles of chemistry.

Around 1930 there were approximately 23,000 public and 2,600 private high schools in the nation, enrolling close to 5,000,000 pupils. Approximately 10 per cent of the pupils in the public high schools were taking chemistry at this time, and the number of schools offering chemistry ranged from 18 per cent in some states to nearly 50 per cent in others.

The first half of the present century has been marked by a gradual trend away from emphasis on basic science principles and toward an emphasis on practical, applied and industrial chemistry.

Commenting on the nature of the high school chemistry course about 1932, Frank[53] said:

> There are at least fourteen different types of chemistry courses given in the various high schools of the country. The names usually suggest the content of these courses; as Elementary Applied Chemistry, Agricultural Chemistry, Technical Chemistry, Textile Chemistry, Industrial Chemistry and Dairy Chemistry. These are all modifications of ordinary general chemistry and are given as a substitute for it.

During the half century under discussion in this section, the percentage of the total high school population enrolled in chemistry fluctuated between 6.9 and 7.7. These percentages can be misleading if some care is not used in their interpretation. In 1900, 7.7 per cent of the total high school population represented an enrollment in chemistry of about 40,000 students. In 1950, on the other hand, 7.6 per cent of the high school population meant an enrollment in chemistry of something over 400,000 students.

Chemistry in the 1950–60 Decade

This period was marked by some interesting developments in the high school chemistry course. Following a slight drop in the percentage of the total high school population enrolled in chemistry between 1950 and 1956, there was a steady increase to nearly 9 per cent of the total high school population in 1959–1960. In the decade 1948–49 to 1958–59, there was an actual increase from 412,000 to 657,000. This was an increase of nearly 60 per cent in terms of the total school population (age group 14–17 years). In the same period, the 14–17 year age group population increased by 22.2 per cent and the total high school enrollment, Grades nine through twelve, by 45.2 per cent. This is an all-time high for the century.

Following the initial work on the revision of the high school physics course by the Physical Science Study Committee, two independent projects were established to revise the course in high school chemistry. These have come to be identified as "C.B.A.," the Chemical Bond Approach and "CHEM," the Chemical Education Material Study.

While the basic approach to these two separate courses is quite different, they have in common the purpose to swing the emphasis in high school chemistry away from a study of technological processes toward the understanding of basic principles of chemistry. Each of these projects has been carried on by grants from the National Science Foundation. The following quotations taken from the literature of the two projects indicate the purposes, nature and present status of each course.

The Chemical Bond Approach Project

The C.B.A. project is an outgrowth of the 1957 Reed College Conference on High School and College Chemistry, supported by a grant from the Crown-Zellerbach Foundation.[54] Among the conclusions of the conference was that a student's first chemistry course could be better presented if it were based on a theme central to, but smaller than, all of chemistry. In 1959 the National Science Foundation awarded Reed College and Earlham College grants so that preparation of text and laboratory materials could proceed, and the course was introduced experimentally in nine high schools.

Among criticisms of the traditional curriculum have been the fragmentary way in which much of the material is presented, the lack of opportunity for real understanding of background material, the emphasis of "practical" chemistry and chemical technology, the highly directive nature of the laboratory program, the lack of correlation between the text and the laboratory, a general feeling that course materials are too narrowly limited by the textbook, and little encouragement of supplementary reading by students.

In an attempt to answer some of these criticisms, the C.B.A. project has developed a completely new program of text materials, supplementary readings, and laboratory experiments. Even though much of the factual and technological material found in the traditional course has been omitted, the students are still introduced to a variety of descriptive chemistry to illustrate the power and limits of the theoretical concepts.

The laboratory experiments are presented as problems and, insofar as possible, the student is encouraged to decide what information and techniques he needs to solve each problem. It is expected that the student will use the text, supplementary readings, and the laboratory for his information, and will synthesize his data into a reasonable solution to the problem. In many cases the solution suggests other paths to explore. While manipulative skills, laboratory techniques, and quantitative numerical answers are developed, they are presented not as ends in themselves but rather as instrumental in the solution of a particular problem.

During the school year 1959–60, the C.B.A. program was used by nine teachers and approximately 800 students. Following extensive revision during the summer of 1960, the evaluation was carried on in seventy-five schools with about 5,000 students. As a result of this evaluation program, revisions were again made in the text and laboratory materials, and subsequently the evaluation has been continued in eighty schools, involving over 5,000 students. More than 4,000 other students in at least 110 other schools have used the materials outside the official study group.

A study has been made of the correlation between an aptitude measure (SCAT) and students' performance on five C.B.A. achievement examinations administered during 1960–61. As was the case in the P.S.S.C. program, there was a general declining correlation between SCAT and successive achievement tests administered during the course. The recency of this course in the high school curriculum precludes any reliable comments on its impact on the schools or on any changes in the adequacy of preparation for later college courses in chemistry.

Chemical Education Material Study

CHEM Study is experimenting with means for making a first chemistry course as profitable as possible for all students who wish to take such a course.[55] The text, laboratory manual, teachers' guide, and motion pictures emphasize heavily the experimental approach to chemistry and the importance of laboratory work. This experimental emphasis has been used to develop the major concepts, such as dynamic equilibrium, rates and mechanisms of reactions, chemical bonding, structural ideas, and the systematics of chemistry in terms of the periodic table. The course tries to present chemistry from the point of view of a person intimately involved in the profession of chemistry, but in terms both interesting to and comprehensible by typical beginning students. A series of tests produced and distributed in cooperation with Educational Testing Service indicates that the general goal of CHEMS has been achieved with the thousands of students throughout the nation who have so far taken the course.

Sources of further information are:

Glenn T. Seaborg. "New Currents in Chemical Education," *Chemical and Engineering News,* **38** (1960), p. 97.

J. A. Campbell. "The Chemical Education Materials Study," *Journal of Chemical Education,* **38** (1961), p. 2.

Lawrence D. Lynch. "Report on CHEM Study Program," *Science World,* **10**, No. 2 (1961), p. 3-T.

J. A. Campbell. "Chemistry—An Experimental Science," *The School Review,* **70** (Spring 1962), p. 51.

CHEM Study Newsletter, obtainable from Chemical Education Material Study, Harvey Mudd College, Claremont, California.

Motion pictures (16 mm., sound-color, running between fifteen and twenty-two minutes) are now available, or in production, covering the areas of kinetics of reactions, catalysis, equilibrium, ionization energy, vibration of molecules, molecular spectroscopy, synthesis of an organic compound, mechanism of an organic reaction, gases and how they combine, and chemical families. Some fifteen other pictures are currently in the planning stage.

CHEMS has also produced some wall charts and special pieces of equipment, which will be available through various suppliers. The commercially published versions of the text and laboratory manual are now available.

BIOLOGY IN THE CURRICULUM

Biology as a subject in the high school curriculum emerged between 1900 and 1910, having developed by consolidation of courses in botany, zoology and human physiology.

Early Natural History and Its Transition, 1800–90

Biology had its roots in an earlier course called natural history, in a way similar to physics, which had its roots in natural philosophy. Some of the better equipped academies offered limited work in biological science around 1800. There were but a few books available in this country. In the decade 1820–30 a few schools, mostly girls' schools, used botany books by Eaton and Sumner. The course centered on the making and classifying of herbarium collections. Classroom work consisted largely of reciting textbook material from memory. One author stated in the preface of his book that the aim of the course was "utility, recreation, religious benefit and cultivating the aesthetic feelings."[56]

Sometime in the decade 1820–30, zoology was first offered in the high school curriculum. The content, method and aim of this early course placed the greatest emphasis on the natural-history aspects of zoology. There was no laboratory work, and classroom procedures consisted largely of reciting memorized pages of a textbook. An interesting historical fact of this period is that when plant analysis was introduced through the study of herbarium specimens, a kind of plant physiology was also introduced as laboratory work. This died out rapidly after about 1830, and did not appear again until 1890. The cause of this is somewhat uncertain, but may have been the result of unverified factual bases and the poor experimental results.

One of the pioneers of this period was Asa Gray, Professor of Botany at Harvard College. As early as 1842, he wrote and published a college text on plant analysis. His influence in the teaching of natural history, especially botany, was immediately evident in the colleges in the decade 1840-50, but it was not noticed in the high school curricula until 1860 and after. Gray's profound influence was greatest in the slow transition from the artificial classification system of Linnaeus to the natural system. Historians of the period report that this transition was not fully achieved until 1875.

Zoology was much less affected than botany during the period of 1840–60. The natural-history methods continued to be emphasized, and the older method of classification was retained. The earliest evidence of a shift in the basis of classification of animal forms was the publication of Morse's *First Book in Zoology*, about 1875. Here one could see the change from emphasis on natural history and classification as the major centers of interest to the problems of internal anatomy and morphology of animal forms.

Just at the close of this period in the history of the biological sciences, the great zoologist Louis Agassiz began to influence the teaching of zoology in a profound way. His influence was first felt on a generation of college teachers, but later carried down into the high schools. College and high school teachers alike were fired with the spirit of research by Agassiz. His methods of teaching were characterized by his motto: "Study nature, not books." This great teacher was one of the major influences that carried the teaching of biological science through a period of transition down to the last decade of the nineteenth century.

The Beginnings of a Laboratory Biology, 1890–1900

By the last decade of the nineteenth century, the influence of the theory of evolution was being felt in the colleges. High school teachers were influenced by this, and emphasis was placed on types or forms of plant and animal life and on a study of structural forms. Thus, high school courses in zoology and botany developed into a study of a series of structural types. Each of these became the subject of intensive laboratory investigation which involved dissection and observation—both gross and microscopic—to be followed later by discussions of the work. These class sessions were usually followed by textbook assignments and further recitation.

This period from 1890 to 1900 was prolific in the production of laboratory manuals. One author reports that more than thirty appeared in the decade. An early manual written by Huxley and Martin in 1883, called *Elementary Instruction in Practical Biology*, emphasized the method of "verification" for laboratory work as opposed to the method of "rediscovery" which had been the theme of Agassiz.

Hunter[57] reports: "These methods became combined in later manuals in the 'note and question' method of Boyer and of Hunter and Valentine."

The earliest indication of the movement toward a one-year course in biological science in the secondary school appeared in 1894 with the publication of Boyer's *Laboratory Manual in Elementary Biology*. At this time many schools still preferred to give a half year of botany and a half year of zoology, even though the Committee of Ten had recommended against this in their famous report.

Toward the close of the 1890–1900 decade there was quite a sharp reaction on the part of schools against so much laboratory work with meticulous directions in biological science. This resulted in a return to textbook work and recitations, with considerable emphasis on field work. One factor that influenced this change was the publication of Davenport's *Zoology* about 1900. Davenport went back to the old natural-history and classification methods of presenting biological science, but, on the other hand, he introduced a kind of laboratory work based on life activities. This put life activities, histories and physiological processes into the forefront of botany and zoology. This textbook was widely used, and had a profound influence on biology teaching in the secondary schools of the period.

Human Physiology Introduced into the High School Curriculum, 1890–1910

The continuing emphasis in high school botany on plant physiology during the 1890's, together with pressures from a group of teachers who felt strongly about human physiology, gradually forced a few textbook writers to extend the study of physiological processes in plants and animals to the consideration of such processes in man.

Another factor that influenced schools to introduce human physiology into the high school curriculum was the crusading work of the Women's Christian Temperance Union. This organization, through vigorous campaigns, had laws passed in many states making obligatory the teaching of the harmful effects of alcohol and narcotics on the human body.

The Science of Biology Emerges

It is difficult to draw hard and fast lines for the appearance of any particular course in the high school curriculum. As can be seen from above, forces and factors that were shaping a new course in biology began to operate as early as 1890 and continued past the first years of the new century. Late in this time span, two very potent influences were at work which put the final pressures on the mold from which biology as a science in the high school curriculum was cast.

The first of these came from the experimental biological scientists in the colleges. Among these were the physiologist, the morphologists and somewhat later the psychologists. While the influence of the college was slow and subtle, yet new teachers were coming from the colleges with a broad view of biological processes studied in plants and animals but applied to man. The study of such processes as tropisms, automatic response, of mental as well as morphological evolution, were generalized to include all living forms.

The second factor that helped to shape the separate sciences of botany, zoology and human physiology into a high school biology offering, was the influence on the public mind of the period of research in preventive medicine and hygiene. It was about the turn of the century that the dramatic experiments were performed that resulted in the control of malaria and yellow fever. The response to the public demand for information about physiological processes and practical applications of biological knowledge such as conservation of natural resources, foods, drugs, narcotics, hygiene and sanitation was soon evident. Textbooks began to appear with more pages devoted to practical science.

Hurd[58] summarizes the 1890–1900 decade as follows:

A consensus of the committee reports on the improvement of biology teaching shows:

1. The desirability of a continuous offering of biological science from the first grade through high school.
2. The establishment of a required course in biological science at the tenth-grade level.
3. The requirement of one year of biology for entrance into college.
4. The need for more uniformity of content in high school biology.
5. The teaching of biology as a laboratory science.
6. The need for an emphasis in biology teaching on the broader principles of the discipline.
7. The importance for all young people to receive instruction in hygiene and human physiology before completing high school."

Biology Comes of Age, 1900–1920

The first courses in so-called high school biology appeared in a few schools in New York, New Jersey, and Pennsylvania in the late 1890's and the early 1900's. The earliest textbooks were little more than abbreviated and uncoordinated courses in the three components botany, zoology, and human physiology. During this period the beginnings of a laboratory experiment phase of biology began with simple exercises or plant and animal tropisms.

The early course in high school biology received considerable impetus from college textbooks of the period. Hunter[59] reports: "Two college textbooks stand out very prominently as guideposts in the unification of biology as a college science. They are Sedgwick and Wilson's *General Biology* published in 1895 and Parker's *Elementary Biology* which appeared in 1897." Hunter goes on to say:[60]

The first course in elementary biology in this country seems to have been that prepared by the Regents of New York State and first offered in 1899. This course at first consisted of three distinct courses in botany, zoology, and human physiology. No text to fit the course was made until 1907 when Hunter's *Elements of Biology* appeared. This was little more than an attempt to place the topics required or suggested by the Regents' syllabus into connected form. But the book met with popular approval, and was followed by others of the same nature by other authors, Bailey and Coleman (*First Course in Biology*, 1908), Bigelow (*Applied Biology*, 1911), Peabody and Hunt (*Elementary Biology*, 1912), Smallwood (*Practical Biology*, 1916). An improvement in correlation was worked out in 1911 in Hunter's *Essentials of Biology*. But in the latter book the treatment was still, plant, animal and human biology, with cross references from one aspect to the other, without any very decided attempt to unify the course on the underlying principle of biology. The later, *A Civic Biology* by Hunter, 1914, *Elementary Biology* by Gruenberg, 1916, and *Civic Biology* by Hodge and Dawson, 1918, came closer to this ideal than previous books, but no biology appeared in this decade that built a course upon *general principles*.

During the decade of the 1920's and even well into the 1930's, it was evident that textbook writers and curriculum makers were reluctant to break away from the older, watertight compartments of the basic biological sciences. However, there were some evidences of a shift in teaching methods during the 1920's. There were rapid changes in the subject matter of biology, especially between 1910 and 1920, which resulted in the application of biological principles to the improvement of the environment of man and of man within his environment.

Later this trend resulted in great advances in scientific medicine, especially in such things as the application of serum therapy, preventive hygiene and sanitation, and finally, in the applications of the laws of heredity to eugenics. All of these factors made for public demand for more and more teaching about the benefits of the applications of biological science to the welfare of man. It was these forces that finally broke the shackles and moved biology toward the integration and unification of the basic principles.

Hurd[61] has summarized the 1910–20 decade in the history of biology as follows:

With each succeeding decade the values to be gained from a study of biology have been redefined. At this time the emphasis was upon the teaching of biology for its importance to human welfare—vocations, health, sanitation, avocations, appreciations, understanding of the environment. Physiology came to mean human physiology and hygiene, ecology replaced morphology and the other sections of the course were selected for their use in daily living. The research biologists and the high school biology course parted company at this point. . . .

It had been the recommendation of most committees that biology be made a more "practical" course. The "miniature college course" taught in high school was thought unsuitable for the average tenth-grade pupil.

Teaching methods advocated during this period were of the nature that called for more active participation by the student. Projects, problems, and questions were seen as a way to increase student involvement. Wider reading, field trips, use of community resources and the study of local flora and fauna were regarded as techniques for improving motivation.

Teachers and scientists alike felt that students in high school should learn about the nature of science. The organization of courses around problems and projects was an effort to develop some understanding of the methods of science. A study of the lives of famous biologists was felt to create an appreciation for the scientific enterprise. While this objective was educationally sound and the methods of attainment promising, the results were disappointing.

Each committee reporting during this period suggested that the broad "ideas" or "principles" of biology should be stressed. . . .

Both general science and general biology were courses that broke with tradition in an attempt to provide a more comprehensive "picture" of science and to meet the educational needs in science for a larger portion of the high school population. The popularity of these subjects with young people is reflected in the enrollment trends. In the textbooks written for these courses one finds a greater emphasis upon the "practical" and the "applied" aspects of each subject. . . .

The Period 1920–40

The decade from 1920 to 1930 has been characterized by Hurd[62] as "the period of curriculum refinement." There were many committees formed during this period and their reports supply interesting historical perspectives. Perhaps the most influential were the report of the Committee on the Reorganization of Science in Secondary Schools[63] and the report of the Committee on Science in Education of the American Association for the Advancement of Science.

The first of these committees was a part of the Commission on the Reorganization of Secondary Education, 1918. It was this group that formulated the now famous cardinal principles of secondary education:

1. Health
2. Worthy home membership
3. Vocation
4. Citizenship
5. Use of leisure time
6. Ethical character

The subcommittee on the Reorganization of Science in Secondary Schools produced one of the finest and most influential documents in the history of science teaching. The following quotation from this bulletin provides some understanding for its point of view on the teaching of biology:[64]

Aims. . . . Biological sciences, in common with other sciences in secondary schools, should contribute to the educational objectives . . . health, worthy home membership, vocation, citizenship, the worthy use of leisure, and ethical character. In particular, biological sciences should have the following specific aims:

1. The World War has emphasized health as a basic end of education. Since much of biology deals directly with problems of health, the course in biology

must accept efficient health instruction as one of its chief and specific ends.

2. The biological sciences should develop the pupil's purposeful interest in the life of the environment by giving a first-hand acquaintance with plant and animal neighbors.

3. They should emphasize some of the most important applications of biological science to human activities and to general and individual human welfare, and especially should familiarize the pupil with the structure and functions of his own body, to the end that he may know why he must live healthfully in order to live happily and usefully.

4. They should train the pupil to observe life phenomena accurately and to form logical conclusions through the solution of problems and through projects essential to the productive work of agriculture, gardening, etc.

5. They should enrich the life of the pupil through the aesthetic appeal of plants and animals studied, to the end that he may appreciate and enjoy nature.

6. They should demonstrate to the pupil the value of intensive study of biological science as a means through which scientific progress is attained. In view of what science has meant to our present day civilization and in view of the measure in which the methods and results of scientific investigations are to-day reflected in intelligent thought and intelligent action, the need of the life sciences in the education of modern citizens can not be ignored.

Hurd[65] summarizes the major ideas from the report of the Committee on Science in Education of the American Association for the Advancement of Science as follows:

1. The citizen uses science both in conclusions and methods for each day's work; he should profit, therefore, from what he understands of scientific facts, principles and occurrences. Possession of scientific knowledge or of the applications resulting from this knowledge must carry with it a knowledge of the proper uses of these possessions; "a sense of moral obligation that will prevent the newly acquired knowledge and method of science serving base ends."

2. The understanding and application of both scientific knowledge and methods to new situations must be made the immediate objectives of school and college effort. There is an acute need to get more science into the school program because of the unparalleled growth and use of science knowledge. The committee encouraged the tendency toward a coherent and cumulative secondary school sequence in science subjects.

3. It is time to re-study the whole situation of science in secondary schools owing to the widespread growth of general science in the junior high schools.

4. After reviewing a number of research studies on curriculum and learning in the teaching of science, the following resolution was adopted: "These studies represent but a beginning in the application of the objectives of scientific method to the problems of science teaching. Such investigations must be multiplied and verified by those truly interested in the scientific solution of such questions."

5. It was felt that the teaching of science was not entirely effective because educational procedures are too hasty; in the hurry to achieve, those arduous

endeavors by means of which lasting results may alone be developed are omitted. Education also fails because it so often misses the main purpose of teaching modern scientific thought and controls.

6. Science is not primarily for the purpose of building dynamos, understanding radio, and producing more corn or better hogs, but for producing better human beings. Teaching for this purpose should include some of the moral responsibilities that go with the achievement of scientific knowledge.

7. Science teachers need to develop a point of view about science. Most have had too little real science study. The committee suggested that science courses for those who are to teach need to be developed with their teaching uses in mind, to the same extent that special courses are developed for those who intend to practice law or medicine; "we need a similar organization in the use of science courses for those who are to teach." It was pointed out that this did not mean less exacting courses but redirected courses relating to the professional uses of science in education. It was recommended that college courses for teachers be developed with a professional outlook instead of restricting them to subjects with only the research outlook. The recommendation of the committee was that "a more thorough-going preparation in the fundamentals of science is needed by all who aspire to teach it."

8. In their discussions the committee noted that neither the methods of scientific study nor the personalities of those who apply them have been objectified with sufficient clarity to make them functional in general education. Even though objectives of science teaching for the past 75 years have had references to "the scientific method," there has been little transmission to young people of how scientists work and study, or even of scientific attitudes. It seems that the schools and society are absorbing the output of scientific work, that is, the practical application, much more rapidly than they are absorbing the culture of the men who contributed it. A liberal education is incomplete without this culture. The following resolution was adopted: "Science as method is quite as important as science as subject matter, and should receive much attention in science instruction."

9. Other recommendations made by the committee were that: (a) a study be made of the situation, tendencies and needs of science instruction in educational systems; (b) the services of a field secretary be secured to work with existing agencies, to distribute information on research in science education, to stimulate further research, to operate as a sort of clearinghouse agent, and to continue the organization of new groups of science teachers and writers for the popularization of science; (c) a national council of science teachers be organized to advance science teaching, to increase public appreciations of science and to secure for science teachers better facilities for teaching.

The second decade (1930–40) of this period witnessed a large number of forces at work that were to influence the teaching of biology in a major way. In this decade the National Society for the Study of Education brought out its *Thirty-First Yearbook—A Program for Teaching Science.* This report, one of the most influential ever to appear on science teaching, recommended that the program in science be a twelve-year sequence, and that science courses be organized around the major concepts and generalizations of science. The committee proposed such principles as the following as a basis for a secondary biology course:

1. Energy cannot be created or destroyed but merely transformed from one form to another.
2. The ultimate source of energy of all living things is sunlight.
3. Microorganisms are the immediate cause of some diseases.
4. All organisms must be adjusted to the environmental factors in order to survive in the struggle for existence.
5. All life comes from pre-existing life and reproduces its own kind.
6. Animals and plants are not distributed uniformly nor at random over the surface of the earth, but are found in definite zones and in local societies.
7. Food, oxygen, certain optimal conditions of temperature, moisture and light are essential to the life of most living things.
8. The cell is a structural and physiological unit in all organisms.
9. The more complex organisms have been derived by natural processes from simpler ones—these in turn from still simpler, and so on back to the first living forms.

Another important report of this period was entitled *Science in General Education*[66] issued in 1938 by the Committee on the Function of Science in General Education of the Progressive Education Association. This report recommended that science should be taught to meet the needs of young people in the following "aspects of living":

1. Personal living.
2. Immediate personal-social relationships.
3. Social-civic relationships.
4. Economic relationships.

This committee recommended—rather than a curriculum of specialized science courses—a broad fields or unified core course in which the major understandings of science would be stressed.

Hurd[67] has aptly summarized the developments in the 1930–40 decade in science education.

1. Science teaching should contribute to the broader purposes of general education and must include content of wide personal and social significance.

2. Science is best learned as an association of facts culminating in a concept expressed as a principle of generalization of science. Facts acquired through a process of memorization have little value in "problem-solving" situations.

3. The skills, attitudes, and methods usually associated with the "problem-solving" aspect of scientific methodology are worthy objectives of science teaching. Most committees and much of the educational research of the period sought to "spell out" this aspect of the "scientific method."

4. The curriculum content is best defined in terms of the principles and generalizations of the subject field. This makes for a more adaptable curriculum and is consistent with the research on learning.

5. There should not be a distinction between class and laboratory procedures; both should contribute to the solution of problems.

6. Testing and evaluation should be in terms of all the objectives of the course. The best test is one that requires the student to apply his knowledge to novel situations.

7. There is need for a balanced program of science with some opportunity for all students to build a background in both the biological and physical sciences.

8. The program of science instruction should be continuous from the kindergarten through high school.

Biology in the 1940's and 1950's

The rapidity with which secondary school science teaching has developed over the past two decades, together with the voluminous body of literature that has accumulated in that period, precludes a more than cursory discussion of the things that have affected the biology curriculum.

Early in the 1940's the teaching of all high school science reflected the trend through the 1930's—namely, that science should be taught largely for life adjustment and consumer needs, and that its importance for general education were more important than that for specialized training. During these years there were many proposals to absorb science into a generalized core, where it was supposed to be unified or integrated with other subjects such as social studies.

This philosophy greatly influenced the biology curriculum, and there was a tendency to organize the course in terms of what it could provide for meeting the everyday needs of individuals. It was deemed important that whatever was learned be immediately useful or functional. Some consideration was given to the importance of the scientific ways of solving problems as these could be taken over and used by the learner in solving his problems of daily living.

During these years there was a growing concern among the scientists of the nation who were disturbed by the "life adjustment" and "needs" philosophy of teaching biology. This group wanted to see a reasonable balance in the secondary school science curriculum between the biological sciences and the physical sciences. They were alarmed over the decline in the scientific manpower situation, and urged that more time and attention be given to the talented pupil in science as a basis for more scientists.

Hurd[68] has keenly analyzed the 1940–50 decade in a summary. He states:

Most of the committees failed to mention modern learning theory and its relation to science teaching. The philosophical assumptions underlying the concepts of "general education" were often hazy or contradictory. The result was that curriculum reforms in science and improved teaching procedures did not materialize in the schools. The seeds were sown, however, for curriculum developments that were to emerge in the next decade.

While the status of science in the secondary school curriculum was never weaker than at the start of this period (1940), the stimulus of the "atomic age" and the acceleration of scientific and technical developments following World War II reaffirmed the need for education in the sciences In brief, the 1940–1950 period represented a decade of divergent points of view about science teaching. Each committee did agree, however, that the science curriculum of the past was not suitable for the youth then in school.

All the committees that considered the science offerings in schools recommended a continuous program of science instruction from kindergarten through high school. They were not unaware of the problems involved in their recommendation—the shortage of qualified teachers, the lack of facilities and equipment and the need to study the grade placement of different science concepts.

Throughout the last decade of this period the high school course in biology has experienced what has been aptly called the years of "confusion and crisis" in secondary school science teaching. Many professional and scientific organizations have either appointed new committes or reactivated earlier committees to deal with a complex of forces and factors related to education in science.

Following World War II, there has been a tremendous increase in scientific knowledge in all fields. This has included breakthroughs in nuclear science, in medicine, in physical biology, in engineering and technology and more recently in space. With the rapid application of many of the new discoveries to the improvement of the environment and the comfort and well being of man, there is now hardly any area of living that is untouched by science and technology.

Life reflects a new cultural frame of reference and there can be no return to the earlier ones. If the science way of life is to be perpetuated and if the nation is to be at the forefront, two things seem inevitable:

1. There must be provided, for both the immediate and more remote future, a reservoir of excellently trained scientific manpower talent.
2. The great masses of nonscientific citizens must be educated to much higher levels of scientific literacy.

The work of several committees and commissions, together with their reports, has provided impacts that served to move biology teaching rapidly toward a new program of revision. These reports will be mentioned here, and the reader is referred to them for more detailed treatment.

From the Harvard Committee report[69] in 1945, and the Steelman[70] report in 1947, there was evidence of the fact that considerably disparity existed between what was deemed essential in modern science education and the present-day curriculum.

The reports of the Southeastern Conference on Biology Teaching[71] in 1954 and the North Central Conference[72] on Biology Teaching in 1955 were the first real major attempts to bring into sharper focus the needs for a more modern and up-to-date approach for high school biology. Both of these committees represented joint efforts of biological scientists, college teachers, high school science teachers, science educators and school administrators.

Another stimulus toward a revision of the high school course in biology was the establishment of a Committee on Educational Policies by the National Academy of Science–National Research Council in 1954. The work of this committee and its subsequent program grew out of a Conference on Biological Education[73] held in Washington, D.C. The general position of this influential Committee has been summarized by Hurd[74] as follows:

1. There is need for agreement among the educators and scientists in this country as to what constitutes biology to be taught in the high school, college, and graduate levels.

2. Biology as taught at the high school level in many areas, does not arouse much interest in the student. There is need for improving the training and qualifications of high school biology teachers, and correspondingly, there is need for stimulating people to go into the teaching of biology.

3. There is need for a "core curriculum" in biology for the student who plans to become a biologist as compared with biology courses given the student who does not intend to continue in this field.

4. There is need for wider exchange of ideas among biology teachers at all levels, through the media of journals, professional organizations, national societies, etc.

5. In conclusion, there is need for a committee composed of biologists, educators, textbook publishers, science writers, and representatives of industry to cover the whole spectrum of biological education from the high school level up.

As early as 1955, the American Institute of Biological Sciences appointed a Committee on Education and Professional Recruitment. This committee considered the problem of developing a program of biological education for all levels of the school curriculum. In the early stages of the work of this group and its several subcommittees, it was thought best to place emphasis on the production of resource materials to help teachers rather than specific course materials. Later the point of view changed somewhat to include the production of course materials in the form of textbooks and laboratory manuals as well as such teaching aids as monographs, films and film strips.

Since this time the Biological Sciences Curriculum Study has been launched under the auspices of the American Association for Biological Sciences and the National Science Foundation. Three experimental textbooks and accompanying supplementary materials have been prepared and have progressed through several years of testing and revision.

The three courses are somewhat different in approach: the *Green Version* is developed from the ecological point of view; the *Yellow Version* is developed from a genetic-evolution point of view; and the *Blue Version* emphasizes a linear or functional approach. The committee used the color idea in distinguishing the various versions to avoid labels of difficulty.

The statement of objectives of the Biological Sciences Curriculum Study is as follows:[75]

1. Most curricular objectives of the study are those which have traditionally guided the teaching of biology in the American school. These may be summarized as conveying to the student an appropriate private understanding of his own body, of the diversities and commonalities of organisms in general, of their relations to the environment, of the means by which we and they are cared for and conserved, and of the organized structures of fact and concept through which biology organizes and guides its inquiries.

2. The materials and organizations developed to serve these aims are also to serve an additional purpose. Through time, we hope to convey a conception of biological science by which the student may identify vocational and avocational interests and master a literate discipline which will render reports of future scientific progress accessible to him. This means that the materials of classroom and laboratory will present biology as a science which is an ongoing, self-correcting and revisionary process as well as a body of currently warranted fact and theory.

3. The specific objectives for biology teaching which have been tentively accepted to serve as a guide in preparing the preliminary courses of study were:

(a) An understanding of man's own place in the scheme of nature; namely, that he is a living organism and has much in common with all living organisms.
(b) An understanding of his own body; its structure and function.
(c) An understanding of the diversity of life and of the interrelations of all creatures.
(d) An understanding of what man presently knows and believes regarding the basic biological problems of evolution, development, and inheritance.
(e) An understanding of the biological basis of many of the problems and procedures in medicine, public health, agriculture, and conservation.
(f) An appreciation of the beauty, drama, and tragedy of the living world.

(g) An understanding of the historical development and examples of some of the concepts of biology to show that these are dependent on the contemporary techniques, technology, and the nature of society.

(h) An understanding of the nature of scientific inquiry; that science is an open-ended intellectual activity and what is presently "known" or believed is subject to "change without notice"; that the scientist in his work strives to be honest, exact, and part of a community devoted to the pursuit of truth; that his methods are increasingly exact and the procedures themselves are increasingly self-correcting.

GENERAL SCIENCE IN THE CURRICULUM

Beginnings

General science, as an offering in the modern sequence of high school sciences, was introduced and gained a substantial acceptance between the years of 1895 and 1915. However, the subject itself has a venerable history even before its modern inception, for textbooks with content similar to more recent books date back 150 years or more. Even in the early academies, courses in general science were sometimes used for information and cultural purposes. There are records from these early schools concerned with roving lecturers in general science who moved from school to school. These lecturers gave demonstrations and explanations of a variety of scientific phenomena.

In the 1840's, a book called *Peterson's Familiar Science, or The Scientific Explanation of Common Things* was written by a Reverend Brewer and published by Applegate & Co. This textbook covered a range of topics quite similar to some of our modern textbooks in general science. For the student interested in the historical background of science teaching, the following quotations should be helpful.

A book called *The Fairy-land of Science*[76] was written by Arabella B. Buckley in 1879. Its table of contents is reproduced here because of the similarity to the content of some books in general science:

TABLE OF CONTENTS

Lecture I.   The Fairyland of Science and How to Enter It.
Lecture II.   Sunbeams, and the Work They Do.
Lecture III.   The Aeriel Ocean in Which We Live.
Lecture IV.   A Drop of Water on Its Travels.
Lecture V.   The Two Great Sculptors—Water and Ice.
Lecture VI.   The Voices of Nature and How We Hear Them.

Lecture VII.   The Life of a Primrose.
Lecture VIII.   The History of a Piece of Coal.
Lecture IX.   Bees in the Hive.
Lecture X.   Bees and Flowers.

In 1896, a little book of laboratory experiments called *Easy Experiments in Physics*[77] was written by Preston Smith, the instructor in natural science in the State Normal School, Fitchburg, Massachusetts. This book was intended for use as a laboratory guide in the "intermediate and grammar grades." In the preface of the fourth edition (1904) the author writes:

As a result of the author's practical experience with pupils of different grades, and from the ideas of other teachers on the subject, he concludes that as a rule, experiment books in physics are too difficult for young pupils. With this idea in mind, these experiments have been written for use in the intermediate and grammar grades, although they may be successfully used with the lower classes in the high school. . . . It seeks to bring each pupil in direct contact with nature, by asking him questions in the form of simple experiments, by having him make careful, accurate observations, used by requiring him to express his thoughts in clear, truthful language.

The range of content of this laboratory manual for use in the upper grades where general science is now taught may be observed from the table of contents:

CONTENTS

Matter
   Illustrations, molecules, spaces, atoms, molecular forces—attractive and repellent, physical and chemical changes, physical and chemical forces, substance.

General Properties of Matter
   Extension, impenetrability, divisibility, porosity, compressibility, density, expansibility, cohesion, hardness, tenacity, brittleness, flexibility, elasticity, malleability, ductility, adhesion, capillary action, absorption, filtration.

States of Matter
   Solid, liquid, gas, solution, crystallization, condition of solids—amorphous and crystalline—mineral waters.

Gravity
   Illustrations, center of gravity, line of direction, centrifugal tendency, equilibrium, falling bodies, stability, pendulum.

Energy
   Potential, kinetic.

Resistance
Inertia, friction.

Mechanical Powers
Forces acting together. Levers: relation between power and weight, illustrated by lever of first class; application to all classes of levers; uses. Pulleys; relation between power and weight; single pulleys, fixed and movable; multiple pulleys; uses. Wheel and axle; relation between power and weight; applications. Inclined plane; relation between power and weight; uses. Wedge. Screw. General application of the relation of the power and power distance to the weight and weight distance.

Mechanics of Liquids
Surface of a liquid; illustrations of pressure; directions of pressure; pressure at varying depths; transmission of pressure. Pascal's law; hydrostatic paradox; hydrostatic bellows, hydraulic press; liquids in communicating vessels; springs, wells, water supply systems, artesian wells, streams, fountains, spirit level, water wheels, Barker's mill; buoyancy; equilibrium of floating and immersed bodies; specific gravity.

Mechanics of Gases
Illustrations and directions of pressure; transmission of pressure; Torricelli's experiment; barometer, uses; principle of pump and siphon; lifting pump; force pump; air pumps—exhausting and condensing—balloons; compressed air in industries: atomizer, pneumatic drill, hammer, tube, tire.

Heat
Sources; temperature; measure of temperature, thermometer; sensible and real heat; effects of heat: solids, liquids, gases; transfer of heat: conduction, safety lamp, liquids as conductors, convection, draft, radiation, reflection, absorption, applications; changes in the state of matter by action of heat: melting, freezing, vaporization, evaporation, boiling, condensation, dew, dew-point, frost, fog, clouds, rain, hail, snow, distillation, sublimation; latent heat; artificial cold: solutions, ice machines; specific heat; steam engine, high and low pressure; gas engine.

Sound
Production; transmission and velocity in different media; reflection; vibration of strings, intensity and pitch; musical instruments, string and wind; musical scale; resonance; human voice; ear.

Light
Sources; transmission; velocity; intensity; shadow: umbra, penumbra, moon's phases, eclipses; reflection, twilight; law of reflection; mirrors: plane—single and multiple—curved: refraction: simple lenses, prism, plate glass, solar spectrum; the eye.

Magnetism
Magnets: illustrations, kinds, poles; law of magnets; magnetization; lodestone; earth as a magnet: compass, dipping needle; magnetic field.

Frictional Electricity
Simple illustrations; electroscopes; positive and negative electricity; law;

induction; electrophorus; Leyden jar; familiar illustrations: lightning, the aurora.

Voltaic Electricity
Simple zinc and copper cell; conductors and non-conductors; effect of current on magnetic needle; arrangement of cells: in parallel, in series; galvanoscope; electrolysis; electromagnet: applications; electric bell, telegraph; thermal and luminous effects.

Simple Measurements
Lines, surfaces, solids, weighing, use of graduates.

Chemistry of Combustion
Carbon dioxide; preparation, effect on combustion, effect on lime-water. Oxygen; preparation, effect on combustion, effect on lime-water, effect on lime-water after burning charcoal in it. Air; effect on combustion, combustion in open air, in confined air, effect on lime-water of pure air and of air after combustion. Nitrogen; preparation, effect on combustion, effect on lime-water. Composition of air; test of exhaled breath with lime-water; necessity of oxygen to sustain life; dilution of oxygen. Ordinary combustion; drafts, ventilation, kindling point of various substances. Manufacture of gases from wood and coal. Combustion; rapid, slow, explosion, rust, decay, animal life. Purification of air; effects of winds, plants, rains.

Early Experiments with General Science as a Subject in the High School Curriculum

General science as a subject in the modern high school curriculum is a little more than sixty years old. Chronologically it had its origin in the late 1890's, at the height of the period when high school science was most technical and specialized. By 1899 there were at least three states in which general science was being offered in at least one high school. These were: Massachusetts, Illinois, and California.

The Illinois experiment was at Oak Park under the direction of J. C. Hanna, principal of the high school. Two years prior, while at East High School in Columbus, Ohio, Hanna had experimented with a course that resembled general science. In reality, this course was an introduction to physical geography, which at that time was the standard offering for first year high school science.

Hanna remarked about his reasons for introducing general science:[78]

It seemed to me that the science teaching of the high schools was not well adapted to the capacity of the pupils and was not so conducted as to challenge and hold their interest, and, further, that it lacked in recognition of the psychology of youth and the ordinary principles of pedagogy as well as in its definiteness of relation to the real things of life.

In Springfield, Massachusetts, as early as 1899, experimenting was in progress with a general-science course. This grew out of an earlier experimental course in biology. The general-science offering was organized into a number of large units, each having a definite relation to the life of the city. Some of the units were: the houses we live in; keeping well; cleansing and dyeing; household electric appliances; the weather; our neighbors in space; what time is it?; water supply; etc.

Some early authors prepared texts on general science with regard to its value as a preparation for later high school science. Others were more concerned with providing the pupil with a better understanding of his environment. A number of the early texts were slightly modified revisions of current physical geography books. Others were divided into two sections: one devoted to physical science, and the other to biological sciences. The very earliest books quite frequently reflected the training and major science interest of the author.

General science was introduced at a rather slow pace. After ten years, by 1909, records show that it was being taught in five schools in Pennsylvania, three schools in Illinois, fifteen schools in Massachusetts, and five schools in California. In the whole of the United States there were probably fewer than fifty schools offering the subject by the end of the first decade. By 1914, more than 223 schools were offering general science in the first year of high school.

Nature of the General Science Course, 1915–30

By 1915 it was generally recognized that general science was a fixture in the high school science curriculum and that it should be organized as a whole and quite without relation to the later, specialized offerings. After 1915 the content began to be selected on the basis of factors of the environment and was generally organized into broad units, where continuity was provided by dealing with phenomena related to one aspect of the surroundings without reference to the basic science from which it was derived.

One of the typical textbooks, written by Percy E. Rowell in 1911, had the title *Introduction to General Science*.[79] The table of contents lists 212 numbered sections ranging from No. 1, Explosions, through such topics as Expansions, Blasting, Animal Heat, First Aid to the Burnt, Radiation of Heat, The Steam Engine, Cooking, The Laws of Motion, Age of the Earth, The Northern Lights, Suction, The Theory of the Kite, Sailing Boat, The Farm a Workshop, Flowers, The Stings of Insects, The Muscles, Dangers of Vitiated Air, The Mind, Nature and Business, How to Plan a House and Barn, Simple Household Remedies, Reading Meters, Economy, Education and Civilization, Manner of Living.

From the preface of this general science textbook one may read:

The value of a General Science course is twofold. Knowing a little about a great many sciences enables the pupil to obtain a birds-eye view of all and a day's lesson in some one of the elementary sciences ceases to be a blind alley,— the other value lies in awakening the mind to the vast possibilities of scientific knowledge and mental attainments.

Another early textbook was that of Caldwell and Eikenberry, called *Elements of General Science*,[80] published first in 1914. Quite in contrast to the hodgepodge of disorganized information found in Rowell's book, these authors presented a course organized in four parts: the air; water and its uses; work energy and electricity; and life upon the earth.

Each of the separate parts of this book was divided into chapters. Each chapter was introduced by a group of "questions for discussion," followed by numbered paragraphs in which the text materials were developed. The book had a separate laboratory manual. From the preface of this book one can read:

Human experience includes results from modern science almost constantly. The scientist's way of working and thinking is recognized and desired as the most reliable method. It is also generally recognized that science in the schools should lead to better understanding and better daily use of the kinds of scientific knowledge which are associated with common human experience. It is the object of this course to develop a useable fund of interesting and worthwhile knowledge about common things. It is also its object to develop helpful and trustworthy habits of thinking about and of judging the common experiences which fall within the field of science.

Still another book of the period, *First Course in General Science*,[81] written by Barber and his associates in 1916, reflects a somewhat different organization of subject matter. The table of contents of this book shows:

Chapter I.   The Production and Use of Light.
Chapter II.   The Production and Use of Heat.
Chapter III.   Refrigeration and Its Uses.
Chapter IV.   The Weather.
Chapter V.   The Seasons—Climate and Health.
Chapter VI.   Ventilation.
Chapter VII.   Food and nutrition.
Chapter VIII.   Micro-organisms.
Chapter IX.   Soil Physics, Water Supply and Sewage Disposal.

The following quotation is taken from the preface of the book by Barber:

General Science has been accused of being a hodgepodge, an incoherent mass of science materials without form, or continuity or order of development.

In this course a conscious effort has been made to select a straight and solid track and to proceed in a well-ordered, common sense manner along it. The train of thought, as it were, runs upon and is guided by, two parallel rails, the one physical, *Energy*, the other sociological, *Human Welfare*. These two supporting rails are everywhere strongly bound together.

In 1923, Carleton W. Washburne published a general-science textbook called *Common Science*.[82] The table of contents of this book shows the following major topics:

1. Gravitation.
2. Molecular Attraction.
3. Conservation of Energy.
4. Heat.
5. Radiant Heat and Light.
6. Sound.
7. Magnetism and Electricity.
8. Electricity.
9. Mingling of Molecules.
10. Chemical Change and Energy.
11. Solution and Chemical Change.
12. Analysis.

The following quotation is taken from the preface of the Washburne book:

A collection of 2,000 questions asked by children forms the foundation on which this book is built. Rather than decide what it is that children ought to know, or what knowledge could best be fitted into some educational theory, an attempt was made to find out what children want to know. The obvious way to discover this was to let them ask questions. . . .

The chapter headings of this book might indicate that the course has to do with physics and chemistry only—but the examples and descriptions throughout the book include physical geography, and the life sciences. Descriptive astronomy and geology have however been omitted. These two subjects can be best grasped in a reading course and field trips.

Another interesting development in the earlier general science course is shown in a book by Bertha M. Clark called *New Introduction to Science*,[83] published in 1928. The book was divided into ten major "Parts" and these were further divided into 31 Chapters:

Part I.	Heat and Fire.
Part II.	Food and Water.
Part III.	Clothing and Fabrics.
Part IV.	Light and Illumination.
Part V.	Health.

Part VI.   Using Some Factors of Our Environment.
Part VII.   How the Work of the World Is Accomplished.
Part VIII.   Using and Generating Electricity.
Part IX.   Life, How It Continues, How it Varies.
Part X.   Learning To Know the Heavens.

Dr. Clark said, in the introduction to her book:

> Someone has said that education is learning to do better those things which we do almost every day of our lives. [This book] explains the important factors in your environment, and suggests how to use these factors wisely. . . . To do an experiment well, you must (1) observe carefully and fully, you must see everything connected with the experiment, and you must (2) see each factor in its proper place and in its relation to everything else. . . .
> Observation is the beginning of an experiment. Reasoning and drawing a conclusion, on the basis of your observation, is the end of an experiment.

During the first three decades of the general science movement, there was a continuing effort to consolidate the variety of factual content from a number of basic sciences and to find some unifying principle that might be used as an organizing pattern. From the inception of the movement, there was considerable uncertainty about whether or not it would achieve a place in the high school science sequence.

As a subject for the early years of the high school it was opposed by teachers of the specialized sciences, because they feared that it would dull the interest for the later study of science. General science was also criticized for being somewhat "thin" in content. It was argued that with such a broad and general coverage it was quite impossible to study any phase of the subject in depth.

Despite the many misgivings and criticisms, general science continued to grow and flourish, as is shown by the increasing number of schools that offered the subject between 1915 and 1930, and the increasing enrollment in the subject.

The following table[84] shows the percentages of different science courses offered at various grade levels of the high school for the years 1908, 1923, and 1930. It is interesting to note the explosive rise of general science as a Ninth Grade science offering over these years, and the steady decline of physiography during the same period.

Figure 1[85] shows the steady growth in enrollment of general science and other high school sciences between 1890 and 1958.

Factors Influencing the Rise of General Science

While there are undoubtedly many general factors which influenced the evolution and development of general science as a high school offering, a few stand out with prominence. The first of these is the fact

PERCENTAGES OF DIFFERENT SCIENCE COURSES OFFERED AT VARIOUS GRADE LEVELS DURING 1908, 1923 AND 1930 AS SHOWN BY RETURNS OF QUESTIONNAIRES

	9TH YEAR			10TH YEAR			11TH YEAR			12TH YEAR		
	1908	1923	1930	1908	1923	1930	1908	1923	1930	1908	1923	1930
General Science	2.5	53.10	66.8		1.93	6.4						
Elementary Biology	10.0	16.09	18.8	7.25	48.13	45.3	2.09	3.47	1.8	1.95	2.67	.28
Botany	21.1	4.37	1.3	29.98	16.22	13.0	7.79	2.5	4.6	8.05	1.85	.85
Zoology	7.5	1.60	.77	26.5	10.41	9.0	7.19	1.87	2.3	4.17	1.44	1.1
Human Physiology	29.17	14.72	3.1	10.72	8.95	2.7	6.29	6.88	4.5	9.01	5.97	6.8
Chemistry				2.52	1.45	6.4	28.14	39.64	48.6	40.55	41.38	28.4
Physics		.43	.26	7.88	2.66	1.5	41.31	40.91	32.0	25.0	39.30	49.1
Physiography	26.11	10.11	3.1	15.46	9.92	6.4	1.81	4.18	3.1	4.72	6.17	2.3
Other Sciences	3.61	.43				1.3	2.39	.41	1.1	6.38	1.44	2.86
Advanced Biology						4.4			2.0			3.1
Agriculture			5.9			7.4			5.1			3.4

that general science appeared at the very height of the period of the rapid development and expansion of the American high school. It was a period when new courses were being sought, and when the hold of the colleges on the public schools was being broken.

The early decades of this century were also years when there was a desire for things practical, for those things in education that would meet the needs of the young people who were flocking to the new high schools in unprecedented numbers. General science would meet this need as it was inaugurated both to give an overview of later sciences and to create interest in the further study of science.

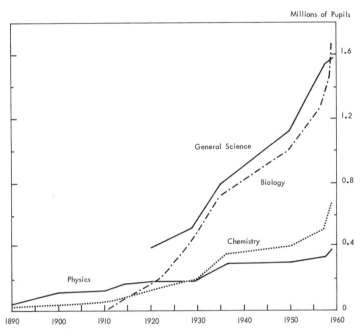

FIGURE 1. Number of pupils in last four grades of public high schools enrolled in certain science courses, 1890–1958.

During its rapid initial rise, general science coincided with the development of the junior high school. Here again it seemed to be a natural, and to fit almost perfectly into the philosophy that was the incentive for the establishment of the junior high schools.

The Committee on the Reorganization of Science in Secondary Schools[86] published its now-memorable report in 1920. The impact of this report was perhaps the one factor that gave greatest impact to general science as an offering in both the junior and senior high schools. The following quotation, taken from that bulletin, gives an idea of its recommendations concerning general science:

This introductory course in science is not a substitute for any one of the special sciences, but should provide a basis for discovery of interest in special sciences and of vocational opportunity. It should prove to be the best training for any pupils who can take only one course in science in high schools.

A. SELECTION AND ORGANIZATION OF SUBJECT MATTER

The subject matter of general science should be selected to a large extent from the environment. It will therefore vary greatly in different communities. The science involved in normal human activities, and especially the science involved in the reconstruction period after the war, presents many real problems which must be met more intelligently than formerly if there is to be the needed increase in effectiveness of the service which individuals and groups are expected to give. Science is universal and constant in the life of our citizens, and hence to be useful to all pupils general science must accept the science of common things as its legitimate field. The science of common use and that of the classroom should be the same. General science should use any phase of any special science which is pertinent in the citizen's interpretation of a worthwhile problem.

The particular units of study should be those that truly interest the pupils. Interest not only secures productive attention but is an evidence of attention. To be substantial educationally, interest must rest upon a sense of value, an evident worthwhileness in the topics considered.

No topic should be selected which is meagre in content or lacking in significant problems. The range of material which can be used is in reality limited only by the capacity, experiences, and needs of the pupils. The materials should be concrete and capable of leading to many avenues of new and untried experiences.

In organizing this material the topic should be the large unit to which many specific pieces of work are related. For example, a general topic such as fire may be selected. Many specific pieces of work will arise—one of practical value being "The Hot Air Furnace," or any other definite system of heating. The problems for solution under this topic will be varied and many, as: What causes the air to circulate? How does it circulate? How should pipe valves be arranged to cause equal circulation in all rooms of a house? To answer these questions many experiments and demonstrations must be made. Again, in the study of the local water system, determine the uses now made of water and the benefits and dangers of the system, construct models of mechanical devices used in the system for securing and delivering water and for disposal of wastes, etc. The following list of subtopics will suggest the content of the whole topic: The common uses of water; local dangers of contamination; sources of supply in use and possibilities for extension of system; relation to public health with typhoid as an illustration; sewage, its uses and dangers.

B. METHODS

The foregoing discussion of selection and organization suggests the point of view in presentation. Topics should be large units. At the outset the topic should be viewed briefly as a whole for the sake of perspective. Such a general view gives a concrete and significant basis to which there should be constant return and to which further and more detailed and more exact studies should be constantly related.

A combination of class presentations of out-of-school experiences of individual laboratory work, and of teacher-and-pupil demonstrations is desirable. Simple materials should constitute most of the laboratory apparatus. The desk demonstration by teacher or pupil is excellent as a means of presenting an experiment for observation and discussion so that the attention of all may be definitely directed to the question in mind. Pupil demonstrations and individual laboratory work also should be used, since they give individual opportunity to handle apparatus and opportunities for active participation by each pupil. There is no objection to the same problem being solved by the whole class as individuals or as groups, provided that the class as a whole feels the importance of the work; but care must be taken when assigning the same task to all to see that the work does not become meaningless for some. Sixty-minute laboratory periods are generally better than longer periods for introductory science courses. An abundance of textbook and other reading matter should be available.

No text in general science can or should supply answers to all inquiries. The textbook should be used as a reading and reference book, and other sources for reading should be extensively used, such as magazine articles which deal with current use of science. References should be specific for children of the age of general science pupils, since they will gladly do much reading if they know just what to read.

Bulletins of available current reading matter prepared by teachers and pupils are an aid in reference work, and are stimulating to teacher and pupil.

Excursions, well directed and with a purposeful plan, are of great value. Excursions should always be definitely planned, carried out as serious exercises, and the results used in later work. Pupils and teacher should look upon excursions as a regular part of the serious work of the course.

Hunter[87] lists four specific factors as the basis for the rise of general science. These are:

1. The mortality in high school enrollment at the Ninth Grade level
2. The lack of environmental science background of pupils studying biology as a second-year high school science
3. The general disatisfaction with the lack of a science sequence in high school
4. The loss of enrollment in later high school sciences

General Science from 1930 to 1960

Bulletin 26 on the Reorganization of Science in Secondary Schools[88] was a landmark document in the history of science teaching in America, for it not only solidified the place of general science in the accepted offerings of the seventh, eighth and ninth grades, but it established the sequence of offerings in high school science for the forty or more years which have followed. From that bulletin the following quotation on science sequence for the secondary school is taken:

The science sequences should vary with the type and environment of the schools. Each year's work should be so outlined as to give the best training without reference to whether the pupils take later courses in science. Many schools will need to make adjustments of a recommended sequence, so that it may best serve the school's particular constituency. The committee has outlined sequences for the following types of high schools:

A. The junior-senior high school.
B. The large four-year comprehensive high school with adequate teaching staff and equipment, usually enrolling over 500 pupils.
C. The four-year high school of medium size, usually enrolling from 200 to 500 pupils.
D. The small high school of not more than 200 pupils.

A. THE JUNIOR-SENIOR HIGH SCHOOL

Seventh or eighth year, five periods a week; or both years with three periods a week in each year—General science, including hygiene.

Ninth year—Biological science, including hygiene; courses may consist of general biology, botany, or zoology.

Tenth year, eleventh year, twelfth year—Differentiated elective courses in sufficient number to meet special needs and interests, as follows:

(a) Chemistry—General chemistry, and chemistry specialized for various curriculum needs, such as household chemistry, industrial chemistry, etc.
(b) Physics—General physics; and physics specialized for various curriculum needs, such as physics of the home; industrial physics, etc.
(c) General geography, or physiography.
(d) Advanced biological sciences.

B. THE LARGE COMPREHENSIVE FOUR-YEAR HIGH SCHOOL

The conditions usually prevailing in these schools make possible a wide differentiation of science courses, since there are likely to be enough pupils with special interests to constitute adequate classes in differentiated science courses. In such four-year high schools the following plan is recommended:

First year—General science, including hygiene.

Second year—Biological science, including hygiene; courses may consist of general biology, botany, or zoology.

Third and fourth year—Differentiated elective courses to meet special needs and interests as follows:

(a) Chemistry—General chemistry, and chemistry specialized for various curriculum needs, such as household chemistry, industrial chemistry, etc.

(b) Physics—General physics; and physics specialized for various curriculum needs, such as physics of the home, industrial physics, etc.
(c) General geography, or physiography.
(d) Advanced biological sciences.

C. FOUR-YEAR HIGH SCHOOL OF MEDIUM SIZE

First year—General science, including hygiene.
Second year—Biological science, including hygiene; courses may consist of general biology, botany, or zoology.
Third year—Chemistry, with emphasis on the home, farm, and industries.
Fourth year—Physics, with emphasis on the home, farm, and industries, general geography or physiography, or advanced biological sciences.

D. SMALL HIGH SCHOOL

First year—General science, including hygiene.
Second year—Biological science, including hygiene; courses may consist of general biology, botany, or zoology.
Third and fourth years—Elective chemistry and physics. . . . In the small high school it is desirable to alternate the courses in chemistry and physics in successive years

The decade 1920–30 witnessed a period of experimentation and innovation in general science as a result of the impact of Bulletin 26. The evidence of the wide variety of these endeavors is given in the listing of textbooks published during these years[89] to be found in the Appendix.

Perhaps the most significant result of the experimentation and innovations of the 1920–30 decade was the development of the unit plan of organization for the content of general science. The basic plan for this pattern of organization was developed by Morrison at the University of Chicago, and by 1930–35 it had become almost universal as a basis for organizing content in general science. The following table of contents from one of the most widely used general-science textbooks of the period will indicate the nature of the unit structure of the textbooks at that time:[90]

Chapter I.   The World of Science

Unit One.   The Air and Man's Uses of It
II.   The Nature of the Air
III.   Doing Work with Air

Unit Two.   Water and How We Use It
IV.   Water and Its Work
V.   Securing a Water Supply
VI.   Keeping Clean with Water

During the period 1930–50 several influential documents on science teaching were written, and they have had considerable influence not only on the course in general science but also on other high school sciences. Each of these will be considered briefly.

The *Thirty-First Yearbook* of the National Society for the Study of Education, Part I, *A Program for Teaching Science*,[91] proved to be another landmark document in the history of science education in America. Its greatest influence has been the impetus provided for the organization of science content around the basic concepts and broad generalizations of various specialized sciences.

While some textbooks in general science and other sciences sought to organize and present the course content around conceptual understandings, the most profound influence of the *Thirty-First Yearbook* was on courses of study and the development of scope and sequence designs for various science courses. The following quotation selected from the *Thirty-First Yearbook* gives some indication of the position in science teaching taken by the committee that prepared it:

In this volume, the Committee has focused its attention upon the essential elements in the program of education; namely, the gradually maturing children on the one hand and the materials of education on the other. The maturing children are organisms endowed with capacity to learn from experience; the materials of education are the products of race experience. The search for specific materials of education is a search for those products of race experience that will most satisfactorily and effectively orient the children in the life of today. The influence on the life of today that is being exerted by developments in the field of science gives to this field a place of prominence in the program of education.

The volume presents: first, a general plan for an integrated program of science teaching; second, an adaptation of this general plan to the successive grades of each of the administrative units of the public school; and third, a suggested program for the education of teachers of science.

The general features of the report are set forth in the first ten chapters. Chapters I to V give in order: (1) the Committee's interpretation of what seem to be best practices in planning the work of elementary and secondary schools, together with the more general features of its own recommendations for science teaching; (2) criticisms of some current practices that must be modified in order to accomplish the program outline; (3) an analysis, with illustrations, that shows some of the contributions to life enrichment that may be expected from the field of science; (4) a definition in the field of science that is at least fairly comprehensive, given in terms of major principles and generalizations that may be used for guidance in selecting the specific objectives of science teaching; and (5) a brief interpretation of the principles of psychology that have guided the Committee in constructing its program.

In Chapters VI to IX, inclusive, there is an analysis of the contributions from educational research that relate to the field of science teaching. In these chapters are presented, in order, interpretations of research relating: (1) to problems of classroom teaching; (2) to problems of laboratory teaching;

(3) to the content of science courses; and (4) to curricular developments in school centers.

Chapters X to XV, inclusive, carry recommendations for each of the administrative units of the public school. These are followed by a chapter (XVI), on rooms and equipment for science teaching, with recommendations for each of the administrative units.

In Chapter XVII, on science teaching on the college level, attention is given to problems associated with the integration of high-school and college courses.

In Chapter XVIII, on the education of teachers of science, it is assumed that the requisites for success in such teaching are: first, that the teacher shall be a liberally educated person; second, that he shall be a specialist in science; and third, that he shall be professionally educated, in the sense that he will be familiar with the problems associated with teaching and in command of the techniques that are necessary for successful work in the classroom. The program for the education of teachers is, therefore, a program of liberal education, including a good measure of specialization, and at the same time a program of professional education.

The reader of this report will find no recommendations for drastic or revolutionary changes. The Committee's effort has been to aid teachers and curriculum specialists to work constructively from present practices toward the attainment of more worthy outcomes. It may be expected in any program of education that many educational experiences will be selected from the field of science. In order that educational values may be realized, it is necessary that the teacher be guided in thinking by a consistent educational philosophy; that he have some understanding of how children learn; and that he have such a comprehensive understanding of the field of science that he will be able to explore deeply into it. It is the hope of the Committee that its report will point the way to the progressive attainment of the standards suggested in these considerations.

In 1938 the Committee on the Function of Science in General Education of the Progressive Education Association's Commission on Secondary Curriculum issued its report, *Science in General Education*.[92] This report sought to influence the teaching of science for certain social values and outcomes which were classified in the following major "basic aspects of living": (1) personal living; (2) immediate personal-social relationships; (3) social-civic relationships; and (4) economic relationships.

The position of the committee toward science teaching may be seen from the following quotations, taken from the preface of the report:

Science in General Education is the report of the Committee on the Function of Science in General Education of the Commission on Secondary School Curriculum. This Commission was established by the Executive Board of the Progressive Education Association in May, 1932, and charged with the task of examining the fundamental problems of education at the secondary level.

Firm in the conviction that educational processes and goals must be relevant to the needs of the learner as he interacts with his social medium, the Commission set up, first, a Study of Adolescents to provide basic information on the problems, interests, concerns, and inclinations of young people in reaction to the situations which confront them in home, school, community, and the wider social scene. . . .

From this outline it will be gathered that the Committee conceives of science teaching within the context of the whole process of general education, that its proposals are relevant both to what the student now is and to what he may become as a responsible member of society, and that it assumes a democratic way of life as a guide to its goals in education. It is hoped that teachers who read the volume will not look upon its specific suggestions merely as materials to be added to the now existing curriculum. Continued accretions have already rendered the offerings in secondary education confused and burdensome. Application of the proposals of this report should instead lead to the revaluation and elimination of many materials now in use, and to the organization of a program consonant with the conception of science teaching proposed.

The year 1947 witnessed the publication of the *Forty-Sixth Yearbook* of the National Society of the Study of Education, Part I of which was entitled, *Science Education in American Schools.*[93] This document, while perhaps not so revolutionary and influential as the *Thirty-First Yearbook,* came at a time when there was a growing need for the revaluation of the purposes and objectives of science education and to consolidate the gains resulting from previous committee reports and recommendations.

The report of the Committee on the Function of Science in General Education, discussed above, gave some impetus to the teaching of science to achieve outcomes of critical thinking. The *Forty-Sixth Yearbook* placed much more emphasis on the less tangible outcomes such as problem solving, scientific attitudes, interests and appreciations. Perhaps the impetus given to these process outcomes, somewhat in contrast to the emphasis given to science concepts and generalizations by the *Thirty-First Yearbook,* was the major contribution of this report to the improvement of science teaching.

The following quotation from the *Forty-Sixth Yearbook* provides some understanding of the general point of view of the Committee:

Several useful reports dealing with instruction in science have appeared during the past two decades. There are, however, a number of considerations justifying the preparation at this time of a yearbook in this area.

First to be mentioned is the scientific progress which has been made during the past decade and more especially during World War II. Advances in transportation have drastically altered our concepts of time and space and consequently of the relationships of peoples and nations to each other. Research in causes and therapy of diseases and improvements in medical and surgical care and techniques have affected both our standards of health and our manner of living. The far-reaching consequences of newly developed methods for releasing atomic energy can as yet be only dimly seen. It is possible that such sources of energy may cause war to be outlawed entirely; certainly they will affect peacetime pursuits in countless and very fundamental ways.

Scientific discoveries and developments affect not only man's material existence but also his thinking. Instruction in science must take cognizance of the social impact of developments produced by science. It is not enough that they be understood in a technical or scientific sense; it is most important that their effects on attitudes and relationships of people be studied and understood. Science instruction has not only a great potential contribution to make but also a responsibility to help develop in our youth the qualities of mind and the attitudes that will be of greatest usefulness to them in meeting the pressing social and economic problems that face the world.

Second, important new movements in science education have appeared which have far-reaching effects. One is the growth of organized science in the elementary grades, which is influencing fundamentally the program through the entire public school. Another movement is the introduction of fused science courses at the upper secondary level. General science at the junior high school level is now well established and is almost universally accepted in this country. The same is true of general biology. However, not many realize that an appreciable proportion of enrollments in senior high school science is now represented in courses called by such titles as "senior science," "consumer science," "survey science," or "physical science." A similar trend is evident at the junior college level where survey courses in biological sciences and in the physical sciences are replacing separate courses in the basic sciences for many college students.

Third, the new research literature in science instruction needs to be synthesized, integrated, and implemented. Although the number of research studies produced in this area since 1930 has been smaller than in the two decades just before 1930, it is the opinion of the committee responsible for the present yearbook that the average quality of investigation has improved. It is important that available research be surveyed critically, analyzed and appraised, and that the findings be related to classroom practice.

PURPOSE OF THE YEARBOOK

The foregoing are some of the most important factors which a yearbook on science instruction should take into account and evaluate. In the light of these needs, the purposes of the present volume may be stated as follows:

A. To present a challenging and workable philosophy which will assist and encourage teachers of science to make the contribution to the welfare of our society which they, through their instruction and professional activities, can make and which society expects them to make. As a means to this end, the committee throughout its work has adhered to the following principles:

1. To make the report as practicable as possible. It has been the aim to present the material from the viewpoint of the classroom teacher and to

show how the daily activities of classroom and laboratory can be made to contribute to the ultimate goals of education in a democracy.

2. To review and appraise available research in science teaching and to suggest desirable types of problems for further study. To enhance the usefulness of research data and conclusions, the citations and discussion of research studies have been introduced wherever they seem pertinent rather than in separate chapters or sections.

3. To select and describe the best practices in science teaching that could be found and to show how they can be adapted to daily use by any qualified science teacher.

B. Another important purpose of this report stems from the movements and trends referred to above. New kinds of courses and new methods and devices in science instruction are being developed in many places. It is the purpose here to examine these developments, to appraise them, and to determine, in so far as possible, what their implications for the future seem to be. Time will reveal to what extent the analyses are significant but the attempt to interpret such movements is regarded as one of the important obligations of the yearbook committee.

C. Although not a major purpose of the yearbook, it should be stated that, as a working principle, the committee decided to make a constant full recognition of the fact that this unity holds chiefly in larger aspects of science instruction, and that such unity does not require, or perhaps even make desirable, unity in detail. To strive toward such unity in larger perspective the committee agreed:

1. To consider in an early chapter perennial issues for which unity in larger aspects offers no single solution, and to make recommendations based on the consensus of the committee.

2. To have all manuscripts read and criticized by each member of the committee, and to approve them in final form only when acceptable to a majority of the committee.

3. To supply specific orientation to all associated contributors as to the point of view to be presented in the yearbook.

4. To share jointly as a committee the responsibility for all chapters in Section I, which is considered basic to the entire report.

The attitude of the committee that prepared the *Forty-Sixth Yearbook* toward science courses in the junior high school may be judged from the following quotation:

ATTITUDES AND APPRECIATIONS

More investigative work has been done on the accompanying phases of scientific attitudes and appreciations, although some of the findings are contradictory and indicate need for further research. Blair and Goodson found that mere exposure to a course in general science does not develop scientific attitudes but that marked improvement in scientific thinking can be achieved by direct teaching. On the contrary, Eberhard and Hunter noted no significant advantage for an experimental group with respect to scientific attitudes after seven months of direct teaching. There may well be a question concerning the comparability of the attitudes taught in these two investigations. Certainly the findings of Eberhard and Hunter are inconsistent with earlier investigations in which the direct teaching of attitudes is reported as successful. In agreement with the study of Blair and Goodson, McKnelly found that scientific attitudes are not formed by free reading in science.

The interest of investigators in superstitions and unfounded beliefs continues. Vicklund's work to reduce credence in superstitions and unfounded beliefs by direct teaching is comparable with that of Blair and Goodson on the direct teaching of attitudes. In six weeks of direct teaching, Vicklund reports, unfounded beliefs of the subjects were considerably diminished. Beliefs in health and mental telepathy and those which relate to religious faiths seemed to be most difficult to change. Ter Keurst tested pupils in Grades VII, VIII, and IX for superstitions and observed that superstitions do not decrease with grade level. Apparently there was no direct teaching with the subjects of Ter Keurst's investigation.

The last report to be discussed in this series is the *Fifty-Ninth Yearbook* of the National Society for the Study of Education, Part I, *Rethinking Science Education*.[94] This report published twenty-eight years after the *Thirty-First Yearbook* and thirteen years after the *Forty-Sixth Yearbook,* is still too recent for any reliable assessment of its influence. The *Thirty-First Yearbook* was prepared almost exclusively by the six members who comprised the committee. The *Forty-Sixth Yearbook,* in some of its parts, sought a much broader base of contributors. The *Fifty-Ninth Yearbook* felt the need of seeking contributions from an even greater number of persons. Thus, perhaps more than any previous major report, it represents the thinking of a broad segment of the science teaching profession. This may prove to be one of its greatest values as its impact is felt over the next decade.

The following quotation from the *Fifty-Ninth Yearbook* provides some insight into the general point of view of the committee who prepared the report:

Although much of modern science is of comparatively recent origin, its "practical" aspects have had far-reaching impact upon our culture. Unfortunately, science is too frequently viewed *only* in this light. Its purely speculative nature, whereby the creative imagination of man seeks unity amid the great variety of nature, is not so well understood. When viewed in this light, science becomes less antagonistic to the other ways by which man seeks order in his world. It is through science that man seeks to understand this order by self-correcting methods that put limiting values on his preconceptions.

Through the practical applications of scientific discovery our civilization is undergoing constant change. In turn, these changes bring about situations which threaten the well-being of future generations. The welfare of our civilization is now almost wholly dependent upon scientific progress. Society must respond with adequate and intelligent control.

There may have been a time when scientists preferred to let others assume the responsibility for our destinies as they relate to technological advances. Not so, today. Scientists are particularly concerned about the ways in which they can help solve problems which have been brought into sharper focus through scientific advancements within the generation. One such problem is the improvement of science teaching in the schools.

In this yearbook the purposes of science education are reassessed in light of the increasing significance of science in our culture. The nature of the learning process as it relates to achievement in science is dealt with at some length. Procedures for planning and implementing science teaching at each level from the elementary schools through the junior college are explained. In recognition of the advanced training exacted of the science teacher, both his preservice education and his in-service professional developments are described.

Colleges and universities have a number of responsibilities for the kind of science teaching that goes on in the schools. They educate the teachers, supervisors, consultants, and administrators. They supply consultant services to schools. They are responsible for most of the research in science teaching. The implications of what has been written in this yearbook for colleges and universities are treated in chapter xvii. The final chapter is devoted to the issues in science education as the committee has seen them emerge through its work in preparing this yearbook.

The attitude of the *Fifty-Ninth Yearbook* Committee toward general science courses in the junior high school may be inferred from the following quotations:

SCIENCE FOR GRADES VII AND VIII

Science for Grades VII and VIII should be general science in the sense that it, like elementary science, should draw upon all the sciences for its content. Its organization, however, should relate to the broad areas of human activity in which the selected contents and methods of science play important roles.

In school systems that have well-organized elementary-science programs, the seventh- and eighth-grade science courses should build upon the elementary program in a clearly defined sequence. Whereas much of the science content in the elementary school is descriptive, the contents of Grades VII and VIII should be less descriptive and more interpretative. Wherever appropriate, theoretical interpretations should be developed.

Definitive research regarding the nature of science concepts that can be learned by pupils at each grade level is lacking. There is evidence, however, that the background of experience of the learner is a primary factor in determining his capacity to conceptualize in science. With pupils coming from the lower elementary school into Grades VII and VIII with more experience in science, it is reasonable to expect them to be able to work with concepts heretofore considered beyond the comprehension of the average seventh- and eighth-grade pupils. . . .

Seventh- and eighth-grade pupils should have special science teachers who have good science backgrounds. Although the science to be taught may appear to be elementary, the problems of adapting the learning experiences to a wide range of abilities and interests requires the efforts of a highly resourceful teacher, especially one who is resourceful in the various sciences. The reported "damping off" of science interests of pupils after the sixth or seventh grade is accounted for in part by the fact that science beyond these levels is too frequently taught by teachers poorly prepared in science. Because of the critical nature of these grades, teachers with the very best preparation should be teaching seventh- and eighth-grade science.

Seventh- and eighth-grade science courses should provide for a wider range of learning experiences than is generally possible in the elementary school. Greater provision should be made for laboratory work of a problem-solving nature. Brandwein has shown that pupils taking general science taught in a perfunctory way, with little or no laboratory work, elect fewer science courses later. Smith has shown how laboratory experiences in general science can be used in developing understanding of selected science principles. If the span from elementary-school science to senior high school science is to be bridged in a developmental sense, laboratory work must become a common experience in seventh- and eighth-grade science. Facilities must be provided.

Although the seventh- and eighth-grade science courses must be clearly organized to insure appropriate scope and effective sequence, they should be reasonably flexible. The courses should be flexible in the sense that the teacher should be free to reduce, extend, or supplement them whenever and wherever such adaptations seem appropriate in order to meet more nearly the needs and abilities of his pupils.

The amount of time per week scheduled for science in Grades VII and VIII should be determined in light of the total curriculum offerings. As much, but no more, time should be scheduled for science as is scheduled for such courses as social studies and English. In order to provide for problem-solving laboratory work in science, however, it is desirable that science be scheduled for a minimum of one hour for each class session. Where periods are shorter than one hour, science classes should be scheduled for one or more double periods a week.

SCIENCE IN THE NINTH GRADE

General science was introduced into the schools as a ninth-grade subject. Since that time, however, much of its content and activities have been drawn upon to develop science courses in the first eight grades. In schools that have a well-developed science program through the eighth grade, the conventional ninth-grade general science is not adequate. Too often it is a repetition of the content previously covered. Many of the learning activities are also repeated.

General Science. At least three different kinds of science courses are appropriate at the ninth-grade level. In schools where there has been comparatively little science in the elementary school, a general science course at the ninth grade would be desirable. The course should draw upon content from all sciences whenever appropriate. It should not, however, be a survey of science in the sense that it will touch many science topics lightly. It should more properly be an orientation to science. The course should be organized around a relatively few unifying areas, selected in terms of their pertinence to the problems facing man today to which both the methods and content of science apply. It should be organized to show the interrelationship of the sciences, both conceptually and as they apply to our technological advancement. It should be a laboratory course that provides experiences in the methods of science. It should be conceptual rather than entirely descriptive.

A general science course of the type described would also be appropriate in schools where young people come into the ninth grade with fairly good backgrounds in elementary science. It would be one of several science courses at the ninth-grade level from which pupils would elect.

Summary

The growth and development of general science as a subject in the high school curriculum may be summarized by period as follows:

Prior to 1900   General science learned as a body of related topics for purposes of general information.

1900–15   The experimental period, when general science was emerging and developing as a separate course but with its content largely in specialized subject-matter blocks.

1915–30   The period of consolidation and integration when general science concepts were being identified and learned for understanding the environment.

1930–60   The period of a developing philosophy of emerging research, and the identification of its contribution to the learning of the processes of science.

OTHER SCIENCES IN THE SCHOOL CURRICULUM

Considerable space has been given to the historical backgrounds of the four major science offerings in the high school curriculum because it is through this perspective that one is able to gain some understanding of the forces and factors which have shaped the trends in the present curriculum.

This section would be incomplete unless mention were made of other science offerings in the school curriculum, together with a brief account of their historical antecedents. A recent survey[95] of the subjects in the high school curriculum conducted by the United States Office of Education revealed more than 110 course titles under science offerings. A listing of these courses offered in the public high schools of the nation gives some indication of the range and diversity of science. It would be quite impossible and undesirable to discuss each of these, so a few that seem to have major implications have been chosen for treatment in this section.

General Science
General Science, 7th grade
General Science, 8th grade
General Science, 9th grade
  Explorations in Science
General Science, 10-12th grade
  Advanced Science
  Bio-physics
  Bio-physical science
  History and theory
  Nature study or science
  Science frontiers
  Science Survey I
  Science Survey II
  Science Survey, Grade 12
  World Science
General Science (Honor), Grade 7 (or
  acc).
General Science (Honor), Grade 8 (or
  acc.)
Talented Science (Grade 9)
Applied Science
  Basic Science
  Practical Science
Applied Science I
Applied Science II
Related Technology
Laboratory Science
  Laboratory Science Assistants
  Laboratory Techniques
Laboratory Science (Life)
  Bio-Lab Techniques
Laboratory Science (Physical)
  Advanced Lab
Biological Science
Beginning Biology
  Natural Science
  Radiation biology
  Terminal biology
Biological Sc. Curr. Study (BSCS)
Practical Biology
  Household biology

Advanced Biology
  Intensive Biology
College Biology
Life Science
  Effective Living
  Science for Modern Living
Biology (Honor)
  Biology Seminar
Bacteriology
Microbiology
Applied Biology
  Basic Med. Tech.
Botany
Zoology
Chemistry
Beginning Chemistry
  Descriptive Chemistry
  General Chemistry
Advanced Chemistry
  Chemistry Honors
  Intensive Chemistry
College Chemistry
Chem. Bond Approach (C.B.A.)
Chem. Ed. Material (CHEM)
Practical Chemistry
  Applied Chemistry
  Basic Chemistry
  Chem.—Nursing
  Chem.—Science
  Med. Chemistry
  Technical Chemistry
Physics
Beginning Physics
  Descriptive Physics
  General Physics
Advanced Physics
  Honors Physics
  Physics Seminar
College Physics
P.S.S.C. Physics (11 or 12)
  P.S.S.C. Science
Practical Physics

Applied Physics
Fundamentals of Electricity
Fundamentals of Machines
Everyday Physics
Basic mechanics and electricity
Electronics
  Radio
  Radio Physics
  Television
Modern Physics
  Atomic Physics
Physiology
Anatomy
  Human Biology
Physical Science
  Acc. Science
  Basic Physical Science
  Science Fundamentals
  Senior Science
  Survey Course
Adv. Phys. Science
Earth Science

Meteorology
  Physical Geography
Earth Science, Talented
Conservation
  Forestry
  Horticulture
Aeronautics
  Pre-flight aeronautics
Astronomy
  Navigation
Research Seminar
  Problems of Analysis
Health Science
  Hygiene
Earth-Space Science
  Astro-Geoscience
  Space science
Industrial Science
  Materials for industry
  Photography
  Science Engineer
Automation

Nature Study and Elementary
Science in the School Curriculum

Nearly seventy-five years before science appeared as nature study in the early grades of the public school, science materials were to be found in children's literature. These books first appeared around 1750, and were no doubt brought from Europe by the early settlers. The greatest influence of these early science writings occurred between 1800 and 1825, according to Underhill.[96] "In the early years of the last century a small amount of science was taught, mostly as nature study, as a part of the school curriculum in connection with, (1) the monitorial system of education, (2) infant schools, (3) reading books, (4) special texts, and (5) geography." Underhill comments as follows about this period:

This period characterized the beginnings of group instruction in the schools, accompanied by the use of special texts and readers embodying the science materials. The books which excited greatest influence on the science programs to follow were published between 1850 and 1870.

In the period between 1860 and 1880, object teaching was brought into American elementary schools transplanted from European educational influences and teachings of the period. This mode of teaching appeared to be, as Underhill comments, "an interlude in the attempt to utilize the study of things and phenomena as a part of the general educative process, during which time the emphasis on a highly formal methodology obscured the direction and purpose of science."

It should be noted, however, that during this period the impetus given to the study of objects had a profound effect on teaching and learning, and this influence is without doubt one of the basic factors which later led to the popularity of nature study, and the emergence of elementary science. As the interest in object teaching waned in the 1880's, attention became focused more on the teaching of science as a subject.

The period between 1870 and 1900 was important in the growth of elementary science, for it was during these years that the earliest courses of study and specific curriculum outlines for the subject began to appear. Underhill[97] suggests several factors which influenced this movement as follows:

(1) the rapid development of the sciences and their application to everyday life, (2) the need for skilled labor in the rapidly developing technology, which emphasized the vocational and utilitarian values, (3) the fruitfulness of the laboratory method in technology, (4) the influence of the "new education" which emphasized pupil activity as a "natural" expression of biological development.

Among those who made impact on the trends of this period should be mentioned William T. Harris, Charles, Frank and Linda McMurry, William S. Jackman, and Francis W. Parker.

The rise of nature study as a popular subject in the elementary school curriculum began about 1890 and extended over the next forty years, well down into the 1930's. Some vestiges of this popular movement still remain as an influence in the present curriculum in elementary science.

Courses of study for a so-called elementary science had appeared prior to the rise of nature study, but interest in this school offering declined for lack of teachers with adequate science backgrounds to teach it. It is interesting to note that today, some seventy years later, there has been a return to this same phase of what appears to be a cycle.

Nature study as a subject in the elementary school was no doubt an outgrowth of the influences of the "romanticism" of the period as well as the influence of the "new education" of the day. There was a flood of courses of study in the subject and many books for teachers appeared that sought to indoctrinate them in the purposes and methods of the subjects. Claims as to the values of the nature study covered a wide range and often bordered on the emotional, as indicated by objectives related to "love of" and "sympathy for" nature.

As a school program, the nature study movement was greatly influenced by Dr. Liberty Hyde Bailey and the Comstocks at Cornell University. This influence for the study of nature at Cornell has persisted down to the present through the outstanding and influential contributions of Dr. E. Lawrence Palmer.

The advent of present-day elementary science was in 1927 when Craig[98] conducted a study that sought to develop objective techniques through which the content of the elementary science curriculum might be developed. This study had a wide influence on elementary science curricula over the country. Perhaps its greatest impact was the placement of emphasis on a continuous and unified science curriculum from the kindergarten through the secondary school.

The *Thirty-First Yearbook* of the National Society for the Study of Education,"[99] published in 1932, had the following to say about the objectives of science in the elementary school:

Certain objectives that are selected for elementary science should conform to these conceptions (1) that greatly influence the thinking of the individuals who learn their meaning, and (2) that have modified thinking in many fields outside of science.

The following satements will illustrate this criterion:

1. The earth is very old as measured in terms of units of time.
2. The surface of the earth has not always had its present appearance and is constantly changing.
3. Space is vast.
4. The earth has been developed as a result of the action of natural forces.
5. The sun is the original source of energy for the earth.
6. The earth's position and relation to the sun and moon are all of great importance to the life of the earth.
7. All life has evolved from very simple forms.
8. Species have survived because by adaptations and adjustments they have tended to become better fitted to the conditions under which they live.
9. The physical environment has great influence, not only upon the structural forms of life, but also upon society.
10. Man has modified plant and animal forms through a knowledge of methods found in nature.
11. Through interdependence of species and struggle for existence there tends to be maintained a balance among the many forms of life.
12. Chemical and physical changes are manifestations of energy.

The *Forty-Sixth Yearbook* of the National Society for the Study of Education[100] commented as follows on science in the elementary school:

Functional understanding of information, concepts, and principles. Science contains much useful information for children. There is a wide range of facts from the various fields of science which children need in pursuance of their own activities. These facts may be useful in that they play an important part in giving children the kind of explanations they need in their normal living, such as the cause of day and night, the nature of lightning, etc. There are also facts that are needed because they directly affect the welfare of the child and have value in changing his behavior in such matters as health and safety. There are meanings which contribute to an understanding of large ideas of science, such as those of space, time, change, adaptations, interrelationships, and evolution. It should be noted that the large ideas involve meanings for all levels of educational advancement, from childhood through the period of adult education. They may have great significance in the development of a constructive outlook on life.

Instrumental skills. There are a number of instrumental skills which are necessary as means of achieving the aims of education discussed earlier in this chapter and which must have consideration in the teaching of science in the elementary school. These include the ability to (1) read science content with understanding; (2) make observations of events; and (3) perform the various science activities.

Elements of the scientific method. There have been few points in educational discussions on which there has been greater agreement than that of the desirability of teaching the scientific method. In recent studies of children's responses it has been found that the scientific method can have its beginnings in the education of children at an early age. However, in the elementary school there are relatively few times when it is appropriate to solve problems through use of all the elements of the scientific method. Such a procedure is too difficult for the maturity level of the majority of the children. The teacher can focus the attention of the children on those elements which seem most appropriate to the problems and to the intellectual development of the children involved.

The elements of the scientific method should contribute to intelligent planning. Science has a great contribution to make to individual and to group planning in a democracy. Children should be given an opportunity to participate in planning to the extent that they are aware of the elements of the scientific method in good planning. The elements of the scientific method should lead to action in life and to scientific appreciations and attitudes. Children should be given an opportunity to participate in planning to the extent that they are aware of the elements of the scientific method in good planning. The elements of the scientific method should lead to action in life and to scientific appreciations and attitudes. Children should be so well educated in the use and implications of these elements that they can participate as individuals and in groups in the advancement of the human race.

Scientific attitudes. It is a difficult matter to disassociate attitudes from the other objectives of science. Attitudes are not secured in a vacuum of verbalizations, but rather are derived out of experiences which have meaning. Characteristic attitudes that may be acquired by children through meaningful content are the following: questioning magic as an explanation of events; searching for an explanation of things which happen; realizing that some natural phenomena have not yet been explained satisfactorily by scientists; rejecting personification, mysticism, animism, anthropomorphism, or gossip in making explanations; realizing that interpretations advanced by scientists today may be corrected and improved by scientists tomorrow; changing one's ideas as the result of new evidence; rejecting guessing and faulty thinking as a means of ascertaining truth; being willing to check conclusions; questioning the accuracy of sources of information; questioning the acceptance of the opinions of those who are not qualified in the field in which the opinions are given; questioning superstition, prejudice, astrology, fortunetelling; placing confidence in the methods and conclusions of scientists.

The use of the elements of the scientific method should result in the attitude of critical-mindedness. At the same time there should be growth in such traits as willingness to consider new information, avoidance of dogmatic attitudes, avoidance of gullibility, willingness to change attitudes, ability to make distinctions between fact and fiction, and willingness to seek and to act upon reliable information.

A more recent statement of the purposes of science teaching in the elementary school appeared in the *Fifty-Ninth Yearbook* of the National Society for the Study of Education.[101]

There are several different ideas today about the function of the school in our society. Should it teach skills only, maintain the status quo, pass along the cultural heritage, or bring about cultural change? Our schools in effect attempt, in some measure, to realize each of these functions. This brings about considerable confusion.

When children study science they draw on accumulated knowledge in order to understand presently observed natural phenomena, Yet, knowledge is not learned just for the sake of learning but to throw light on children's current questions and problems. By teaching children the methods of science we are, in a sense, transmitting the culture of the past. But the methods give us the key to discovering valid new knowledge and to solving new problems.

In this century, characterized as it is by the scientific and technological advances, scientific attitudes are not the motivating attitudes of a majority of our population. Most people accept scientific knowledge as valid within small spheres of their life and look to other sources of knowledge for behavior guidelines in many aspects of living. This results in a real dilemma. Children who in science are taught to be open-minded, to be tolerant of various points of view, and not to jump to conclusions are confronted on every hand with decisions which are not to be questioned, superstitions and magic, advertising that is false and authoritative, and other evidences of unscientific beliefs and behavior. One of the greatest cultural problems which elementary-science teachers face is that of helping children see the spheres which scientific inquiry and behavior are appropriate, though perhaps sometimes not accepted.

The most recent development in the curriculum in elementary science is represented by several projects supported by the National Science Foundation,[102] in which various groups of educators and scientists are working together to develop new materials for the science curriculum at the elementary level. The following descriptions of a few of the projects give a clear idea of the present point of view and directions which these endeavors are taking:

MID-TWENTIETH CENTURY DEVELOPMENTS IN ELEMENTARY AND JUNIOR HIGH SCHOOL SCIENCE[103]

The phase of science curriculum development which began with the Physical Science Study Committee moved through the specialized sciences of the senior high school and into the junior high and elementary schools. The National Science Foundation continued to support many separate projects. No doubt some of these projects ultimately will make greater impact and gain wider usage than others. It is wise in establishing historical perspective, however, to take account of as many developments as possible and it is in this spirit that the following brief resumes are presented.

Junior High School Science Project (Princeton University)

The course, Time, Space, and Matter: Investigating the Physical World, is centered upon earth science and consists of a series of interrelated, sequential investigations conducted by students, structured toward their discovering through direct observation and inference something of the nature and history of the earth. It is intended that students will gain knowledge of some of the ways in which scientists learn about the nature of the physical world by experiencing scientific inquiry themselves. Materials developed and revised for further experimental classroom use include: teachers' text and student record book, Part I, *On the Nature of Things*.

School Science Curriculum Project (College of Education, University of Illinois)

The project is working on the design of science curricula, K-9, and on development of specific teaching materials. Work on both objectives proceeds concurrently, but not yet uniformly in all fields. Small groups of scientists and teachers sketch out tentative guidelines and prepare whatever preliminary materials seem indicated—written materials, apparatus, filmstrips, film loops, and the like. These are tried out with local classes and with small, informal groups of children. The results of tryout are observed directly and, along with broader criticism, provide the basis for revision and extension. The project expects to put its materials through several revisions before they are released for general use.

During the summer of 1963 work was begun in the general areas of animal behavior, animal and plant metabolism, mapping, motion and energy, and "pre-earth science" (kinematics and introductory dynamics of fluid flow of water and air, change of state, wave behavior, classification principles based on an experimental analogy for the formation of rock). Currently these sequences are being extended, and others are being undertaken. A few design studies are being pursued, some as instructional activities for children, others, as in the case of an elementary school microscope, in quest of improved apparatus.

Physical Science Study Committee-Junior High Physical Science (Educational Services Incorporated)

The objective is to prepare a course in physical science for the ninth grade. The project is in the first stage of development; seven chapters are in print in a preliminary version; several more chapters will be ready for use in pilot schools during 1963–64. The major emphasis in the course is on the study of matter. Student laboratory work is of primary importance. To emphasize this, laboratory instructions are incorporated in the body of the text; the results are not described. Since many junior high schools have little or no laboratory facilities, the equipment accompanying the written materials has been designed in such a way that the students can perform the experiments in ordinary classrooms. The course is intended to be suitable for use both as a terminal course in physical science and as preparation for the study of biology, chemistry, and physics.

Science Curriculum Improvement Study (Department of Physics, University of California)

The Study is exploring a concept of science education based on communicating scientific literacy. The large scale organization of the curriculum is to be determined by the structure of science, by the increasing maturity of the pupils, and by the pupils' preconceptions. Single lessons or groups of lessons are designed to lead students to discover the significance of certain scientific concepts. These lessons include individual pupil activities and experimentation, group activities, and class-wide demonstrations and discussions. They will be planned so that a secure connection is achieved between the pupils' preconceptions or common-sense attitudes and the concepts that embody the modern scientific point of view. Concepts include interactions between objects as causes of phenomena, physical systems (including living organisms), relativity of position and motion, equilibrium, entropy, and organic evolution.

Elementary School Science Project (Department of Botany, University of California)

A group of scientists at the University of California, Berkeley, are working to create science materials for the elementary school curriculum. An experimental approach is maintained in preparing and testing the material. All materials are tried in public schools of the area, utilizing regular teachers and students. The materials cover a wide range of areas of science such as: *How I Began: A Comparative Study of the Development of Human and Chick Embryos; What Am I?; Coordinates; The Nervous System; Animal Coloration.* Units on the following topics are also under development: force, wave motion, chemistry, animal variation, natural selection, population dynamics, animal behavior, the outdoor laboratory, botany, genetics, and paleontology.

Elementary School Science Project (College of Education, and Department of Astronomy, University of Illinois)

Project activity has centered on astronomy. The professional astronomers, science education specialists, and classroom teachers who make up the project staff are guided by two principles: (1) whatever science is taught to children should be sound and correct; (2) what is taught should reflect the essential structure of the subject. Astronomy is a prime example of an interdisciplinary field in the physical sciences, and basic astronomical themes rely heavily on content from mathematics, physics, and chemistry. One of the early tasks was to identify the major themes. Each summer since 1961 has been devoted to their development in a series of six books for children (grades 5–8) plus accompanying teachers' guides. Evaluation of project material is obtained from cooperating teachers in writing and through interviews, from project staff who visit classrooms where the books are being tested, and from written tests administered to the children.

Elementary Science Study (Educational Services Incorporated)

It is assumed that children learn science best when they are given the chance to be scientists themselves. This requires that some of what adult scientists call the physics, biology, or chemistry of a complex world be brought into the elementary grades in forms which the children can work with and understand. The project is attempting to develop sequences, materials, activities, and experience which can assist teachers to do this, and thereby create the conditions in which good science will be well learned.

The participating scientists and teachers have developed, observed, and revised new approaches and materials. The diversity of materials is indicated by the units under development: animal temperature, astronomy, butterflies, cells, chemistry, electricity, gases, kitchen physics, light, molds, playground physics, pocket reckoning, sound, structures.

Elementary School Science Improvement Project (Department of Physics, Utah State University)

This project is developing a series of lessons in science and mathematics for grades 1 and 2 designed to reveal some of the basic unifying ideas of science through investigation of everyday experiences of the child. Pupils identify differences or changes in comparison-type puzzles and are led through activities requiring the use of all the senses to observe and solve puzzles. They observe such phenomena as stretching a spring, sympathetically vibrating a tuning fork, or lighting a lamp with electricity. Attention is focused on the objects and the changes which take place in them. The child learns that interactions of objects are not isolated and unique, but are related to events which they have observed at other times. Acoustical interactions, for example, involve vibrating objects whether they are tuning forks or mother's vocal chords. A spiral type of approach is used, in that many experiments are repeated in several different units, each time emphasizing a different aspect of the problem.

AAAS Commission on Science Education (American Association for the Advancement of Science)

The Commission on Science Education, established in 1962, has the responsibilities: (1) to maintain a continuous review of work on improvement in science instruction, grades K-9; (2) to develop interest within the scientific community and recruit scientists to work on the development of elementary and junior high school science materials; (3) to arrange conferences, communications, and exchange of materials among various groups working in this area; (4) to assist with evaluation of materials prepared; (5) to serve as an advisory board to persons interested in the establishment of new programs or centers for the development of science materials, and to agencies that might be interested in providing financial support for such activities; and (6) to provide interpretation and help in the selection and use of any new science materials.

The Commission has initiated the preparation of a set of science materials for elementary schools. During the summer of 1962, two 8-day conferences were held. The conferees agreed that children will appreciate science only if all aspects of the subject are taught from the earliest grades. Science can be viewed as having three interrelated facets—processes, content, and concepts. The Commission, decided to adopt a process approach for the earliest grades. This would include content and would lead to consideration of concepts and broad themes in higher grades.

During the winter and spring of 1963, a panel set up by the Commission, made detailed plans for a summer writing session. For eight weeks the writing group devised and tested exercises for kindergarten through third grade. The material was written for teachers rather than for children. Special laboratory equipment was constructed and has been provided to the tryout teachers.

The major thrust of the exercises is to develop in children skills and competencies (observation, communication, measurement, inference, etc.) which they will need as they study science in later grades. The objectives of each exercise are stated clearly at the outset, and the teacher is provided with an appraisal activity to use at the end, so that he may determine whether the children have achieved the skills and competencies.

Earth Science in the Secondary School Curriculum

At the beginning of this century, when general science was introduced as an experimental course, earth science, more commonly known as physical geography, or physiography, was the most common science offering at the Ninth-Grade level. General science and biology were standard offerings in the ninth and tenth years respectively by the close of the first decade of this century. During the same period, interest in physical geography began to wane, and as a result the percentage of the total high school population that enrolled in this course gradually declined. By 1949 the course had all but disappeared from the high school curriculum, except for selected units included in general science.

The following table shows the decline of earth science as a curriculum offering between 1900 and 1949.[104]

The Committee of Ten[105] in its report recommended physical geography as the course offering for the first year of high school, and that more advanced phases, together with meteorology, should be elective in the last year of high school. These subjects were regarded by the

NUMBER AND PERCENTAGE OF PUPILS, GRADES NINE-TWELVE, ENROLLED IN EARTH SCIENCE IN PUBLIC HIGH SCHOOLS (1900–49)

YEAR	NUMBER	PER CENT
1900	154,513	29.8
1910	155,401	21.0
1915	178,693	15.3
1922	97,140	4.5
1928	81,017	2.8
1934	78,559	1.7
1949	20,575	0.4

committee as offering excellent opportunity for the correlation and organization of the scientific knowledge gained from the study of other sciences.

While 1957 is usually used as the reference date for the revival of interest in earth science, it is significant to note that New York State was well on the way toward a statewide earth-science course when the Russians lofted Sputnik I as the first man-made satellite in 1957. This state had been experimenting with the course and had prepared and adopted a new earth-science syllabus by 1955.

In 1959 Pennsylvania produced a *Teaching Guide for Earth and Space Science*.[106] By this time several other states had begun introducing new earth-science materials into science courses at various levels. The pioneer work in New York, followed by the widely copied course guide in Pennsylvania, seemed to be the detonators of a sudden spurt of interest over the nation in earth/space-science courses. A survey conducted by a major book-publishing company in 1961 indicated that twenty-four states had or were planning earth-science courses or units. Most of these were to be offered at the Ninth-Grade level.

It is difficult to judge at this time whether or not the revival of interest in earth-science will persist. In New York State, where the newer prototype of the earth-science course was pioneered, it has shown sudden and remarkable growth. In 1961 more than 30,000 students in that state were enrolled in the course. The earth-science offering in New York State is restricted to the upper one-third or one-fourth of the class, so it seems evident that it is not being used as a dumping ground for those pupils who are unable to cope with other science courses.

In Pennsylvania the course is now taught in about 450 schools. There is evidence that the course enrollment here, as well as in other states, is steadily increasing.

The table of contents from the Pennsylvania course of study in earth-space science is included below to indicate the nature of the subject matter.[107]

The developing interest in the Earth Sciences has created a need for concerted efforts among scientists and educators to provide a project similar in concept to those supported by the National Science Foundation in other areas. Following is a brief account of the Earth Science Curriculum Project.[108]

Earth Science Curriculum Project (ESCP)—Boulder, Colorado

The Earth Science Curriculum Project is an interdisciplinary program in which astronomers, geologists, geophysicists, meteorologists, oceanographers and physical geographers are combining their talents and efforts with those of science educators and secondary school earth science teachers to develop up-to-date resource materials for use in secondary school earth science courses and to improve the training of earth science teachers. ESCP will develop a textbook, a set of laboratory experiments and demonstrations, one or more teachers' guides and a variety of other learning aids. The teacher preparation committee will plan and conduct related conferences and programs for pre-service and inservice training of teachers.

The project has conducted several studies to provide information for use in planning new course materials: a survey and assessment of current and planned secondary school earth science programs, an investigation of the scope and sequence of earth science subject matter for grades K-12, and a review of secondary school earth science texts.

A group of 20 earth scientists, secondary school teachers, and science educators prepared rough outlines for the text, laboratory experiments and demonstrations and teachers' guide during a ten-day conference held at the University of Colorado in August, 1963. In developing the outlines the participants attempted to incorporate the following unifying themes: science as inquiry, universality of change, the flow of energy, adaptation to environmental change, conservation of mass and energy, significance of components and their relationship in time and space, uniformitarianism, comprehension of scale, and prediction. The outlines were revised for use by writers participating in a two-month writing conference during the summer of 1964.

In developing course materials, ESCP made no attempt to cover the entire body of knowledge in the earth sciences choosing, rather, to develop a system of basic concepts and principles.

The Physical Science Course
in the High School Curriculum

The present course in physical science included in the curriculum offerings of large numbers of high schools has roots that go back at least to the closing decade of the last century. In a book written by Dr. A. P. Gage entitled *Introduction to Physical Science,* published in 1892,[109] one may read from the preface:

I venture to hope, in view of the kind and generous reception given to the *Elements of Physics,* that this attempt to make the same methods available in a somewhat more elementary work, may prove welcome and helpful. It has been my aim in the preparation of this book to adapt it to the require-ments and facilities of the average high school. With this view I have en-deavored to bring the subjects taught within the easy comprehension of the ordinary pupil of this grade (12), without attempting to "popularize" them by the use of loose and unscientific language or fanciful and misleading illustrations and analogies, which might leave much to be taught in after time. Especially has it been my purpose to carefully guard against the intro-duction of any teachings not in harmony with the most modern conceptions of Physical Science.

This quotation at least implies that some of the purposes for such a course in physical science today also prevailed in the 1890's.

Available statistical records of course offerings and enrollments for science between 1890 and 1949 show with respect to physical science, that it was insufficiently enrolled in the public high schools to be included in the listings included in the Biennial Survey of Education in the United States,[110] published by the U. S. Office of Education.

A study made by Watson in 1940[111] indicated that a course described as physical science was offered in some fifty-four cities of the nation of over 25,000 population. These cities were distributed over twenty-six states. A study made at the U.S. Office of Education by Johnson[112] in 1947-48 indicated a sharp decline in the physical-science offering during the years of the second World War. Johnson's study, based on a random sample of 755 public high schools, revealed only seven places where physical science was offered during these years.

The committee that wrote the *Forty-Sixth Yearbook* of the National Society for the Study of Education commented as follows about the nature and function of the physical-science course:[113]

WHAT SHOULD BE THE NATURE AND FUNCTION OF THE PHYSICAL-SCIENCE COURSE?

Many "fused" courses of physical science have been introduced into the senior high during the last decade. Moreover, the number of such courses seems certain to increase. It is quite as logical to develop such a course at the present time as it was to begin the development of general biology about thirty-five years ago. The formulation of a satisfactory course in physical science, however, has been retarded by a variety of different approaches to the problem, reflecting nebulousness and confusion of ideas with respect to the nature and functions of such a course. The following considerations, therefore, are deemed to be fundamental to a satisfactory solution of the problem of providing a satisfactory course in physical science.

(a) The content should be planned so as to develop concepts and principles important not only in physics and chemistry but also in other branches of physical science, namely, geology, astronomy, and meteorology. For example, an understanding of the principle of gravitation may appropriately be developed by presenting applications dealing with falling bodies, decantation and precipitation, air currents, erosion, tides, and movements of heavenly bodies.

(b) Practical considerations dictate that the course should be planned for one year and not for two. There is, of course, more than enough material of unquestioned worth to justify a two-year course, but such a course would not have extensive election because too few pupils would find time in their crowded programs to take both years of the work. The failure of the promising two-year program of physical science prepared for use throughout one of the middle-western states about twenty years ago reveals the difficulties encountered in carrying on such a two-year course. In the typical situation many pupils in the last two years of the high school would be able to take only one more year of work in science and hence must take either the first or second half of a two-year course. Relatively few, and these chiefly the ones corresponding to those who now elect both physics and chemistry, would be able to take the entire two years' work. Consequently, the numbers of pupils who would secure special training in physical science would be even smaller than where the one-year course is offered, because a large proportion of those who might elect a year of physics or of chemistry would be unlikely to elect one-half of a two-year physical-science course.

(c) The values of a course of physical science are likely to be largely sacrificed if attempts are made to simplify it too greatly. Deeply concerned over the decreasing elections of physics and chemistry resulting from the formidable reputations of these subjects, some pioneers in the physical-science movement sought to assemble, under a variety of course and book titles designed to camouflage the nature of the course and thus to allay pupil prejudices against it, materials which would be easy enough for the ready comprehension of any of the pupils. These efforts in some cases resulted in courses that were practically on the level of effortless entertainment. They were less demanding of pupil effort and thought and, on the whole, provided a less valuable orientation in physical science than does a good course in general science intended for the junior high school. The worth of many of these early physical-science courses was further lessened by the omission of laboratory work.

There are obviously grave difficulties in the way of organizing a course in physical science which will prove simple enough for ready comprehension by pupils of limited abilities and still retain the unique, intrinsic values attainable within this area. There seems no doubt, however, that a course of this nature can be evolved which can achieve its desired objectives through a much less technical and mathematical approach and with many more contacts with the daily lives of boys and girls than do the conventional present-day courses in physics and chemistry. If, however, physical science is to realize its full potentialities, it must be made to serve both as a "college-preparatory" and as a terminal course.

The devising of satisfactory courses in physical science is one of the greatest challenges in the field of secondary-school science. Their development is especially important for the smaller schools in which the equipment and scheduling of separate courses in physics and chemistry is often a serious problem.

In 1954 the U.S. Office of Education began a series of recurring studies of offerings and enrollments in high school science. These studies tend to indicate that the course in physical science made a comeback in the decade following World War II. In the 1954 study of offerings and enrollments Brown[114] did not find a sufficiently large enrollment in the physical-science course to warrant separating it for statistical purposes from a category called "other sciences." In 1956, in a report of this study, Brown and Obourn[115] reported from a 10 per cent random sample that 77,900 pupils or 1.1 per cent of the ninth- to twelfth-grade population was enrolled in a course called "advanced general science." In 1958,[116] the data from a subsequent repeat of this study revealed that enrollments in the advanced general science course had increased to 98,000. These data show clearly that the course is increasing in popularity. To convey some idea of the nature of the course content of current physical science offering, the following sample course outlines have been selected:

MODERN PHYSICAL SCIENCE[117]

Unit 1. Understanding Chemistry
1. Science and Your Daily Life
2. The World of Matter
3. Atoms and Molecules
4. Gases of the Air
5. Acids, Bases, and Salts

Unit 2. Metallurgy and Metals
6. Metallurgy and Iron
7. Metallurgy of Other Common Metals
8. Precious Metals and Alloys

Unit 3. Applying Chemistry
9. Water and the Chemistry of Its Treatment
10. Chemistry in the Home
11. Materials for Building
12. Rubber and Plastics
13. Natural and Synthetic Fibers

Unit 4. Fuels and Heat
14. Heat as a Form of Energy
15. Fuels as a Source of Energy
16. Petroleum

Unit 5. Forces
17. Force and Motion
18. Force and Machines
19. Engines
20. Force and Flight

Unit 6. Forces Acting on Matter
21. Behavior of Matter
22. Work, Power, and Energy

Unit 7. Meteorology
23. Weather and Climate
24. Air Masses and Fronts

25. Storms and Forecasts

Unit 8. Earth Science
26. The Structure of the Earth
27. Physiography
28. Oceanography

Unit 9. Astronomy and Astronautics
29. The Solar System
30. Planet Earth and Its Moon
31. Space Science
32. The Universe

Unit 10. Sound
33. Wave Motion and Sound
34. Music

Unit 11. Light
35. The Nature of Light
36. Light and Lenses
37. Wave Motion and Color

Unit 12. Electricity
38. Electric Circuits and Currents
39. Effects and Electric Currents
40. Electromagnetism

Unit 13. Electronics
41. Electrostatics
42. Radio Electronics
43. Modern Electronic Devices

Unit 14. Nucleonics
44. Nuclear Changes
45. Atomic Energy

Appendix (Periodic Table of the Elements)
Glossary
Index

PHYSICAL SCIENCE—A BASIC COURSE[118]

Unit I. The Earth As It Began
1. The Earth—Its Origin
2. Waters of the Earth
3. The Earth's Atmosphere

Unit II. Earth, The Abode of Man
4. The Earth—Its Shape and Motions
5. Rocks of the Earth (1)

PHYSICS AND CHEMISTRY—A UNIFIED APPROACH[119]

10. The Activity List of Metals
11. Oxygen
12. Valence and Oxidation Numbers
13. Water
14. The Atomic Theory
15. Weight Calculations in Chemical Reactions

Unit 3
16. Pressure in Liquids
17. Pressure in Gases
18. The Kinetic Theory and the Gas Laws
19. Volume Calculations in Chemical Reaction

Unit 4
20. Temperature and Expansion
21. Heat and Its Measurement
22. Heat from Electricity
23. Evaporation and Vapor Pressure
24. The Liquefaction of Gases
25. Carbon
26. Carbon Dioxide
27. Heat Energy in Chemical Reactions

Unit 5
28. Parallel Forces
29. Forces Acting at a Point
30. Velocity and Acceleration
31. Accelerated Motion
32. Newton's Law of Motion
33. Momentum and Gravitation

Book Two

Unit 6
34. Faraday's Laws of Electrolysis
35. Rate and Extent of Chemical Reactions
36. Ionization Theories
37. Acids and Bases
38. Water as an Electrolyte
39. Neutralization
40. Electrolysis
41. Voltaic Cells

42. Oxidation-Reduction Reactions

Unit 7
43. Reflection of Light
44. Refraction and the Speed of Light
45. Lenses and Optical Instruments
46. Waves and Their Properties
47. Spectra
48. The Electromagnetic Spectrum
49. Electric and Magnetic Fields
50. Interactions of Particles and Fields

Unit 8
51. Mendeleeff's Periodic Classification
52. Atomic Structure
53. The Modern Periodic Classification

Unit 9
54. The Halogen Family
55. The Sulfur Family
56. The Oxides and Oxyacids of Sulfur
57. The Nitrogen Family
58. Some Compounds of Nitrogen
59. Some Metals
60. Some Chemical Industries
61. What Are Colloids?
62. Types of Colloids

Unit 10
63. Energy in Atoms
64. Natural Radioactivity
65. Transmutation and Artificial Radioactivity
66. Fission and Fusion

Unit 11
67. Compounds of Carbon and Hydrogen
68. Other Families of Carbon Compounds
69. Isomerism
70. Some Reactions of Organic Compounds

EXPLORING SPACE
A Resource Unit for a Course in Physical Science[120]

The Earth's Atmosphere

Exploring Space from the Earth

Exploring Outer Space

Equipment and Supplies
Films
Bibliography

The 59th Yearbook of the National Society for the Study of Education commented as follows on the course in physical science as a subject for the Ninth Grade:[121]

General Physical Science. The generalized physical-science course should also be an orientation rather than a survey course. Its orientation should be toward the development of a better understanding of the methods of investigation that have been used effectively in the physical sciences; selected unifying concepts of matter and energy that man has developed by using these methods; and ways in which man has applied both methods and concepts to control matter and energy. Both the general biological science and the general physical science should be laboratory courses with a maximum of problem-solving experiences.

It would be desirable to make all three of these courses—general science, biological science, and physical science—available to ninth-grade pupils. In some schools this may be impossible. In such schools decisions regarding which one of the three will be offered will have to be made in terms of a number of factors such as: the nature of the elementary-science program, the number and qualifications of science teachers; and the science program for tenth, eleventh, and twelfth grades.

For Discussion and Further Study

1. Although Marshall's quotation in the introduction to this section emphasizes the uncertain manner in which science courses have been developed, are there clear-cut forces that do determine the content and organization of courses and programs of study?

2. What assets or liabilities would accompany the establishment of a central agency to develop and revise science courses for all schools in a county, state, or nation?

3. To what extent should the peculiar nature of a community be reflected in the content and organization of the science courses to be taught in the schools of the community?

4. How can school science courses, or the amount of school time to be devoted to science, be adjusted to stay in step with the proliferation of science?

5. Is it true that the procedures, logic, history, and philosophy of science can be taught without attempting to touch on each of the separate discoveries and inventions of science?

References

1. J. Stanley Marshall. "The New School Science." A Report to School Administrators on Regional Orientation Conferences in Science, AAAS Misc. Publ. 63–6. Washington: American Association for the Advancement of Science, 1962, p. 3.

2. Reprinted by permission of the publishers from Joseph J. Schwab and Paul F. Brandwein, *The Teaching of Science*. Cambridge, Mass.: Harvard University Press, Copyright 1962, by the President and Fellows of Harvard College. P. 102.

3. Samuel R. Powers. "The Thirty-First Yearbook in Retrospect and a Look to the Future," *Science Education,* 37 (February 1953), pp. 33–35.

4. Francis D. Curtis. "The Thirty-First Yearbook in Retrospect and a Look to the Future," *Science Education,* 37 (February 1953), pp. 33–35.

5. C. R. Mann. *The Teaching of Physics*. New York: The Macmillan Company, 1917, p. 58.

6. G. R. Twiss. *Principles of Science Teaching*. New York: The Macmillan Company, 1922, p. 188.

7. National Education Association. *Cardinal Principles of Secondary Education*. Report of Commission on the Reorganization of Secondary Education. Washington: U.S. Bureau of Education Bulletin 35, 1918.

8. Otis W. Caldwell and Committee. *Report of Subcommittee on the Teaching of Science*. Bulletin 26. Washington: U.S. Bureau of Education, 1920.

9. American Association for the Advancement of Science. "On the Place of Science in Education," *School Science and Mathematics,* 28 (June 1928), pp. 640–64.

10. National Society for the Study of Education. *A Program for Teaching Science,* Thirty-First Yearbook of the National Society, Part I. Bloomington, Ill.: Public School Publishing Company, 1932.

11. Wilbur R. Beauchamp. *Instruction in Science*. Monograph No. 22, Bulletin 1932, No. 17. Washington: U.S. Government Printing Office, Office of Education, 1933.

12. Committee on the Function of Science in General Education, Commission on Secondary School Curriculum, Progressive Education Association. *Science in General Education*. New York: Appleton-Century-Crofts, 1938.

13. National Committee on Science Teaching, American Council of Science Teachers. *Science Teaching for Better Living*. Washington: National Education Association, 1942.

14. National Committee on Science Teaching, American Council of Teachers. *Redirecting Science Teaching in the Light of Personal-Social Needs*. Washington: National Education Association, 1942.

15. Educational Policies Commission. *Education for All American Youth*. Washington: National Education Association, 1944.

16. Harvard Committee. *General Education in a Free Society*. Cambridge, Mass.: Harvard University Press, 1945.

17. National Society for the Study of Education. Forty-Sixth Yearbook of the National Society, *Science Education in American Schools*. Chicago: University of Chicago Press, 1947.

18. National Society for the Study of Education. Fifty-Ninth Yearbook of the National Society, *Rethinking Science Education*. Chicago: University of Chicago Press, 1960.

19. National Science Teachers Association. *It's Time for Better Elementary School Science.* Washington: The Association, 1958.
20. National Science Teachers Association. *Planning for Excellence in High School Science.* Washington: The Association, 1961.
21. E. E. Brown. *Making of Our Middle Schools.* New York: Longman's, Green & Company, 1902, p. 184.
22. *Ibid.,* p. 307.
23. C. Riborg Mann. *The Teaching of Physics.* New York: The Macmillan Company, 1917, p. 31.
24. *Ibid.*
25. Blair. *A Grammar of Natural and Experimental Philosophy.* 1822.
26. C. Riborg Mann. *The Teaching of Physics.* New York: The Macmillan Company, 1917, p. 32.
27. *Ibid.,* pp. 32–33.
28. *Ibid.,* p. 31.
29. *Ibid.,* p. 44.
30. Hall and Bergen. *Textbook of Physics.* New York: Holt, Rinehart & Winston, 1892.
31. *Report of the Committee of Ten of the National Education Association.* New York: American Book Company, 1894, p. 119.
32. John F. Woodhull. *The Teaching of Science.* New York: The Macmillan Company, 1918.
33. Coleman, in Woodhull, *Ibid.,* p. 97.
34. Millikan and Gale, "Elements of Physics," in Woodhull, *Ibid.,* p. 97.
35. Hoadley, in Woodhull, *Ibid.,* p. 98.
36. Crew and Jones, in Woodhull, *Ibid.,* p. 99.
37. Robert W. Fuller, Raymond B. Brownlee, and D. Lee Baker. *Elementary Principles of Physics.* New York: Allyn and Bacon, 1924, p. iv.
38. N. Henry Black and H. N. Davis. *New Practical Physics.* New York: The Macmillan Company, 1934, p. v.
39. American Association for the Advancement of Science. "Report on Broad Improvement in Science Education," *Science Education News* (December, 1961), p. 14.
40. S. R. Powers. "The Teaching of Chemistry in Early American Secondary Schools," *School and Society* 24 (October 23, 1926), pp. 497–503.
41. J. O. Frank. *The Teaching of High School Chemistry.* Oshkosh, Wis.: J. O. Frank and Sons, 1932, p. 8.
42. Eliot and Storer, in Woodhull, *The Teaching of Science.* New York: The Macmillan Company, 1918, p. 90.
43. J. D. Steele. *Fourteen Weeks in Chemistry.* New York: A. S. Barnes and Company, 1873.
44. *Ibid.*
45. John F. Woodhull. *The Teaching of Science.* New York: The Macmillan Company, 1918, p. 90.
46. Elroy M. Avery, in Woodhull, *Ibib.,* p. 91.
47. A. P. Gage, in Woodhull, *Ibid.,* p. 91.
48. Carhart and Chute, in Woodhull, *Ibid.,* p. 93.
49. Elroy M. Avery, in Woodhull, *Ibid.,* p. 93.
50. Cooley, in Woodhull, *Ibid.,* p. 93.

51. Hortvet, in Woodhull. *Ibid.*, p. 94.
52. Torrey, in Woodhull, *Ibid.*, p. 94.
53. J. O. Frank. *The Teaching of High School Chemistry.* Oshkosh, Wis.: J. O. Frank and Sons, 1932, p. 12.
54. American Association for the Advancement of Science. "Report on Broad Improvement in Science Education," *Science Education News* (December, 1961), pp. 5–6.
55. *Ibid.*, p. 6.
56. George W. Hunter. *Science Teaching.* New York: American Book Company, 1934, p. 25.
57. *Ibid.*, p. 28.
58. Paul DeH. Hurd. *Biological Education in American Secondary Schools 1890–1960.* Biological Sciences Curriculum Study Bulletin No. 1. Washington: American Institute of Biological Sciences, 1962, pp. 17–18.
59. George W. Hunter. *Science Teaching.* New York: American Book Company, 1934, p. 34.
60. *Ibid.*, p. 32.
61. Paul DeH. Hurd. *Biological Education in American Secondary Schools 1890–1960.* Biological Sciences Curriculum Study Bulletin No. 1. Washington: American Institute of Biological Sciences, 1962, pp. 39–41.
62. *Ibid.*, p. 43.
63. Otis W. Caldwell and Committee. *Report of Subcommittee on the Teaching of Science.* Bulletin 26. Washington: U.S. Bureau of Education, 1920, pp. 12–13.
64. *Ibid.*, p. 30.
65. Paul DeH. Hurd. *Biological Education in American Secondary Schools 1890–1960.* Biological Sciences Curriculum Study Bulletin No. 1. Washington: American Institute of Biological Sciences, 1962, pp. 49–51.
66. Committee on the Function of Science in General Education, Commission on Secondary School Curriculum, Progressive Education Association. *Science in General Education.* New York: Appleton-Century-Crofts, 1938.
67. Paul DeH. Hurd. *Biological Education in American Secondary Schools 1890–1960.* Biological Sciences Curriculum Study Bulletin No. 1. Washington: American Institute of Biological Sciences, 1962, p. 71.
68. *Ibid.*, p. 106.
69. Harvard Committee. *General Education in a Free Society.* Cambridge, Mass.: Harvard University Press, 1945.
70. John R. Steelman. "Manpower for Research," Vol. IV. *Science and Public Policy,* Appendix II. Washington: The President's Scientific Research Board, 1947.
71. John Breukelman and Richard Armacost. "Report of the Southeastern Conference on Biology Teaching," *The American Biology Teacher* 17(1) (1955), pp. 4–55.
72. Richard Armacost and Paul Klinge. "Report of the North Central Conference on Biology Teaching," *The American Biology Teacher,* 18(1) (1956), pp. 4–72.
73. National Academy of Sciences—National Research Council. *Conference*

on Biological Education, March 10, 1953 (mimeographed). Washington: The Academy, Division of Biology and Agriculture, 1953.

74. Paul DeH. Hurd. *Biological Education in American Secondary Schools 1890–1960*. Biological Sciences Curriculum Study Bulletin No. 1. Washington: American Institute of Biological Sciences, 1962, p. 116.

75. *Ibid.,* p. 136.

76. Arabella B. Buckley. *The Fairy-land of Science*. New York: Appleton-Century-Crofts, 1879.

77. Preston Smith. *Easy Experiments in Physics*. New York: The Morse Co., 1904, p. 3.

78. W. L. Eikenberry. *The Teaching of General Science*. Chicago: University of Chicago Press, 1922.

79. Percy E. Rowell. *Introduction to General Science*. New York: The Macmillan Company, 1911.

80. Otis W. Caldwell and W. L. Eikenberry. *Elements of General Science*. Boston: Ginn & Company, 1914.

81. F. D. Barber *et. al. First Course in General Science*. New York: Holt, Rinehart & Winston, 1916.

82. Carleton W. Washburne. *Common Science*. Yonkers-on-Hudson: World Book Company, 1923.

83. Bertha M. Clark. *New Introduction to Science*. New York: American Book Company, 1928.

84. George W. Hunter. *Science Teaching*. New York: American Book Company, 1934, p. 49.

85. Kenneth E. Brown and Ellsworth S. Obourn. *Offerings and Enrollments in Science and Mathematics in Public High Schools, 1958*. Office of Education Bulletin No. 5, OE-29021. Washington: U.S. Government Printing Office, 1961.

86. Otis W. Caldwell and Committee. *Report of Subcommittee on the Teaching of Science*. Bulletin 26. Washington: U.S. Bureau of Education, 1920.

87. George W. Hunter. *Science Teaching*. New York: American Book Company, 1934, pp. 36–37.

88. Otis W. Caldwell and Committee. *Report of Subcommittee on the Teaching of Science*. Bulletin 26. Washington: U.S. Bureau of Education, 1920.

89. J. O. Frank, *How to Teach General Science*. Philadelphia: P. Blakeston's Sons & Company, 1926, pp. 73–76.

90. Otis W. Caldwell and Francis D. Curtis. *Everyday Science*. Boston: Ginn & Company, 1943, pp. ix–x.

91. National Society for the Study of Education. *A Program for Teaching Science,* Thirty-First Yearbook of the National Society, Part I. Bloomington, Ill.: Public School Publishing Company, 1932.

92. Committee on the Function of Science in General Education, Commission on Secondary School Curriculum, Progressive Education Association. *Science in General Education*. New York: Appleton-Century-Crofts, 1938.

93. National Society for the Study of Education. Forty-Sixth Yearbook of the National Society, *Science Education in American Schools*. Chicago: University of Chicago Press, 1947.

94. National Society for the Study of Education. Fifty-Ninth Yearbook of

the National Society, *Rethinking Science Education*. Chicago: University of Chicago Press, 1960.

95. U.S. Office of Education. *Offerings and Enrollments in High School Subjects, 1960–61*. (In process)

96. Orra E. Underhill. *The Origins and Development of Elementary Science*. Chicago: Scott, Foresman & Company, 1941.

97. *Ibid.*

98. Gerald S. Craig. "Certain Techniques Used in Developing a Course of Study in Science for the Horace Mann Elementary School." New York: Columbia University Press, Teachers College, 1927.

99. National Society for the Study of Education, *A Program for Teaching Science,* Thirty-First Yearbook of the National Society, Part I. Blooming-ton, Ill.: Public School Publishing Company, 1932, pp. 134–35.

100. National Society for the Study of Education. Forty-Sixth Yearbook of the National Society, *Science Education in American Schools*. Chicago: University of Chicago Press, 1947.

101. National Society for the Study of Education. Fifty-Ninth Yearbook of the National Society, *Rethinking Science Education*. Chicago: University of Chicago Press, 1960.

102. "Science Course Improvement Projects," National Science Foundation, Bulletin 64–8 (July 1964), Washington, D.C.

103. *Ibid.*

104. Federal Security Agency, Office of Education. *Offerings and Enrollments in High School Subjects*. Washington: U.S. Government Printing Office, 1950, Chapt. 5.

105. National Education Association. *Report of the Committee of Ten*. New York: American Book Company, 1894.

106. Pennsylvania Department of Public Instruction. *Teaching Guide for the Earth and Space Science Course*. Harrisburg, Pa.: The Department, 1959.

107. *Ibid.*

108. "Science Course Improvement Projects," National Science Foundation, Bulletin 64–8 (July 1964), Washington, D.C.

109. A. P. Gage. *Introduction to Physical Science*. Boston: Ginn & Company, 1892.

110. U.S. Office of Education. *Offerings and Enrollments in High School Subjects, 1960–61*. (In process)

111. Donald R. Watson. "A Comparison of the Growth of Survey Courses in Physical Science in High Schools and Colleges," *Science Education,* 24 (January, 1940), pp. 14–20.

112. Philip G. Johnson. *The Teaching of Science in Public High Schools,* U.S. Office of Education Bulletin No. 9. Washington: U.S. Government Printing Office, 1950.

113. National Society for the Study of Education. Forty-Sixth Yearbook of the National Society, *Science Education in American Schools*. Chicago: University of Chicago Press, 1947.

114. Kenneth E. Brown. *Offerings and Enrollments in Science and Mathematics in Public High Schools, 1954,* Office of Education Pamphlet 118. Washington: U.S. Government Printing Office, 1956.

115. Kenneth E. Brown and Ellsworth S. Obourn. *Offerings and Enrollments in Science and Mathematics in Public High Schools, 1956*, U.S. Office of Education Pamphlet No. 120. Washington: U.S. Government Printing Office, 1956.

116. Kenneth E. Brown and Ellsworth S. Obourn. *Offerings and Enrollments in Science and Mathematics in Public High Schools, 1958*. Office of Education Bulletin No. 5, OE-29021. Washington: U.S. Government Printing Office, 1961.

117. William O. Brooks, George R. Tracy, and Harry E. Tropp. *Modern Physical Science*. New York: Holt, Rinehart & Winston, 1962.

118. John C. Hogg *et al. Physical Science—A Basic Course*. Princeton, N.J.: D. Van Nostrand Company, 1959.

119. John C. Hogg *et al. Physics and Chemistry—A Unified Approach*. Princeton, N.J.: D. Van Nostrand Company, 1960.

120. New York State Education Department. *Exploring Space—A Resource Unit for a Course in Physical Science*. Albany: State Education Department, 1957.

121. National Society for the Study of Education. Fifty-Ninth Year Book, *Rethinking Science Education*. Chicago: University of Chicago Press, 1960, p. 161.

16

Recent Trends and Influences in Science Curriculum Offerings

What are the changes that are likely to become more notice-able in the years ahead? In what directions are our science curricular changes heading? Let me put my vision of these changes (I will not call them trends) into a few bold state-ments. Change from much subject matter to relatively less subject matter. . . . Change from one problem-solving method to many relatively unstructured methods of in-quiry. . . . Change from use of a book in a series to the use of many books. . . . Change from an emphasis on ac-cumulating knowledge to an emphasis on how to find out and create knowledge. . . . Change from facts and factual concepts as instructional goals to skills in inquiry as the teaching goals. . . . Change from teacher-selected concepts as instructional goals to concepts as they may arise in the process of confirming or rejecting hypotheses. . . . Change from reliance on qualitative observations to more and more stress on securing and recording quantitative observations. . . . Change from science experiences as prep-aration for secondary school science to experience for basic education of all students. . . . Change from science as something to be learned from books to science as some-thing that grows out of a series of experiments. . . . Change

from a science program based on topics to a science program based on a more fundamental frame of reference. . . . Change from emphasis on technology to emphasis on science. . . . Change from science that must be developed from a limited understanding of mathematics to science that is built on mathematics.[1]

Philip G. Johnson   1962

It appears that . . . more attention is being directed to the broad-concept idea of chemistry . . . that teachers are being trained, retrained, and updated with stresses placed more on the academic areas in which the teacher will be teaching. . . . As experimentation on learning progresses, students are becoming better educated than ever before and . . . sophisticated ideas are being presented much more readily than in the past.[2]

Robert J. Silber   1962

The trend in science instruction [in Sweden] is toward more individual laboratory work and an elimination of non-essentials; from the morphological to the physiological in biology; from the mathematical to the more practical in physics; in general, toward making the science training more like that in the United States, though retaining its own desirable features.[3]

Holger F. Kilander   1931

"Problem solving" . . . is currently a popular phrase in the schools and is supposed to mark a new and higher conception of means and ends in education. But when the problems posed are examined and the "solving" inspected, "problem solving" turns out to be little more than the meticulous application of given procedures to situations which follow strictly the model problem on which the procedures were learned. Rarely indeed is the challenge one of modifying a given procedure so as to adapt it to situations which depart in a few respects from the known and standard form of the problem. Even rarer is the opportunity to discover that there are related or neighboring problems for which we have no ready methods of solution.[4]

Joseph J. Schwab   1962

The rapid progress true *science now makes, occasions my regretting sometimes that I was born so soon. It is impossible to imagine the height to which may be carried, in a thousand years, the power of man over matter. . . . O that moral science were in as fair a way of improvement, that men would cease to be wolves to one another, and that human beings would at length learn what they now improperly call humanity![5]*

Benjamin Franklin   1780

If science teachers are concerned about teaching the attitudes and methods of science so that they relate in a more functional manner to the education of young people in a democracy, they need to direct both the content and methods of their courses toward the achievement of positive overt behaviors.[6]

J. Darrell Barnard   1953

While any attempt to predict trends, even for a short period ahead, must be somewhat speculative, there seems to be some evidence to support the following trends and influences currently emerging in the science curriculum:

1. There is still a considerable influence toward general science in Grades One through Six, although some experimentation is in progress toward the organization of isolated units or topical strands in physics, biology and chemistry for these grades.
2. There is a general influence toward the inclusion of more sophisticated concepts in the elementary science course.
3. There is a general trend toward more laboratory work in science at all grade levels.
4. Although the general trend and influence is toward general science in the Seventh and Eighth Grades, there is evidence of specialization for these levels in some state courses of study.
5. There is definite trend toward making the science offering in the Ninth Grade a year of specialized rather than general science. There is, however, great uncertainty as to exactly what the course content should be. In some schools general biology is offered, in others earth

263

science, in a few an integrated physics-chemistry, and in many the traditional general science is still offered.

6. The influence of the course content revision committees sponsored by the National Science Foundation is being felt in each of the traditional high school sciences. The most profound impact has been in the increased emphasis on basic science concepts with a corresponding lessened emphasis on technology and applications of science.

7. There is a clear-cut trend toward the introduction of advanced courses in physics, chemistry and biology as well as an increase in sophisticated and academic research seminars in science, especially at the Twelfth-Grade level.

8. Perhaps the most profound influence resulting from many causes is the trend toward teaching science scientifically. That is, the increasing recognition that the processes of scientific enquiry have equal importance with the concepts of science.

For Discussion and Further Study

1. At a meeting of science educators in 1950, the program featured predicting trends in the teaching of science by extending changes noted between 1925 and 1950 to 1975. One prediction suggested that just as botany and zoology had become the general biology course, the coming twenty-five-year period would see a comparable fusion of chemistry and physics into a physical science course. What factors are related to the accuracy of this prediction?

2. Do the changes suggested by Johnson in the introduction to this section hinge on major changes in the attitudes children bring with them into their science courses? On major changes in the training of teachers and their supervisors?

3. Is the science teaching profession susceptible to fads? How can a potential fad be distinguished from a continuing trend?

4. Is the attention that is being directed toward teaching the procedures of science indicative of a fad or of a trend?

5. Which seems to change more readily: the content and organization of courses, or pedagogical tactics and strategy:

References

1. Philip G. Johnson. "Emerging Curriculum Studies in Elementary and Junior High School Science," *Supervision for Quality Education in Science*, DHEW, Office of Education Bulletin No. 3, OE-29039. Washington: Government Printing Office, 1963, pp. 132–39.

2. Robert J. Silber. *Advances in Secondary-School Science Education*. Proceedings of the conference in nuclear education held at Gatlinburg, Tennessee, August 20-22, 1962. Oak Ridge, Tennessee: U.S. Atomic Energy Commission, Report TID-7638, 1962, p. 23.

3. Holger F. Kilander, in Francis D. Curtis. *A Third Digest of Investigations*

in the Teaching of Science. Philadelphia: P. Blakiston and Sons Publishing Co., 1939, p. 218. Used by permission of McGraw-Hill Book Company.

4. Reprinted by permission of the publishers from Joseph J. Schwab and Paul F. Brandwein, *The Teaching of Science.* Cambridge, Mass.: Harvard University Press, Copyright 1962, by the President and Fellows of Harvard College. P. 39.

5. Benjamin Franklin, Letter to Joseph Pristley, February 8, 1780. Quoted by the Rand Corporation, *Scientific American,* 198 (April, 1958) p. 26.

6. J. Darrell Barnard, "Teaching Scientific Attitudes and Methods in Science," *The Bulletin of the National Association of Secondary-School Principles,* 37 (January, 1953) pp. 178–83.

17

On Relationships
Between Science and
Other Courses
in the
Total School Program

There is a higher correlation between reading ability and the ability to recognize mathematical concepts in high-school physics than between reading ability and computational ability. . . . The ability to recognize the mathematical concepts in high-school physics bears an important relation to performance in physics. . . . The fundamentals of mathematics are not thoroughly enough mastered by a large percentage of high-school students to enable them to apply these fundamental processes in a field such as physics.[1]

William R. Carter 1932

In a properly constructed society the philosophy which underlies the definition of one's political doctrine, one's religious, poetic and artistic theory must be identical with the philosophy of the natural sciences which is determined by nothing more that the logical analysis of the experimentally verified theories of the natural sciences to bring out their primitive, ontological assumptions and their methodological and epistimological assumptions.[2]

F. S. C. Northrop 1948

Art is practical, Science is speculative: the former is seen in doing; the latter rests in the contemplation of what is known. . . . Art is the parent, not the progeny, of Science; the realization of principles in practice forms part of the prelude, as well as of the sequel, of theoretical discovery.[3]

William Whewell 1847

Hence we must believe that all sciences are so interconnected, that it is much easier to study them all together than to isolate one from all the others. Therefore, if anyone wishes to search out the truth of things in earnest, he should not select any one special science; for all the sciences are conjoined with each other and interdependent: let him think only about how to increase the natural light of reason, not in order to solve this or that difficulty of a scholastic nature, but that his understanding may direct his will to its proper choice in every contingency of life.[4]

René Descartes 1629

Without further argument it will, we think, be admitted that the sciences are none of them separately evolved—are none of them independent either logically or historically; but that all of them have, in a greater or less degree, required aid and reciprocated it. Indeed, it needs but to throw aside hypotheses, and contemplate the mixed character of surrounding phenomena, to see at once that these notions of division and succession in the kinds of knowledge are simply scientific fictions: good, if regarded merely as aids to study; bad, if regarded as representing realities in Nature.[5]

Herbert Spencer 1854

By no means do the science courses within a typical school program operate apart from the other courses which make up the full schedules of students. In fact, if a student is enrolled in a biology, chemistry, or physics course, he will very probably be enrolled concurrently in English, social science, foreign language, mathematics, physical education, art, music, business or industrial education, and other so-called major or minor courses. During the few minutes permitted students to move from one to another classroom, they must shift their interests and thought processes from one to another discipline. In effect, students are expected to pursue one discipline at, say, nine o'clock, another at ten, another at eleven, and so forth. Furthermore, when a group assembles for a science class quite often the students come immediately from classes in a variety of disciplines, and different students will, therefore, need to make different kinds of shifts in their mental activities to be ready to take part in the science class. In general, students seem to expect these abrupt transitions and, apparently, solve their own problems of integrating one class with another. This does not mean, however, that the science teacher cannot improve his teaching by keeping in touch with what the other departments in the school are doing or hope to do and using this knowledge to facilitate the integrative process. The so-called Harvard Report[6] of 1945 emphasizes the importance of a well-integrated education. Many of the ideas in the paragraphs to follow are drawn from this report.

Nearly all secondary schools require their students to enroll in one or another kind of English course during each of the school years. This requirement stems from the belief that reading, writing, speaking, and listening in the English language are basic skills that all students must develop to communicate effectively and thereby be able to comprehend and appreciate other educational opportunities and experiences. Furthermore, the creation of literature is in itself one of the endeavors that is adequate to capture the minds and hands of men and women. One of the recognized functions of the courses offered by departments of English is to give students some of the satisfactions that derive from efforts to compose essays, stories, poems, and other types of literary production. A student coming to a science course immediately from an English course may need to shift abruptly from whatever an English teacher felt is associated with the pursuit of literary endeavors to whatever the science teacher has planned for the day. Obviously, whenever the abruptness of this transition can be tempered, assuming that the mind works most efficiently when there is unity and continuity to its functioning, the total school program will operate more efficiently.

The traits and characteristics of mind fostered by education in general become the most promising bridge whereby students may pass from one to another discipline. For example, to think effectively, to communicate thought, to make relevant judgments, and to discriminate among values, are abilities not, in practice, separable, nor to be developed in isolation. As worded, these aims of education can be professed with almost equal validity by teachers of both English and of science. Assuming adequate communication between the two departments, many opportunities arise to let students see that it is mainly differences in topic that distinguish their participation in science and English courses. Among educational opportunities provided in either course are improved abilities to think effectively, to communicate thought, and to demonstrate similar traits and characteristics of mind.

Another bridge connecting English and science courses derives from each being a human endeavor. The creation of a literary essay or poem can engage the mind of a man or woman in a manner quite comparable to the way a puzzling event or circumstance that is yet to be adequately described engages the mind of the scientist. When the student attempts to look over the shoulder of the writer at work the better to comprehend and appreciate the creative process at work in literature, the student is in very much the same role he must play when he attempts to comprehend and appreciate the pursuit of science. Doubtlessly the student will recognize that there are different motivations present in the two disciplines, that the tactics and strategy within the two pursuits will differ, and that the two disciplines perform different functions in a society. Despite differences, unity can be restored by realizing that literature and science are together human endeavors, that each is something men and women do. Although the two pursuits may seem to differ, differences are seen to stem more from goal and function than from basic variations in their pursuers.

One or more courses derived from the social sciences are generally required in each of the years of the secondary school program. This practice follows the conviction that all students should be given some sense of the nature and value of the inheritance—which they did not achieve, but which they must help maintain—as well as some understanding of that principle of continuity with the past that is possible only through the study of the past. There is no way to maintain that perspective, that sense of proportion essential to good citizenship, without some understanding of the forces that have gone into the making of the age in which the student finds himself. Furthermore, students deserve a scholarly introduction to the goals and values, the organization and the processes, the problems and conflicts in the political structure, the economic life, and social relationships existent in the society of which he is becoming increasingly a part.

If it is true that science is that human endeavor that seeks to describe with ever-increasing accuracy those events and circumstances that occur in nature, it would seem that there would be a close similarity between this human endeavor and the attempt to describe phenomena arising from the interactions between and among men. Equally clear-cut phenomena should arise in the two domains—social and natural—and the pursuit of adequate descriptions of the two sets

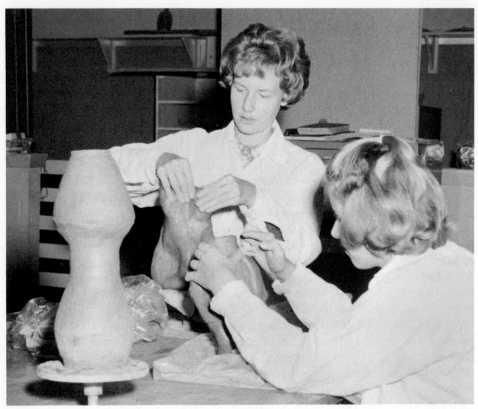

of phenomena would evolve along quite similar lines. But such has not been the case, and students experience sharp transitions as they move between their classes in the natural and social sciences. Much of the abruptness of these transitions stems from the basic restrictions applied to the teaching of the social sciences, in contrast to the heralded freedom permitted the teaching of the natural sciences. In the natural sciences, the investigator is not only permitted but also required to identify with equal clarity each of the events and circumstances that accompany or precede the occurrence or existence of a phenomenon. Not so in the social sciences. Whole areas of social events and circumstances exist in a domain of "controversial issues" and the social scientist or the social-sciences teacher knows that the description of any social phenomenon must proceed with caution, if it is to be permitted to proceed at all, when a truly accurate and complete description must touch on relationships between the event that is being described and certain ethical, religious, or economic events and circumstances—events and circumstances that impinge sharply on the interests of influential persons or groups in the community.

270

FIGURE 2. Ringing bells to mark changing from classroom to classroom does not insure that students coming from widely diverse activities will automatically switch their minds to the topic a science teacher has in mind to teach.

Of all human endeavors, it is probable that history, sociology, geography, psychology, and the other social sciences will experience the longest delay in being pursued within as they are pursued outside of the classroom. For example, the methodology of history is today much, much less clearly defined than are the methods of science and the boundaries of, say, sociology, delimit its domain much less exactly than do the boundaries of physics delimit the domain of physics. For these and other reasons, students coming into natural-science classes immediately from social science classes can continue to expect differences in their roles as students of the two subjects. Because of these differences, students who enjoy success in their social science courses may become particularly frustrated and dissatisfied with the content and goals of their natural science courses. In turn, there will be students who, although they fail to be stimulated toward intense intellectual participation in their social science courses, may rise to relatively high degrees of success in their natural science courses. Perhaps a clear-cut discussion of the differences in the spirit, structure, and function of the natural and social sciences will ease transition of students between courses in the two disciplines.

At least in theory, a student's transition between classes in science and in mathematics should involve no great problem. When mathematics is defined as that human endeavor which seeks to describe with ever-increasing accuracy those quantitative relationships inherent in the universe, mathematics becomes a discipline quite similar to the discipline of science. An oft-quoted definition of mathematics, however, identifies it as an endeavor in which the practitioner does not know what he is talking about nor does he know whether what he is talking about is true. In general, science teachers complain about the difficulty with which students transfer their achievements in mathematics courses to their performance in science courses, and many facets of this difficulty may stem from instances in which the science teacher assumes that his students have been taught mathematics courses consistent with the former of these definitions, whereas the teachers of the mathematics courses have embraced the latter definition.

Students of the pursuit of mathematics can be expected to exercise the ability to analyze a concrete situation into its elements, to synthesize components into a related whole, to isolate and select relevant factors, defining them rigorously, meanwhile discarding the irrelevant; and the ability to combine these factors, often in novel ways, so as to reach a solution. These abilities resemble quite closely many of the powers of the mind that are exercised in the pursuit of science, and it seems that this resemblance could serve as a bridge whereby students may pass easily between classes in science and mathematics. Perhaps it is differences in the kinds of concrete situations being analyzed together with differences in relevancy that places obstacles across such a bridge. The mathematician insists that the situations to be analyzed can be created entirely from the intellectual activity of the human brain and that these situations can be purely abstract, totally apart from any real, concrete, segment of nature. Relevancy in the analysis of a mathematically derived situation depends solely upon consistency with the established set of presuppositions. In other words, the mathematician retains the freedom to subject any set of postulates to a sequence of logical inferences. His postulates may or may not be true or consistent with those of another mathematician's, but he remains true to the spirit of mathematics, consistent with its methods, and complementary to its function so long as any conclusions he derives are logically consistent with his postulates.

When a student moves abruptly from a mathematics class to a science class, it becomes necessary for him to sense subtle differences between the two disciplines in the origins of episodes. Although science tends to operate within a smaller number of generally agreed upon postulates, they receive much less direct attention; in fact, a student in science may proceed through several years of study before he senses any use of postulational thinking.

Especially if the student is enrolled in a college preparatory program, his course of study will include classes in a foreign language. It is the intent of such classes to develop the ability to understand and speak the language in daily living situations, to read the language without conscious translation, and to write acceptably those things that he has first mastered orally. Students acquire these abilities through exercising audiolingual skills either accompanied or followed by practice in free reading and writing.

Only the specially gifted teacher of a foreign language is able to develop with his students very profound comprehension and appreciation of a language as being anything beyond a means of communication. Although many teachers hope their students will gain insight into another culture through study of its language, just as the science teacher hopes that the vocabulary of science will be recognized by the student as a key to its comprehension and appreciation, neither of these hopes seems to be automatically achieved by having students enroll in the usual courses. In both cases the teacher must make overt efforts to interpret the culture through its language or vocabulary. Another goal of foreign language instruction is to illuminate English both in syntax and vocabulary. Obviously, the science teacher finds many opportunities to help students make the transition between classes in a foreign language and in science by citing instances wherein the root meanings of words can be invoked.

The factor that causes the most difficulty for the most students as they travel between classes in science and in foreign language will probably always stem from the relatively greater use of sheer memorization in foreign language classes. The dutiful student, who enjoys mastery of a foreign language by exertion of efforts whereby vocabulary and syntax are memorized, will be extremely frustrated in a science course in which he must exercise the wider array of the powers of mind that are exercised in the pursuit of science. This hazard should be identified and clarified early in science courses as one more effort to ease the abrupt transitions that students must make as they move from one to another of the classes included in their total daily programs.

Although seldom required to do so, students are encouraged to include one or more courses in the arts in their daily programs. The arts, like languages and mathematics, are forms of intellectual communication, in fact they constitute an almost universal form of communication. Not only do the arts provide sustenance for the inner man but they also provide a method for utilizing ideas, concepts, techniques, and materials from all other human endeavors. Furthermore, the arts provide a direct method of fostering and cultivating creativity.

A student coming into a science class from a class in one of the arts may regret the abrupt transition from actually dabbling in an artistic pursuit to taking on a much less dynamic role in the science class. Almost from the very start of a course in the arts, the students are expected to exercise their minds and hands in actually being an artist, regardless of how naive they may be. Only rarely are courses in these disciplines arranged with the early sessions devoted to laying a groundwork of basic ideas or the development of a basic vocabulary or array of fundamental skills. Teachers in the arts devote only a small fraction of their time to exhibition of the works of great masters, and when they do so it is to help the novice bend his own efforts to produce something of which he will be proud.

To observe students at work in arts classes provides one of the greatest endorsements of the point of view (1) that each discipline holds intrinsic means of motivating its students, (2) that students respond to the satisfactions inherent in exercising their minds in the pursuit of the discipline and (3) that, through such exercise, the students advance rapidly toward proficiency in the actual pursuit of the discipline.

Health and physical education classes are included in the daily programs of many public school students. Although many opportunities arise in which the contents of these courses can be readily correlated with the content of science courses, students seem to experience no sharp difficulties when they move between classes in science and in physical education.

Unfortunately, the limited number of classes permitted the student in the four years of secondary school all too often require him to choose between rather than combine classes in science with classes in home economics or business or technical education. Strong cases can be

FIGURE 3. Some segments of the teaching profession involve their students in full pursuit of the human endeavor being taught.

made for including in their programs classes that seek to prepare young people for effective home and family living, classes which have as their goals the provision of an awareness and understanding of the motives, organization, and interrelationships between business, government, and society, and classes that give their students the skills they need in technical vocations and occupations.

When students do move between science classes and classes in one or more of the vocations, the greatest hazard seems to be that they will encounter a change in the general climate of opinion regarding the two areas of human activity. Unfortunately, vocational education in too many schools carries a second-class status. When this situation prevails, it is up to the science teacher to do what he can to restore dignity to productive, creative, and constructive efforts be they basically intellectual or manual in nature.

Again, the science courses included in a student's daily schedule are only one of the many parts of his total educational program. It is possible for the student to integrate these parts on his own, but the need for some kind of integrative process is felt. The concept that each subject of the school program derives from a human endeavor can be a valuable integrative theme, and especially so if teachers in the separate departments adjust their pedagogical strategy to the subtle differences in the spirit, structure, and function of each of the major human endeavors.

For Discussion and Further Study

1. Is there a significant problem in the fact that only the ringing of class bells marks the transfer of a student's mind from one to another discipline?

2. What special consideration should be given to the student who does very well in other subjects but achieves no satisfaction in his science courses?

3. In what respects is the pursuit of science similar to other human endeavors? Is the spirit of science antagonistic to the spirit of any other human pursuits?

4. How can the science teacher join forces with teachers of other disciplines so as to achieve common goals?

5. What is the significance of the large fraction of college students who change their majors at least once during the four-year college program?

References

1. William R. Carter, in Francis D. Curtis. *A Third Digest of Investigations in the Teaching of Science.* Philadelphia: P. Blakiston and Sons Publishing Co., 1939, pp. 136–37. Used by permission of McGraw-Hill Book Company.
2. F. S. C. Northrop. *The Logic of the Sciences and the Humanities.* New York: The Macmillan Company, 1948, p. 361.
3. William Whewell. *History of the Inductive Sciences.* London: John W. Parker, 1847, p. 351.
4. René Descartes. *Rugulae ad Directionem Ingenii,* 1629. Quoted by the Rand Coporation, *Scientific American,* **198** (March 1958), p. 28.
5. Herbert Spencer. *The Genesis of Science,* 1854. Quoted by the Rand Corporation, *Scientific American,* **198** (January 1958), p. 22.
6. Harvard Committe. *General Education in a Free Society.* Cambridge, Mass.: Harvard University Press, 1945.

18

On Teaching Methods
in General

The complete enquiring classroom would have two aspects. On the one hand, its materials would exhibit science as enquiry. On the other hand, the student would be led to enquire into these materials. He would learn to identify their component parts, detect the relations among these parts, note the role played by each part, detect some of the strengths and weaknesses of the enquiry under study. In short, the classroom would engage in an enquiry into enquiry.[1]

Joseph J. Schwab 1962

There is no evidence in the data given . . . that high-school pupils acquire skill in scientific thinking as a necessary by-product of the study of scientific subjects as at present taught. It would appear from these results that ability to think scientifically is a complex of a number of component abilities and that these develop at varying rates and differently in different communities.[2]

Elliot R. Downing 1933

If resourcefulness is really one of the qualities upon which success in life is founded, then we should present more problems involving resourceful activity in our class room teaching, our quizzes, examinations and tests. . . . If experience is one of the foundations of resourcefulness, then good training in the schools should include many experiences with actual objects, in varied fields of activity, related as frequently as possible to actual situations of practical living. The solution of simple perplexities gives training for more complex dilemmas.[3]

Robert O. Beauchamp and Hanor A. Webb   1927

Extensive reading of general science apparently of itself serves to give some training in scientific attitudes; but such gains as may thus be secured are inconsiderable as compared with those made when definite instruction in scientific attitudes is given.[4]

Francis D. Curtis   1924

A given method which to one teacher may be of great value, may lose much of its value in the hands of another teacher, especially if that teacher believes that a different method is better.[5]

George W. Hunter   1921

Data . . . indicate that specific information, which is represented by exercises requiring the naming of animal structures, is most quickly forgotten; that information of more general application is more permanent; and that during the 15-month period there was no loss in the ability of students to apply important zoological principles to new situations, or to interpret data obtained from experiments. If these results are substantiated by further investigations, it is clear that the permanent results of the college education are not the specific items of information recalled, and that the organization of courses and the development of examinations should center around those objectives which are found to have more permanent value in college education.[6]

Ralph W. Tyler   1930

The bulk of the evidence . . . indicates that the ability to recall and the ability to infer . . . are different abilities.

278

*The only group of students . . . who could infer a fair
number of generalized science principles from rather typical
general-science situations was the upper 25 per cent in
intelligence.*[7]

Ralph C. Bedell 1934

*Many of the theories in science are being taught as facts
by many of our best teachers. Teachers as well as pupils
fail to distinguish clearly facts from theories. . . . Many
teachers tend to propagandize their material when there
is no specific evidence for the statements they make. Teachers do not consciously attempt to develop the characteristics
of a scientific attitude. If pupils have acquired these characteristics, it has come by some process of thinking or
experiences outside of the science classroom.*[8]

Ira C. Davis 1935

*In so far as aims are a criteria of actual work being done
. . . teachers of junior-high-school science are doing their
work better and with more understanding than teachers
of the senior high school. Teachers of neither level show
much evidence of humanizing science through the development of an appreciation of the work of scientists. Teachers
of the upper level seem to be held more closely by convention and college requirements, there appearing to be little
relationship between the major aims of the two levels.*[9]

George W. Hunter 1931

*The science teacher gets his job done only by what he
induces, motivates, cajoles, inspires, forces, or challenges
his students to do, and to do in such a way that they
"learn." The misuse or overuse of certain methods is one
of the hazards that students have to face. The skillful
teacher will have many offerings in his repertoire and will
employ . . . a melding of approaches that help students
develop their own powers of learning, their own insights,
perceptions, and increasingly sophisticated understanding
of science as content, as process, as attitude, as part of the
cultural heritage, and as a socioeconomic vector.*[10]

Robert H. Carleton 1963

All who seriously study the history of education in our times must agree that, although it may be long ere we can cry Eureka! Eureka! *of an ideally perfect system, recent experience justifies the assertion that we shall hasten the advent of that desirable time if we seek to minimise the didactic and encourage heuristic teaching; for the progress made of late, which is very considerable, is unquestionably due to the introduction of heuristic methods and exercises. . . . I first came across it [heuristic teaching] in an eminently suggestive paper by Professor Meiklejohn, one of the most valuable by far of those read at the International Conference on Education held in connection with the Health Exhibition at South Kensington in 1884. Heuristic methods of teaching are methods which involve our placing students as far as possible in the attitude of the discoverer— methods which involve their* finding out *instead of being merely told about things. It should not be necessary to justify such a policy in education. Unfortunately, however, our conceptions are blunted by early training or rather by want of training. Few realize that . . . discovery and invention are divine prerogatives, in some degree granted to all, meet for daily usage: consequently, that it is of importance that we be taught the rules of the game of discovery and learn to play it skillfully. The value of mere knowledge is immensely over-rated and its possession over-praised and over-rewarded; action, although appreciated when its effects are noted, is treated as the outcome of innate faculties and the extent to which it can be developed by teaching scarcely considered.*[11]

Henry E. Armstrong   1910

The fundamental characteristic that is common to both children and science is that both are actively involved in interpreting the objects and events of the environment.[12]

Gerald S. Craig   1958

Especially for the new teacher, the problems of how to meet the immediate needs of organizing ones classes and handling the paper work that goes with teaching may loom large. In fact, there will be those new teachers who feel so bogged down by the multiplicity of housekeeping details or the apparent rebellious noncooperation of the students in some schools that they will wonder if teaching the pursuit of science is any significant fraction of what they are on a payroll to achieve.

How to solve these kinds of problems is more within the domain of other courses ordinarily included in teacher-training programs, particularly the general principles of teaching and educational or adolescent psychology. The importance of finding solutions to these problems does, however, justify devoting some space in this book to them.

Much of the paper work for which classroom teachers are responsible stems primarily from such sources as (1) the necessity for the school to know who its students are and where they are at any time during the school day and to report these data to whatever central agency dispenses the funds upon which the school operates, (2) the need to know who a school's teachers are, their qualifications and where they can be reached during the school day, (3) the need to maintain and be ready to present to authorized persons or institutions a record of courses attempted and completed by each student and the grade received during each marking period as well as final grades, and (4) the need to maintain inventory control of all equipment, materials, and supplies owned by the school and to be able to replenish or supplement them when needed. In addition to these primary sources of paper work, there are always the unscheduled memoranda regarding the peculiar problems of individual students, requests for cooperation with various community projects, and the more or less officially sanctioned but always abundant student social, civic, and athletic events.

How an individual teacher sets out to take care of his paper-work responsibilities depends, obviously, on his attitude toward same. This attitude can range from acceptance of this responsibility as a fact of the profession to looking upon it as aggravatingly antagonistic to what the teacher wants and feels he should be doing.

In general, for reasons not at all peculiar to the teaching profession, the new person stands a better chance of becoming an influential member of his group if he meets his paper-work responsibilities pleasantly, promptly, and as accurately as the briefing instructions permit. This does not mean that he should delay indefinitely exercise of his right—nay, duty—to protect his classes from needless intervention and interruption. The hazard is that administrative officers tend to equate a teacher's ability to handle paper work with the degree of judgment reflected in all of his professional opinions and suggestions. And griping about his paper work responsibilities seems to be an oft-recurring factor in the syndrome of the less than competent teacher, an observation complicated by the high probability that the true genius in the profession can also wax quite eloquently when discussing paper work before the usually sympathetic audience to be found in the teachers' lounge. Administrative officers, in turn, can seldom avoid subtracting from their opinions of the genius' total value to the school whatever they feel it costs to have to do or redo his paper work themselves. For these reasons, it is not sheer preachment to encourage new teachers to meet their paper-work responsibilities as pleasantly as possible.

To meet these responsibilities promptly is next to impossible unless some degree of orderly procedure is established. The effort to establish an orderly system should begin at the briefing sessions customarily held for new teachers prior to officially opening the school term. At these sessions, the new teacher is shown and told how to process such items as enrollment cards, daily program cards, locker assignment forms, excused absence slips, unexcused absence slips, library permits, hall passes, to-the-nurse passes, unauthorized absence report form, textbook inventory form, and whatever other forms deemed necessary to get the school organized and underway. Perhaps it is not so with the exceedingly well-self-disciplined new teacher, but the usual person comes from these briefing sessions overwhelmed rather than properly enlightened. This confusion can be somewhat avoided by completing a sample of each form as it is presented, either asking for specific situations or, if the session is too foreboding, by trying to create or imagine a situation in which each form would be the right one to use.

The calendar provides an excellent ordering device to take the new teacher's confusion out of his paper work responsibilities. Despite apparent disorder, each piece of paper is to be used at a predictable time of the day, week, month, or year. This time can be noted on the sample form and then a "to-do" schedule prepared accordingly. Unless he is blithely ignorant, each teacher realizes that he will be under pressure that first day when the school becomes populated. The need to take care of the paper work can easily become submerged by feelings of greater need to make a good impression on the students with whom the teacher knows he must work and live for the next nine months. Unfortunately, the two needs may be vitally interlocked.

Almost immediately upon meeting their new teacher, students start asking in one way or another whether or not he is in command of the situation, whether or not he knows his way around this business of being a teacher. Despite his mastery of his subject and enthusiastic urge to get on with teaching it, to proceed confidently to get the scheduled paper work out of the way may be the best thing the teacher can do as phase one of establishing a "good" impression. Few established teachers, however, deny the urge to greet their new classes with something more in keeping with the spirit, structure, and function of the subject they teach.

Many new teachers fall into the trap of admitting to their students that they know not which forms were actually the ones referred to by the public address system reminder and therefore need help. True, there will always be the sympathetic student who does know his way around the school who will volunteer the needed help. The outcome of this is obvious, painfully so to the supervisor who so many times has seen the potentially gifted new teacher be cast from the profession by that thoughtless, misguided fraction of any school population who persists in requiring each new teacher to prove himself against the archaic "hickory-stick" image.

An equally dangerous hazard exists for the new teacher who has been told, "Come see me if you really want to learn how to handle the paper work." The hazard lies in the antecedent of the "me." Invariably, in contrast to the all too often misleading "self-appointed supervisor," there is someone whose professional status and official reason for being in the organization hinges on how accurately and promptly this work is done. To be aware of the hazard should be adequate to cause any normally intelligent new teacher to proceed accordingly.

Although the new teacher feels he has been told much about classroom management, especially discipline, he often finds, upon confronting his first classes, that he has learned little. He soon becomes a candidate for that school of opinion the members of which extol the individuality of each teacher and each group of students. These people toss off a teacher's ability to conduct a class with the sloganistic apology: "He either has it or he doesn't." The inference is that "it" is some mystic, genetically controlled pattern of traits and skills. Actually there are many traits and skills that any teacher can adopt which prevent or dissolve discipline problems. Similarly, there are also traits and behaviors that will arouse or otherwise contribute to the delinquency of any teacher's classes. The new teacher who stays always within the bounds of human dignity and common courtesy, who always maintains the poise of the well-groomed and appropriately dressed person, has working for him the greatest possible advantage. True, the new teacher may remember fondly the "dear old Mr. Chips" of his own student days and realize how often this person flaunted each of these restrictions, but mark the adjective "old."

To return to the central theme of *Teaching the Pursuit of Science,* teachers can find within the spirit and structure of science ways and means to avoid and dissolve discipline problems. It is a rare class that cannot be captured by a puzzling event or circumstance, the members of which are so undisciplined that they cannot be caused to observe it, that are so utterly devoid of cerebral endowment that they are totally unable to associate what they see now with what they may have seen in time past. Ironically, at the same time it avoids some kinds of problems, this pattern of teaching invokes its own kind of discipline problems. Problems stemming from boredom, lack of intellectual stimulation, and nonrecognition of the significance of instruction are avoided or diminished. In their place will arise the confusion of multiple conversations and verbal battles being waged to defend one against another point of view. Many established teachers recoil briskly from tentative efforts to do this kind of teaching because their repertory of discipline techniques and strategies has been accumulated on a spinal core of the "I give—you take" concept of teaching. If these teachers would stay with this participation-stimulating pattern of teaching until they gain experience in its administration, they would develop equally effective discipline procedures even though their students were participating in their classes with much more spontaneity and enthusiasm.

The key to discipline is control. Either the students must be doing what the teacher planned and expected them to do, or the teacher must leave the impression that he expected the students to do what they are doing. If a teacher presents an event or circumstance that is intended to introduce ultimately a segment of science, it is axiomatic that his students observe what the teacher does. Thus the teacher's instruction can well be: "To give everyone a chance to exercise his ability to observe things, will each of you write down each thing you see happen that you think is related to the main event." This instruction not only is pedagogically sound but, more importantly, it maintains an orderly climate in the room and, while the students are recording their notes, the teacher gains a few minutes to put his wits in order.

When the hypothesis stage of the lesson is reached, again order can be maintained by such an instruction as: "Rather than blurting out and spoiling the lesson for your classmates, let's take five or so minutes to write down the best guess we can come up with regarding what we have seen." To summarize the point being developed here, when the teacher moves toward thought-stimulating, student-participating procedures, it becomes increasingly necessary for him to invent increasingly astute class management and control tactics. When the teacher arouses advanced intellectual exercise, he should be ready to invoke equally advanced pedagogical strategy.

For a final note on discipline, the new teacher must realize that nearly every class will enroll a few students who will not respond to courteous, poised, and dignified treatment. It is no sign of weakness to call on the "office" for help in dealing with these students and this should be done before the new teacher tries in clumsy fashion the kinds of last-resort discipline measures that can be taken by disciplinary officers.

The teaching profession has always been portrayed as placing upon its practitioner a heavy burden of lessons to be prepared, examination papers to be graded, conferences to be held with students and parents, and all manner of other time- and energy-consuming demands. And the profession can be what this image suggests. It is up to each teacher to budget his time and energy and assign to each demand no more than its due. Teachers soon learn how relentlessly tomorrows come and tend more and more to using their time to prepare for tomorrow rather than to mark yesterday's papers or read last week's laboratory reports. It cannot be denied that four or five hours a day in the exhilaratingly demanding environment of the classroom is mentally and physically exhausting. Assuming a teacher does this kind of teaching, he should be permitted to use student readers for quiz papers and for laboratory reports, laboratory assistants for assembling and storing equipment, and do only as much of this kind of work as is necessary to stay in touch with the appropriateness and effectiveness of his teaching.

To summarize, from the time a teacher greets the students entering his home room and on through the morning classes, the lunch hour, the afternoon classes, and the ubiquitous "overtime" conferences and meetings, the successful teacher radiates competence and the ability to take things in stride. This means not that he must be aggressively domineering, but simply that he knows what his duty and responsibilities are and is sufficiently well organized to meet them as they come. He is accustomed to maintaining courteous, poised, and dignified relations, but is well enough aware of the ways of the world to be not unduly upset when he is faced with the crude, inelegant, even assaultive behavior of which the offspring of his fellowmen are capable. He learns to separate himself from such as promptly as possible and to return to the satisfactions that come with starting new generations of young people along their pursuit of science. The experiences gained day by day quickly become adequate to eliminate many of the conditions that threaten to restrict the success of his classes and occasional glimpses of how to do things well are gradually developed into polished procedures. With this maturity, the teacher lingers longer in the hypothesis phase of teaching, because he knows that his students need not be convinced every day that he is competent, that he is in command, and that he knows his way not only in this school but in the pursuit of science.

Any one lesson in science begins with a clearly defined segment of the pursuit of science which has been chosen by the instructor or designated by a course of study as the target for the day. The instructor knows the total perspective from which the segment has been selected and its relationship to other segments.

Being familiar with the characteristics and abilities of his students, the instruction which has preceded or will follow this lesson, and the time schedule and other physical limits imposed upon the lesson, the instructor plans how he will approach the target for the day. These plans include a reasonably accurate budgeting of time to each phase of the lesson.

Few students enter a classroom or lecture hall with their minds already at work on the topic upon which the instructor has planned the day's lesson. Students who are sufficiently docile will drop the topics and thoughts which occupied their minds on their way to the classroom, open their notebooks, be visibly oriented, and have their minds apparently enmeshed with that of the instructor before the echoes of the class bell are lost in the hallways. In contrast to this type of student behavior, however, instructors know that many students will continue to think about the things they were talking about on the way to the classroom until something of greater interest captures their minds. The ends to which any instructor should go to expedite "mind capture" are, of course, dictated by the circumstances of any one teaching-learning event. There are no exceptions, however, to the necessity of having "mind capture" occur in order to insure the efficiency of the teaching-learning event. Mind capture, either overtly or inadvertently, must be accomplished during the opening phases of any lesson.

Beyond the point of the preceding paragraph, nothing equally arbitrary can be said about the sequence of the phases of any one lesson nor is sequence inferred in the order chosen to discuss the phases likely to occur as a lesson unfolds or evolves. Mark these verbs, *unfolds* or *evolves*. Sooner or later, the students must recognize clearly the segment of the pursuit of science upon which the lesson is based. As the lesson evolves, the natural phenomenon, laboratory skill, tactic of investigation, or whatever the instructor has set for his goal of the day, must stand out clearly within all supporting, enriching, or other pedagogical activities.

At any time during the action of a lesson, the instructor must be ready to equate his goal for the day with the characteristics and aims of the discipline of which his course is a part. The sense here is not that the instructor is to justify his course as an educational enterprise but to increase the efficiency with which his subject is taken up by his students. This increase in efficiency is to be gained by not only reviewing the characteristics and aims of whatever branch of science is involved but also seeing these factors reflected and illustrated in specific episodes, events, or circumstances.

Ideally, the presentation of the lesson remains consistent with the structure and methodology of the subject being taught. Under the worst possible conditions, teaching methods and the structure of the lesson would be contradictory to the spirit and structure of the subject. For example, to impose upon a class the end products of an investigation without sooner or later inviting evaluation of the evidence upon which these end products are based would surely contradict the spirit of science, and be not at all consistent with the usual sequence of events in the pursuit of science.

Efficiency of instruction is influenced sharply by how similar the classroom approach to a segment of a discipline is to the approach of that segment within the discipline itself. To cause a phenomenon to be exhibited within the classroom, for example, insures reality at least up to the point of interacting, preceding, or consequent phenomena. Actual, meaningful practice in a skill is more realistic than watching others perform the skill. Conducting a self-initiated investigation anticipates the reality of the pursuit of science far more efficiently than does plodding through an exercise conceived and planned by someone else.

Progress toward achievement proceeds most efficiently when advancement can be measured. In teaching the pursuit of science, tests and examinations serve this purpose and must be included in planning any teaching-learning event. As stated earlier in connection with the characteristics and aims of science, an instructor must be ready to equate the intellectual or manual performance he seeks on a test or examination with the performance expected from a scientific worker in the laboratory, field, or library. Of course, to do this requires the instructor to be competent in designing, administering, and interpreting an array of different kinds of evaluation devices and procedures. The efficiency with which evaluation is done depends, in many cases, upon the instructor's ability to isolate individual intellectual processes and design exercises within the limits of a teaching-learning situation, which reliably measure his students' performance of these intellectual processes. Ideally, these exercises show valid correlation with out-of-classroom performance.

Closely related to the "mind-capturing" phase of a lesson is the "mind-extending" phase. Just as science is a knowledge generating process, if a lesson imparts one segment of the pursuit of science, the germs of new, related segments should arise within the minds of the students. Thus, a lesson begins by linking a new segment of science to segments already familiar, and closes by pointing toward segments yet to be explored. The body of the lesson identifies relationships and interrelationships and their immediate and ultimate consequences.

The efficiency of any instructor in any teaching-learning situation is influenced by his ability to choose the most appropriate lesson plan and format. To possess a wide repertory of possible plans and formats is, therefore, a very useful advantage for any teacher. The array that appears in this book has been gleaned from many teachers. It is assumed that each reader will examine these examples and create adaptations that are in keeping with his own concept of the teaching-learning phenomenon and the grade level and subjects in which he tends to specialize.

All lessons, however spectacular they may be, owe their basic value to how much they contribute toward mastery of the spirit, structure, and function of the discipline of which they are a part. It is to this point that the following section is devoted.

For Discussion and Further Study

1. How can a teacher capture quickly the attention of his students in a manner that is consistent with the pursuit of science?

2. What obvious and subtle symptoms distinguish the teacher who teaches in a manner that is true to the spirit of science from the teacher who may give only lip service to the nature of science and the characteristics of scientists?

3. What are the assets and liabilities associated with the use of metaphors or "black boxes" to teach the logic and procedures of science? How can these pedagogical aids improve upon the use of actual episodes in science?

4. Are motivation problems best solved by basing lessons on (1) the skills, attitudes, and information needed by citizens to perpetuate the state, (2) the social, personal, civic, or economic needs of individuals, (3) the psychology of the learning process, or (4) the interest that seems to be intrinsic to the pursuit of science?

5. What kinds of examination questions or items complement versus compromise the spirit, structure, and function of science?

References

1. Reprinted by permission of the publishers from Joseph J. Schwab and Paul F. Brandwein, *The Teaching of Science*. Cambridge, Mass.: Harvard University Press, Copyright 1962, by the President and Fellows of Harvard College. Pp. 54–56.

2. Elliott R. Downing, in Francis D. Curtis. *A Third Digest of Investigations in the Teaching of Science*. Philadelphia: P. Blakiston and Sons Publishing Co., 1939, p. 279. Used by permission of McGraw-Hill Book Company.

3. Robert D. Beauchamp and Hanor A. Webb, in Francis D. Curtis. *Second Digest of Investigations in the Teaching of Science*. Philadelphia: P. Blakiston and Sons Publishing Co., 1931. Used by permission of McGraw-Hill Book Company.

4. Francis D. Curtis. *A Digest of Investigations in the Teaching of Science*. Philadelphia: P. Blakiston and Sons Publishing Co., 1926, p. 115. Used by permission of McGraw-Hill Book Company.

5. George W. Hunter in Curtis, *ibid.*, p. 59.

6. Ralph W. Tyler in Curtis, *A Third Digest of Investigations in the Teaching of Science*, Philadelphia: P. Blakiston and Sons Publishing Co., 1939, p. 307. Used by permission of McGraw-Hill Book Company.

7. Ralph C. Bedell in Curtis, *ibid.*, p. 73.

8. Ira C. Davis in Curtis, *ibid.*, p. 273.

9. George W. Hunter in Curtis, *ibid,*, p. 203.

10. Robert H. Carleton. Adapted from an editorial, *The Science Teacher*, 30 (October 1963), p. 10.

11. Henry E. Armstrong. *The Teaching of Scientific Method and Other Papers on Education*. London: The Macmillan Company, 1910, p. 236.

12. Gerald S. Craig. *Science for the Elementary-School Teacher*. New York: Ginn and Company, 1958, p. 2.

19

Lesson Formats and the
Spirit and Structure
of Science

*The artistry of teaching science is dependent on how skill-
fully the teacher blends several of the methods into a
unified teaching lesson. The nature of the lesson, the personality and goals of the teacher, the climate of the class,
and the interests and needs of the students will determine
the ultimate selection and utilization of appropriate teaching methods in science.*[1]

Nathan S. Washton 1961

*At the earliest level of instruction, the individual needs to
learn how to observe, how to figure, how to measure, how
to orient things in space, how to describe, how to classify
objects and events, how to infer, and how to make conceptual models. These capabilities he will use all of his
life.*[2]

Robert M. Gagne 1963

*It is well known that specialists scorn the idea of special
techniques in science instruction. Hidden behind micro-*

scopes, or atom-smashers, or lost in their test tube forests, they believe that if a teacher "knows his material" well enough, or if he has written much, or has made a reputation for original research, he is ipso facto a good science teacher. These are false assumptions.[3]

Kenneth B. M. Crooks   1958

The most successful teachers are often those who let the students behave as practitioners of a given discipline.[4]

Thomas G. Aylesworth   1963

To magnify thought and ideas for their own sake apart from what they do . . . is to refuse to learn the lesson of the most authentic kind of knowledge—the experimental— and it is to reject the idealism which involves responsibility. To praise thinking above action because there is so much ill-considered action in the world is to help maintain the kind of world in which action occurs for narrow and transient purposes. To seek after ideas and to cling to them as means of conducting operations, as factors in practical arts, is to participate in creating a world in which the springs of thinking will be clear and ever-flowing.[5]

John Dewey   1929

To spend too much time in studies is sloth; to use them too much for ornament is affection; to make judgment wholly by the rules is the humor of a scholar. They perfect nature, and are perfected by experience, for natural abilities are like natural plants, that need pruning by study; and studies themselves do give forth directions too much at large, except they be bounded in by experience. Crafty men condemn studies, simple men admire them, and wise men use them, for they teach not their own use; but that is a wisdom without them, and above them, won by observation.[6]

Francis   Bacon   1625

Whereas the most visible end-products of lessons in science revolve around purveying information, practicing skills, or identifying relationships, teaching the pursuit of science includes additional responsibilities less tangible to describe but none the less important. These intangibles carry various labels. One instructor will say, "I want my students to get the feel of science," and another, "Students should know the spirit of science." The negative approach is reflected when failure on the part of a student is attributed to the student never realizing what the laboratory is for or never seeming to grasp what it was that kept the Curies in their laboratory, that gave Jenner the courage to try his vaccination on a human being, that restored the patience with which Gregor Mendel carried on his cross-pollination studies, or, in general, whatever it is that drives a man or woman in the pursuit of science.

Some teachers believe that these intangibles can be taught. Others say they must be caught. In either case—taught or caught—few teachers can enjoy the satisfactions which come with complete success unless they feel that these intangibles are taking shape in their students.

To cause students to achieve the intangible goals of the pursuit of science may require extemely subtle methods. Overt methods to teach the spirit of science, for example, may be less effective than to expose the student to environment which is pervaded by the spirit of science in action. Nonexistence of a formula or equation whereby an instructor can assay the spirit that prevails in his classroom does not allow him to proceed as though he were not responsbile for creating or influencing the subtle attitudes toward science that gradually form in the minds of his students. If not the instructor's, whose responsibility is it? Is there a phase of the educational enterprise, for example, more adequate to transmit the spirit of chemistry to young people than a course that specializes in chemistry? Similarly, should the physics instructor defer to historians and philosophers an appreciation of the cultural climate in which physicists, Galileo and Oppenheimer, for example, sometimes find themselves?

An instructor as he plans or executes a lesson may gain valuable guidance by asking himself: Will I be willing to have the overall climate of my classroom, lecture hall, or laboratory contrasted with the spirit that prevails wherever science is being pursued?

What should determine the order or structure of a lesson? When planning a lesson, what framework will allow a segment of the pursuit of science to unfold or evolve most efficiently? Are some frameworks more likely than others to radiate the spirit of science? In approaching these questions, consider briefly the major frameworks that have been either inadvertently adopted, overtly fabricated, or otherwise evolved within the science teaching profession.

The simple chronological order in which nature's events and circumstances have captured and held man's curiosity provides an obvious framework for a science course and its component lessons.

In some situations, instructors are encouraged to use as the core of their lessons the skills, abilities, attitudes, and information which are held to be required by a citizenry to perpetuate the state. This is one of several attempts to encourage instructors to look outside their individual disciplines for pedagogically determined methods or procedures.

The needs of the specific group of students being taught are sometimes claimed to be an appropriate skeleton to be furnished with whatever segments of a discipline hold greatest promise of meeting these needs. This point of view has been subjected to quite divergent interpretation. In general, however, needs are more likely to have social, economic, or personal connotations than the simple need to achieve learning.

The psychology of the learning event has been explored by some instructors in their search for the most efficient plan or scheme for a lesson. They argue that if there is order or structure in the learning process itself, such order or structure should dictate the scheme and sequence of a lesson. If the would-be learner, for example, learns isolated units less efficiently than when these units appear in meaningful episodes, this suggests that the mastery of vocabulary or basic skills cannot be "got out of the way" before really approaching a topic or block of subject matter.

Finally, the previous paragraph suggests another type of framework upon which a lesson may be planned and presented. Sheer logic can suggest how a lesson is to be designed. If an episode in the pursuit of science appears, for example, to consist of the step-by-step contributions of many individual scientists, a series of lessons would cover the total episode with each lesson featuring one or more individual scientists. A second and more arbitrary example would assume that the mastery of a block of subject matter boils down to the accumulation of a specific vocabulary. Individual lessons would be devoted to sheer vocabulary drill. A third and less arbitrary example might be based on the belief that any episode in science consists of clear-cut steps— statement of a problem, gathering data, forming an hypothesis, experimenting, stating a conclusion, for example, and each lesson would reflect the identity of one or more of these steps.

For at least three reasons, namely (1) the absence of valid data proving that any one lesson structure is more efficient than any other, (2) the rugged individualistic nature (sometimes invoked as academic freedom) that is so characteristic of the teacher, and 3) the widespread differences in the skills, attitudes, and information involved in the pursuit of sicence, no single lesson structure should be held to be either sacred or evil, universally intellectually superior or pedagogically

inferior. Instructors should know and be able to exploit the potentialities of any framework upon which a lesson can be planned, and, in
a similar vein, recognize its limitations and not allow them to unknow-
ingly set limits to the instructor's efficiency.

The important thing is that a lesson has a well-ordered structure
and that the instructor be ready to have the structure he chooses for
any lesson be subjected to the best that is known about the psychology
of the learning process, and examined to determine whether it parallels
or contradicts the structure, tactics, and strategy of the pursuit of
science.

Increasing attention is being given to the use of teaching aids by
instructors at all levels of the educational enterprise. In many cases,
models, charts, slides, and other flat or motion pictures can decrease
markedly the amount of time needed to bring a segment of the pursuit
of science before a group of students. The same comment applies to
the use of natural-history specimens or similar items actually involved
in the topic of any lesson.

In effect, the value of any teaching aid is determined by how
efficiently it brings a phenomenon into the classroom, triggers or brings
data to bear on hypotheses, clarifies the design or interpretation of
experiments, aids in the validation of conclusions, or portrays the
immediate and ultimate impact of man's understanding of the phenomenon. Many of the available teaching aids can be adapted to cause
them to serve the desired purpose. The lack of appropriate aids for
the teaching of many phenomena, however, challenges the inventiveness of the science teaching profession.

The not-always-ill-advised parody—"by their tests and examinations
shall instructors be known"—introduces the final phase of lesson planning. How an instructor expects to measure progress toward achieving
what he hopes to accomplish holds two significant items. His evaluation
techniques must be consistent with those techniques that measure the
pursuit of science, and he must be ready to equate what he hopes to
accomplish with the hoped-for accomplishments of science. If, for
example, to establish the relationships among a set of observations is
closer to the true aim of science than to simply accumulate these
observations, an examination question that requires the student to
identify a relationship would be more easily defended than one that
simply requires him to recall isolated observations.

The preface of a remarkably pertinent little booklet, *You and Your
Students*[7] says:

In the Massachusetts Institute of Technology [and in many other educational institutions at all grade levels] there are many excellent teachers. For
the most part, these men have gained their ability as teachers by hard
individual work, by a deep interest in their students' progress and welfare,

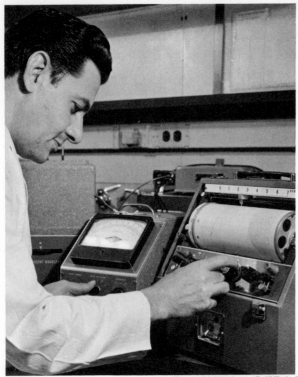

FIGURE 4. It is the recurring pattern in the procedures they use that provides a unifying theme for the widely diverse investigations of science.

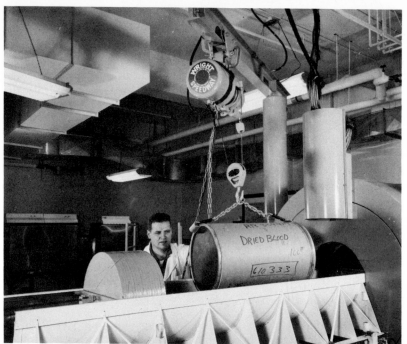

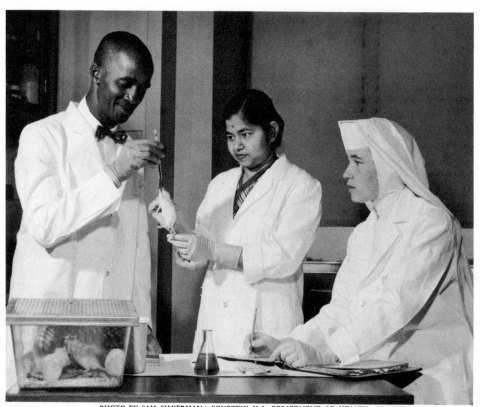

and usually over a long road of individual experimentation and development. Good teachers are made, not born. Yet how few of us regularly spend even one per cent of our annual professional time deliberately studying the mechanism of teaching—with a view of self-criticism and self-development. In the long run, such time is well spent, and it repays itself many-fold in improved efficiency and in actual time saved.

The repertory of lesson formats that follows is presented in exactly the same spirit as was *You and Your Students*. The repertory "is not intended as a formula to tell experienced and successful teachers how to teach. Rather it is an effort to distill from their success those principles which have a recognized soundness, and to set these down in an orderly fashion as a starting point for further development and improvement."[8]

For Discussion and Further Study

1. Does the point of view expressed by the quotation from Crooks in the introduction to this chapter have significance for teachers below the college or university level?

2. Are teachers justified in claiming to nurture the development of traits or skills the development of which cannot be measured?

3. How far should a teacher go in attempting to stretch his personality to include in his repertory lesson formats for which he feels no inherent fitness?

4. What advantages and disadvantages accompany encouraging a teacher to specialize and thus become especially proficient in a single type of science lesson?

5. Is there a tendency for whatever teaching aids are available to establish the kinds of lessons a teacher presents? What are the implications of this for the designers of teaching aids?

References

1. Nathan S. Washton. *Science Teaching in the Secondary School.* New York: Harper & Row, 1961, p. 228.
2. Robert M. Gagne. "The Learning Requirements for Enquiry," *Journal of Research in Science Teaching,* 1 (Spring 1963), pp. 144–53.
3. Kenneth B. M. Crooks. "Suggestions for Teaching the Scientific Method," *The American Biology Teacher,* 23 (March 1961), pp. 154–59.
4. Thomas G. Aylesworth. *Planning for Effective Science Teaching.* Columbus, Ohio: American Education Publications, 1963, p. 9.
5. John Dewey. *The Quest for Certainty.* Quoted by the Rand Company, *Scientific American,* 198 (June 1958), p. 24.
6. Francis Bacon. *Essays 50. Of Studies,* 1625. Quoted by the Rand Corporation, *Scientific American,* 205 (November 1961), p. 48.
7. Massaachusetts Institute of Technology. *You and Your Students.* Cambridge, Mass.: The Institute, 1950.
8. *Ibid.*

20

The Straight
Lecture-Discussion

The control group was exposed to the conventional lecture method. Reading and interpretation of the textbook by the lecturer took up part of the lecture time for the experimental group. . . . The experimental and control groups showed no significant differences at the 5 per cent level, for the Cooperative Physics final test, and for the final grade in Physics.[1]

Haym Kruglak   1955

On the basis of achievement as measured by percental attainment, *by* lasting impression *on the minds of elementary school pupils, by* persistence in memory, *by* encouragement of independent thought and self reliance, *and by* popularity among the pupils, *the three methods rank* . . . experiment method, lecture method, book method. . . . *Since the experiment and* lecture *methods approach each other in so many respects, either may be profitably used. Each produces good results.*[2]   **Jacob E. Mayman   1912**

If one objects that it is easy to feign attentive listening while the mind can dwell on remote idylls, the objection can be minimized if the lecturer requires his audience to respond mentally to rhetorical questions, if he uses transitional words and phrases effectively, and/or if he requires his audience to take notes based upon his presentation. . . . To equate physical passivity with mental inactivity is to admit ignorance of logic, semantics, and psychology.[3]

Melvin P. Heller   1962

In the lecture *method the teacher imparts to the learner by word of mouth the knowledge which the former possesses and the latter lacks.*[4]

Elliot R. Downing   1936

A lecture is defined as an extended, formal discourse for the presentation of knowledge. It is the dominant instructional method in college and university teaching. It is used less often for the less mature students of the secondary school. In fact, the two adjectives "extended" and "formal" become decreasingly applicable to what is basically the lecture method as it is used in the secondary and elementary school years.

In keeping with the above definition, almost any kind of discourse on any kind of knowledge becomes a lecture. Sometimes even the sermon is defined as a lecture on one's conduct or duty.

Strengths and Weaknesses

Because of its widespread usage, the effectiveness of the lecture format in any one instructional situation is very likely to be influenced by the audience's prior experiences with the use of the format. The novice and amateur teacher almost automatically adopts the lecture method. It is the method toward which the least dedicated teacher may gravitate, and yet inspired teachers often reach their greatest heights by mastering this method. Fond memories of famous teachers, especially at the collegiate level, invariably involve a spellbinding lecturer whose efforts were fascinating adventures either because of their intellectual content or dramatic presentation.

The lecture invokes active intellectual rather than physical participation on the part of the student. Some students who are more accustomed to having their physical rather than their intellectual participation exercised tend to become restless and inattentive until they come to accept the lecture format for what it is worth.

The lecture format places the instructor in complete control of the classroom situation. Students have only a minimum of opportunities to interrupt if they fail to comprehend or grasp what is being presented. The format assumes that the lecturer knows the verbal abilities of his students and their degree of prior sophistication in the subject matter of his lecture. If either of these assumptions is invalid, gross inefficiency will follow.

Effective lecturers claim they can stay attuned to failure or success in following their lectures by watching expressions on students' faces. This may be true, especially if the lecturer has developed this skill by repeatedly testing his students for their comprehension and retention of the materials of his lectures.

The lecture provides a way to present a closely knit and organized body of information in the least possible amount of time. Decisions regarding what to exclude, include, and emphasize can be made in advance rather than following the less predictable cases of a class discussion. The lecture provides an ideal opportunity to give perspective and integration to the outside reading, textbook study, laboratory activities, and other instructional procedures that may be used in the total course.

Somewhat counteracting the "perspective and integration" strength of the lecture format is the belief that learning is basically an individual assimilation affair. A lecture can be a perfect example of perspective and integration, but the lecturer can only hope that each student will be able to assimilate the material as it is presented or to reconstruct the lecture and assimilate its content by a more leisurely perusal of lecture notes.

The lecture has the well-established tradition of providing for the student clear-cut comprehension of what the lecturer believes is important. Wherein this tradition prevails, the lecturer takes upon himself a very significant function. His lectures must reflect the true dimensions of the discipline of which his lectures are a part. If properly exploited, this factor can render the lecture format very effective. On the other hand, if the lecturer has a limited concept of the total dimensions of his discipline, and his students realize that the examinations for the course are based solely on the lectures, the students will gain nothing more of the course than was possessed by the lecturer.

Illustrations of the point in the preceding paragraph can be gained from hypothetical approaches to a chemistry course. A lecturer might present the course as a series of lectures each dealing with the occurrence, preparation, properties, and uses of representative elements and compounds. Because of the recurrence of this scheme, his students would come to look upon chemistry as consisting simply of the occurrence, preparation, properties, and uses of elements and compounds. By repetition, this point of view could be firmly established in the minds of the students. The lecturer, however, might be criticized for presenting a limited concept of chemistry. To consider a contrasting example, suppose the instructor believed that episodes in chemistry have their origins in some puzzling event or circumstance in nature which arouses man's curiosity and leads him to elaborating tentative explanations. These explanations are subjected to some kind of verification, usually experimental. This verification leads to a precise description of antecedents and consequences of the originally puzzling event or circumstance. If students were to be subjected to a series of lectures each of which was prepared around this central theme, it can be argued that the students would come to accept the scheme itself as an essential feature of the total discipline of chemistry. This scheme, however, provides an almost unlimited framework for the lecturer to build his chemistry course on.

Examples and Illustrations

The first illustration of the lecture format is provided by a totally inexperienced, beginning teacher. He chose for his topic, "The Atomic Nucleus." Preliminary to the example cited here, this teacher presented a lecture consisting of listing the names and basic characteristics of the nuclear particles in the order in which they have been identified. The lecture followed quite closely the material dealing with this topic in the students' textbooks. Although the students realized that this lecture provided a good opportunity to contrast static descriptions of nuclear particles, the lecture provided little insight into the actual pursuit of science. Furthermore, there is little evidence to prove that students will retain this kind of information better when presented by the lecture method than by textbook study.

On this basis, the teacher was advised to prepare a second version of the same lecture but to attempt to have it reflect more of the total pursuit of science. A transcription of his second attempt provides the first example of the lecture format.

THE ATOMIC NUCLEUS

I'm going to talk today about a lot of unfinished business in science, particularly in atomic physics. There's been a lot of work done and discoveries made in this field, and a lot of work remains to be done. I'd like to illustrate just how some of these discoveries were made, so that you may see how a scientist goes about completing a bit of work, how he conducts his research. His work, naturally, is to explain a little bit better, a bit more exactly, what is happening in our universe—but never really reaching completion at least throughout the years covered in this lecture. There are always new and fresh questions.

Today scientists know a great deal about the atom and how it is put together. They need and want to know a great deal more. Fifty years ago, almost none of the current theories about the atom and its make-up was even dreamed of, and none of the information we have today about protons and electrons, about neutrons and atom bombs was known. To illustrate how all this knowledge came into being, let's look at the case of the positron. It is an excellent example of the procedure scientists use to push back the frontiers of the unknown and to explain hitherto unobserved phenomena. The procedure is basically this: The hypothetical invention of a theory, the experimental evidence to support the hypothesis; and a verification of the evidence as indicative of the theory being true.

In 1928 the atom looked something like this (diagram), and the behaviors of those known parts, the proton and the electron, were pretty well determined from a theoretical as well as an observational standpoint. But in this year, 1928, an English physicist and mathematician, P. A. Dirac, was working with a set of quantum equations dealing with the theoretical behavior of electrons. Everything was working out fine: the answers agreed with the observed behavior of the electron—except for one thing. Besides these answers, he got a set of negative answers, which didn't agree with the behavior of the electron at all. As a matter of fact, they indicated the possibility of a particle similar to the electron in mass and size, but of the opposite charge: that is, a positive charge. Now this was puzzling, because no one had ever seen any indication of a particle of this type at all, or even thought about such a possibility. After all, protons are positive and electrons are negative, and they neutralize each other in the atom, and why should there be another positive particle floating around to mess things up? Everything seemed so neat up to this time. A great many other workers in this field, physicists and mathematicians (Robert Oppenheimer was one) worked out Dirac's equations again, and sure enough, they got the same answer; but they didn't quite believe those results.

Now, in 1932, a physicist out at the California Institute of Technology was investigating cosmic ray phenomena in a Wilson cloud chamber. Cosmic rays have been much in the news lately, and you may know that they are radiations of a very high energy level that come from outer space. And a Wilson cloud chamber is a device for detecting the various types of subatomic particles. If a proton or an electron passes through a cloud chamber, it leaves a visible trail of white vapor, just like the vapor trails of high-flying airplanes, and these trails are distinctive for the type of particle involved. A proton, which is a much heavier particle than an electron, will leave a much shorter but thicker trace. If an electrostatic or magnetic field is put into the chamber, it will curve in a different direction than an electron, since it is positively charged and the electron is negatively charged. Anderson knew about all this, and he identified a great many proton and electron tracks in his cloud chamber photographs. He put lead plates into his cloud chamber to see what happened when electrons and protons struck them. On one of these photographs, he saw something he had never before observed. The picture looked something like this (diagram).

Anderson thought of several possible explanations for this picture: (1) A positive particle of small mass penetrates the lead plate and loses about two-thirds of its energy, (2) two particles are simultaneously ejected by the lead; a positive particle of small mass in one direction, an electron in the opposite direction, (3) an electron penetrated and left the plate, tripling its energy in traversing the lead. (4) the chance occurrence of two independent electron tracks so placed as to give the appearance of one particle traversing the lead plate. Anderson took more pictures of his cloud chamber and varied the circumstances in order to determine which one of these explanations was the right one. He came to these conclusions. Explanations 2 and 4 are to be excluded on a probability basis, and number 3 is disregarded because there seemed to be no reason that a particle would increase its energy by passing through a plate of dense metal. That left explanation 1. That a positive charge of small mass penetrated the lead plate and lost about two-thirds of its energy.

Anderson accepted this as the most probably correct explanation. It agreed with Dirac's equation, and therefore he expected it, or rather, half-expected it. Those people who had redone Dirac's work were astonished when Anderson published the results of his work. They duplicated his experimental conditions and came to the same conclusion. The existence of the positron was added to the store of knowledge of the atom. It is a positively charged particle comparable in mass and in magnitude of charge to an electron.

It is interesting to note that after the positron had been identified that several scientists, looking through their files of photographs, found cloud chamber pictures of cosmic rays which indicated the existence of positrons. There were probably reasons to account for their failure to recognize them, but Anderson must be commended as a scientist with enough imagination to interpret acute observations in a new manner.

It may be asked at this point: what happens when a positron and an electron unite? It appears that the positive and negative charges neutralize each other and the particles are annihilated leaving only energy in the form of radiation. This would be an example of the destruction of matter. It is also known that when high-energy radiation, for example that of cosmic rays, interacts with matter that the energy can be converted into a positron-electron pair; this is an example of the turning of energy into matter.

The positron suggests an interesting question: if the electron and positron can just disappear in the form of radiation, then, keeping in mind the role electrons and protons play in all matter, isn't it a pleasant accident that the electron and proton do not behave similarly. Why don't they just go away? Positron and electron pairs do.

The second illustration of the lecture format has been provided by an experienced instructor. It is a lecture used to introduce high school students to the study of genetics. A transcription follows:

GREGOR MENDEL (1822–1865–1884)

The origin of traits and their transmission to offspring has puzzled man almost from that instant when "transcending himself and nature, he left behind the animal forbears from which he sprang: [and] the questioning spirit of man was born."[5] How does one acquire the color of one's hair, the shape of one's nose, the number of fingers on a hand? In fact, whence the hand? Why not a flipper, a claw, or a wing?

Gregor Mendel marks one of the milestones in man's efforts to answer these questions. From the lowly garden peas which he so patiently tended in his Augustinian cloister garden, Mendel gained penetrating insight into things heretofore only dimly seen or vaguely hypothesized.

For example, a fable of the Burjats, a primitive tribe, tells us: "The striped chipmunk always collected nuts. One time the bear asked it for some of the nuts, with which request the chipmunk complied. In appreciation, the bear stroked the chipmunk thereby causing it to be striped."[6]

Aristotle about 330 B.C. wrote that: "Maimed parents produce maimed children; and so also lame and blind parents produce lame and blind children . . . such marks have often been handed down for three generations . . . the circumstances, however, are rare; and sound children are generally produced from lame parents; nor is there any complete certainty in these matters; and children resemble their parents or their grandparents, and sometimes they resemble neither."[7]

Less well known today but probably widespread during Mendel's time was the "Boxes in a Box" idea developed by Charles Bonnet (1720–1793). "Every female individual contains within her the 'germs' of all the creatures that originate from her, the one generation within the other, and thus, the first female of every species had contained within her, all the individuals of that species that have ever been produced and will be produced for the end of time."[8]

Although it is difficult to determine its effect on the work of Gregor Mendel, the ability of breeders and fanciers to select varieties of plants and animals toward meeting a predetermined pattern was a well-developed art and practice in his day. This also caught Charles Darwin's attention. Quoting Lord Summerville, who was speaking of what breeders have done for sheep, Darwin reports: "It would seem as though they had chalked out upon a wall a form perfect in itself and then had given it existence."[9] Although herdsmen and fanciers were very adept in using selection to establish their breeds, according to Darwin, all of them "are firmly convinced that the several breeds to which each has attended are descended from so many aboriginally distinct species. Ask, as I have asked, a celebrated raiser of Hereford cattle, whether his cattle might not have descended from Long Horns, or both from a common parent stock, and he will laugh you to scorn.[10]

Thus it would appear that while Charles Darwin was seeking to clarify his understanding of the origin of species in England, and we in America were caught up in our own affairs of the mid-nineteenth century, Gregor Mendel's mind could well have been racked with the idea so vividly reflected in Bonnet's "Boxes in a Box" theory, by instances leading him to both accept and question the transmission of acquired traits, and with the reshuffling of traits and characters which herdsmen and gardeners were doing in the domestication of their animals and plants. The transmission of traits from parents to offspring must have appeared to him as a combination of vague general influences and precise, almost mechanistic, determiners.

Mendel's experiments suggest that he knew how the pollen and egg cells form the link between generations of plants. Someone had taught him how to artificially cross-pollinate dissimilar varieties of the same or closely related species. He hypothesized that each character may exist in different forms or varieties, that each character is transmitted independently (he learned, however, that some dissimilar characters seem to be linked with each other), and that the determiner for a character may be totally suppressed (recessive) in one generation, but can be transmitted to an offspring in which, lacking a dominant determiner for an opposing variety of the character, it becomes fully expressive.

In designing his experiments, Mendel either consciously or otherwise chose to prove the existence and nature of his determiners by amassing an array of instances which would allow him to invoke a positive version of the canon that nothing is the cause of a phenomenon in whose presence the phenomenon fails to occur.

In the design of his experiments, Mendel followed the transmission of seven clear-cut characters by artificially cross-pollinating pea plants in which two varieties of each character were contrasted. For example, the seeds were either round or wrinkled, the endosperms green or yellow, the plants tall or short, etc. "Each two of the differentiating characters were united by cross-fertilization. . . . Furthermore, in all the experiments, reciprocal crossings were effected in such a way that each of the two varieties which in one set of fertilizations served as seed-bearer in the other set was used as a pollen-parent."[11]

Mendel harvested these seeds from his first generation crosses and when these were planted, he could observe "In the case of each of the seven crosses, the hybrid character resembles one of the parental forms so closely that the other either escapes observation completely or cannot be detected with certainty. . . . It was furthermore shown by the whole of the experiments that it is perfectly immaterial whether the dominant character belonged to the seed-bearer or to the pollen-parent; the form of the hybrid remains identical in both cases."[12]

In turn, the seeds which formed in these hybrid plants (self-pollinated) produced, when planted, a new generation. "In this generation there reappear, together with the dominant characters, also the recessive ones with their peculiarities fully developed, and this occurs in the definitely expressed average proportion of three to one, so that among each four plants of this generation, three display the dominant character and one of the recessive."[13]

Seed collected from the generation bred from the hybrids, when planted, produced a third generation. "Those forms which in the first generation (F2) exhibit the recessive character do not further vary in the second generation (F3) as regards its character; they remain constant in their offspring. It is otherwise with those which possess the dominant character in the first generation (bred from the hybrids). These two-thirds yield offspring which display the dominant and recessive characters in the proportion of three to one, and thereby show exactly the same ratio as the hybrid forms, while only one-third remains with the dominant character constant."[14]

By experiments such as these 287 hand pollinations on seventy plants for the hybrid cross and 5,123 self-pollinated plants for the F2 generation, Mendel gained complete confidence in his hypothesis that each characteristic is transmitted independently and that certain determiners capable of transmitting characteristics from parent to offspring exist in the pollen and egg cells.

Familiarity with mathematics helped Mendel interpret his experiments. To him, these character determiners showed the same behavior as is involved in an ordinary mathematical combination series. For example, if he combined wrinkled seed (a) with smooth seed (b), it became $(a+b)$ $(a+b)=aa+2ab+bb$. Thus one offspring would receive only wrinkled determiners, two would receive one for smooth and one for wrinkled, and one would receive only smooth determiners. He sensed the parallels between the numbers of different individuals be could observe in his garden when keeping track of two, three, or more characters simultaneously and combinations of terms which appear in a mathematical series. [Try this with $(a+b+c)$ $(a+b+c)$]. These data strengthened his faith in the accuracy of his hypothesis.

Mendel's papers remained unnoticed for thirty-five years. By the time of the rediscovery of his papers, so many other facets of research had matured that it is difficult to determine just how much impetus was added by the re-discovery of his work. Had the results of his investigations been publicly examined during that period in which scientists were so actively considering Charles Darwin's theories regarding the origin of species, we can theorize that both of these branches of the life sciences, evolution and genetics, would have moved forward much more rapidly than they did during the closing years of the nineteenth century.

In any case, the knowledge given us by Mendel enables us to explain and predict the transmission of any trait for which we can answer these questions: How many different kinds of genes for this trait exist in the total population? How many appear in any one individual, and how do unlike genes behave if they are combined in the same individual?

For Discussion and Further Study

1. Is the argument valid that inasmuch as the pursuit of science is an intellectual enterprise, each of its elements can be nurtured through an intellectually stimulating lecture?

2. Successful use of the lecture method assumes certain responses from students. Is this a valid statement and, if so, what hazards accompany the assumption?

3. How can a teacher determine whether or not students are participating in the lecture format as the instructor assumes they are?

4. What advantages and disadvantages accompany clear-cut separation of the lecture format from class discussion rather than combining the two formats?

5. What criteria distinguish the "spell-binding" lecturer from the kind who puts his students to sleep? Is the former type the ideal lecturer?

References

1. Haym Kruglak. "Instruction in Textbook Reading and Achievement in Elementary Engineering Physics at the University of Minnesota," *Science Education,* **39** (March 1955), pp. 156–60.
2. Jacob E. Mayman in Francis D. Curtis. *A Digest of Investigations in the Teaching of Science.* Philadelphia: P. Blakiston's Sons & Company, 1926, p. 30.
3. Melvin P. Heller. "Learning Through Lecture," *The Clearing House,* **37** (October 1962), pp. 99–100. Reproduced by permission.
4. Elliot R. Downing. *An Introduction to the Teaching of Science.* Chicago: University of Chicago Press, 1936, p. 126.
5. Lincoln Barnett and the Editorial Staff. "The World We Live In," *Life,* December 8, 1952, p. 4.
6. Hans Kelsen. *Society and Nature.* Chicago: University of Chicago Press, 1943, p. 145.
7. Aristotle. *The History of Animals.* Written about 330 B.C. Richard Creswell, trans. London: Bell & Sons, 1878, p. 188.
8. Erik Nordenskiold. *The History of Biology.* New York: Tudor Publishing Company, 1936, p. 245.
9. Charles Darwin. *The Origin of Species.* New York: Mentor edition, The New American Library of World Literature, 1958, p. 8.
10. *Ibid.,* p. 46.
11. Gregor Mendel. *Experiments in Plant-Hybridization.* Originally published 1865, and reproduced in W. Bateson, *Mendel's Principles of Heredity.* Cambridge University Press, 1902, pp. 322–23.
12. *Ibid.,* pp. 324–25.
13. *Ibid.,* p. 326.
14. *Ibid.,* p. 329.

21

The Lecture
as Case History
or Case Analysis

The theme of this paper is that the use of historical materials can serve as an effective means of achieving these desirable and important outcomes (scientific appreciations, attitudes, and interests) in high school science teaching.
. . . To show these students how scientists actually go about the complex task of finding new facts, organizing them, and testing hypotheses through experimental confirmation of predictions, several universities have explored the use of "cases." A "case" involves the critical study of the development of a major scientific concept . . . not only involves the final results of the scientific inquiry, but stresses the scientists who were involved, the information available to them, their search for better facts and explanations, and the intellectual and social climate in which they worked.[1]

Leo E. Klopfer and Fletcher G. Watson   1957

My interest in the history of science stems from the conviction that there is no better way for non-scientists to develop insights into the methods and impact of science than by careful analysis of the classical documents of scientific literature and a study of the intellectual and social context in which these documents are rooted.[2]

Auley A. McAuley 1958

The Conant case-history method and its emphasis upon the "strategy and tactics of science" (VS) . . . the contemporary problem-solving method . . . in which class arguments or discussions were initiated through such devices as newspaper clippings or challenging statements and questions in order to be scientifically resolved and evaluated with as much instructor-class planning as possible, and with individual experimentation.

. . . There were no significant differences between or among the methods in the two designs on the written scientific thinking test or on the outside criterion tests for science subject matter achievement.[3]

James S. Perlman 1955

Papers by scientists reporting scientific research have two major advantages as materials for the teaching of science as enquiry. One advantage is obvious. They afford the most authentic, unretouched specimens of enquiry which we can obtain. . . . The second advantage of original papers consists in the richness and relevance of the problems they pose for enquiry into enquiry. Each individual paper poses the problem of discovering its basic parts (problem, data, interpretation, and so on). Each poses the further problem of discerning the relations among these parts: why the data sought were the appropriate data for the problem; why the data actually acquired depart from the data sought; what principles justify the interpretation of the data. . . . Their full-scale use is appropriate for the curriculum aimed at identifying and attracting to science the student of original mind and a bent for frontier investigation—the potential fluid enquirer for whom we have great need.[4]

Joseph J. Schwab 1962

History has often proved the shortsightedness of the practical men and vindicated the "lazy" dreamers; it has also proved that the dreamers are often mistaken. The historian of science deals with both kinds with equal love, for both are needed; yet he is not willing to subordinate principles to applications, nor to sacrifice the so-called dreamers to the engineers, the teachers, or the healers.[5]

George Sarton 1952

308

THE CASE HISTORY

A key feature of the rationale underlying the case-history type lecture or discussion is the investment of the time available for a course in a few selected episodes in science rather than in a more superficial treatment of a greater number of episodes. This allows the instructor greater opportunity to identify the spirit in which the scientist worked, the tactics and strategy forming the structure of his procedures, and the immediate and ultimate relationships between his work and other facets of the total culture.

A case history begins with the selection of an episode in science. Although any episode can become a case history, the instructor will do well to choose those moments of discovery or invention for which there exists an adequately documented history. Furthermore, to give balance and scope to a course, episodes should be selected which are stellar examples of as many as possible of the characteristics and traits of scientists at work.

A case history can be introduced by reviewing or announcing the state of man's knowledge prior to the beginning of the selected episode. To economize on time, this phase is usually covered rather abruptly by citing a minimum array of the end products of prior episodes which form the background for the new.

The next phase requires very detailed treatment. Its purpose is to ferret out the precise events and circumstances that formed the clues leading to the new hypothesis or glimpse of a possible discovery or invention. Despite its extremely great significance to those who are beginning the pursuit of science, this phase is one of the most difficult to achieve. In all too many cases, the investigator has just plainly forgotten or failed to record the steps of the early phases of his investigation. His reports quite often omit the blind groping or unplanned coincidences from which arose a flash of insight. And yet many of these events are reproduceable and, as such, could easily become effective training exercises for young people who would pursue science.

At the same time that it is difficult to identify the events and circumstances that may have contributed to a flash of insight, this is an exceedingly interesting phase of the preparation and presentation of a case history. For episodes already buried in history, the search is likely to include occasional happy excursions into literature, art, politics, and other human endeavors. For recent episodes, this phase provides justification for very valuable visits to the laboratories of practicing scientists or, if more convenient, scientists can be invited into the classroom where "cross examination" can ensure that each student follows each step of the scientist's investigation, regardless of how tortuous it may have been.

During phase three of the presentation of a case history, the students are caused to examine closely the tactics and strategy reflected in the design, conduct, interpretation, and validation of whatever experiments or investigations are included in the episode. The importance of this phase in science teaching is comparable to the role of experimentation in the pursuit of science. In fact, all comments regarding phase two apply with added emphasis to phase three.

Instructors will vary widely in the degree to which they develop phase four, namely, estimating the immediate and ultimate impact of the episode. Those who shy away from subjective material will spend little time here. They, in effect, defer to the social scientists. Some scientists, on the other hand, hesitate to delegate this responsibility and, albeit hesistantly, are willing to take a fling at interpreting the cultural impact of an episode in science. Students invariably receive an interpretation which reflects the wisdom of an expert in science or in social science but seldom in both. The hazards are less if this interpreation is done by the scientist—assuming, of course, that the scientist proceeds under the same discipline with which he pursues science.

The final phase of a case history parallels the opening phase. Again by straightforward announcement, the students are brought up to date on what has been learned about the topic during the years following the episode that was featured in the case history. Although this phase seems to be considered necessary by students, it lacks the intellectual involvement of the preceding phases and, therefore, is given a minimum of time by some instructors.

Strengths and Weaknesses

The initial reception by students of the historical emphasis may be unenthusiastic if they are accustomed to looking on the history of science as nonessential garnishment for the basic content. In some cases, even fairly sophisticated science students are very naive in history, philosophy, and logic, and will encounter severe frustration in examining rather than simply accepting an episode in science. The instructor, in turn, is likely to become frustrated by the apparent inability of his students to grasp quickly the tactics and strategy underlying the episode.

Few fully developed case histories are available. Considerable time is required to compose an authentic case. Furthermore, something seems to work against the adoption of case histories by one instructor that have been worked up by another. In practice, in order to present a case history enthusiastically and with validity, each instructor needs far more saturation in an episode than is provided by the material actually presented to the students.

The case history approach is open to all of the criticisms that are leveled against any of the block-and-gap types of courses. Notwithstanding the complete inability to cover fully any branch of science in any one course, there are always those people who feel that the instructor should give equal time and attention to surveying many facets rather than treating in depth selected episodes. On the other hand, a few blocks of subject matter can become the firm foundations from which students on their own can explore the intervening gaps.

Properly executed, a case history provides an opportunity for students to rediscover, at least vicariously, scientific principles by retracing classical episodes. Concurrently the interrelatedness of all knowledge stands out in clear contrast to the oftentimes compartmentalized patterns of separate courses. Men of science become individuals; in fact, the case history approach almost invites dramatization to the point of glamorization.

Examples and Illustrations

The references at the end of this section particularly entry six,[6] provide good examples of case histories that have been developed for general education college courses. Some exploration in the use of case histories at the secondary school level has also been accomplished. References to these explorations are included.

Presented here is a case history as developed and taught by a teacher at the junior high school level.

WILLIAM HERSCHEL'S INVESTIGATION OF URANUS AND ITS SATELLITES

I. Introduction

A. *Background of William Herschel*

William Herschel was an 18th century English astronomer who was as skilled at making fine lenses as he was at observing the heavens.

It was the lens making that developed his curiosity about the distant stars and other bodies in the sky. For years, he studied and worked as an apprentice to a skilled lens craftsman until he became master of the art. This intent interest on the focusing power of his homemade lenses led him eventually to examine astronomical guides and other materials concerning the stars and the Solar System.

Herschel set up an observatory in his home at Bath, England and began to scan the heavens in the vicinity of known constellations or stars at periodic intervals in hopes of identifying double stars and nebulae previously unknown to man.

B. *State of man's knowledge before Herschel's discoveries*

From the astronomer's point of view several conditions concerning man's intellectual thinking were prevalent. These conditions were as follows:

1. From man's beginning until the 18th century, only six planets were known to be part of the Solar System.
2. The total number of known stars in the world did not exceed 3,000 according to the 18th century British Catalogue.
3. In examining 18th century texts one would find that more time was devoted to the study of the solar system than toward the study of stars. *Note*: The majority of lenses of the 18th century did not magnify greater than 270 power. These lenses were good for observing large objects like the sun, the six known planets, the moon, and a few occasional comets, but the lenses lacked the fine quality to examine thoroughly the distant and seemingly small stars.
4. There was very little known about the fixed stars beyond their relative positions in our sky and the fact that being at an enormous distance from our sun, they must be self-luminous. A very slight proper motion of certain stars amongst the rest had been detected and the existence of variable stars was also known.
5. Satellites were known to be heavenly bodies associated with particular planets.

II. Origin and Investigation of Two Related Hypotheses

A. *Discovery of Uranus*

There are no words which can more adequately express the ideas which run through the mind of a scientist during this phase of his discovery than the words of the discoverer of that event. Therefore, I submit these statements from the notes of William Herschel concerning his discovery of Uranus.

"On Tuesday, March 13, 1781 between 10 and 11 in the evening, while I was examining the small stars in the neighborhood of H Geminorum, I perceived one that appeared visibly larger than the rest. Being struck with its uncommon magnitude, I compared it to H Geminorum and the small stars in the quartile between Auriga and Gemini and finding it so much larger than either of them, suspected it to be a comet.

"The magnifying power used when I first saw the comet was 227. By applying higher powers (460, 932, 1536, 2010—6450), the diameter of the comet increased in proportion to the power while the diameters of the stars to which I compared it were not increased in the same ratio.

"March 19. It moves according to the order of the signs, and its orbit declines but very little from the ecliptic.

"April 6. The comet, appeared perfectly sharp at the edges and extremely well defined."[7]

The "comet" was observed all over Europe. Its orbit was computed by various astronomers and its distance from the sun was found to be nineteen times that of our earth. This was no comet but a new major planet. The discovery of the amateur astronomer of Bath was the most striking since the invention of the telescope. It had absolutely no parallel, for every other major planet had been known from time immemorial.[8]

B. *Discovery of satellites orbiting around Uranus*

Again, I choose to use the words of William Herschel in analyzing his discovery of the Uranus satellites.

"I had frequently directed large telescopes to this remote planet to see if it were attended by satellites, but failed for the want of sufficient light in the instrument I used.

"In the beginning of January 1787, I found that my telescope used as a front view gave much more light. On the 11th of January I selected a sweep which included the Georgian Planet, and noted down the places of the small stars near it. The next day two of these were missing. To satisfy myself I noted down all the small stars on the 14, 17, 18, and 24th of January, and the 4th and 5th of February, and though I had no longer any doubt of existence of at least one satellite, I thought it right to defer this communication till I could see it actually in motion. Accordingly, I began to pursue this satellite on February 7 at about 6 o'clock in the evening, and kept it in view till 3 in the morning of February the 8th and during those 9 hours I saw this satellite faithfully attend its primary planet and describe a considerable arc of its proper orbit.

"While I was attending to the motion of this satellite, I did not forget to follow another small star which I was pretty well assured was also a satellite.

"The first-discovered satellite, Oberon, is the farthest from the planet and I shall call it the second satellite; the last discovered, Titania, I shall call the 1st satellite."[9]

During an eight year period 1787–1794, Herschel discovered six satellites orbiting about Uranus.

1st satellite—the interior one of Jan. 18, 1790
2nd satellite (Titania)—the nearest old one of Jan. 11, 1787
3rd satellite—the intermediate one of Mar. 26, 1794
4th satellite (Oberon)—the farthest old one of Jan. 11, 1787
5th satellite—the exterior one of Feb. 9, 1790
6th satellite—the most distant one of Feb. 28, 1794.[10]

Note: Uranus was first called planet Georgium Sidus.

III. Impact of His Discoveries

William Herschel through his visual labors in scanning the heavens at regular intervals became the father of sideral astronomy. (Systematic study of the stars.)

With the advent of the discovery of Uranus, he made men think toward the possibility of other planets existing in space.

His method for discovering satellites has been applied to the discoveries of satellites (additional) around Jupiter, Uranus, and Neptune.

THE CASE-ANALYSIS APPROACH

The case-analysis approach has been given its identity primarily by the Intercollege Committee on the Evaluation of Science Objectives. This committee worked as a part of the Cooperative Study of Evaluation in General Education which was sponsored by the American Council on Education during the years following 1949. The quotations in this section are from the committee's report.[11]

The key feature of the case analysis approach is the examination of reported episodes in science in order to foster the:

1. Ability to recognize and state *problems*
2. Ability to select, evaluate, and apply *information* in relation to problems.
3. Ability to recognize, state, and test *hypotheses*
4. Ability to recognize and evaluate *conclusions*, *assumptions*, and *generalizations*
5. Ability to recognize and formulate *attitudes* and take action after critical consideration.

A second feature is reflected in the "opinion of the Committee that many of the basic activities essential to the development of the students' ability to deal with problems can be initiated by organizing textbook materials for this purpose."

Phase one of the preparation and presentation of a case analysis is, of course, the selection of a topic or block of subject matter.

Phase two attempts to help students "to discover and formulate problems from textbook selection [by presenting] an overview of the material before the students engage in its concentrated study."

Phase three proceeds to identify within the written materials key statements and ideas and to differentiate between simple facts and generalizations. In some cases the instructor must point out examples of these and establish the identifying characteristics of each. Concurrently, the student "has necessarily made some evaluation of the relationship of each piece of information to the problem."

A fourth phase is devoted to establishing the meaning of hypotheses and a recognition of the antecedents of their elaboration. Instructors will realize that as students read textual material, identification of the hypothesis stage may never occur unless prompted by instruction. This instruction needs be nothing more than advising the student to speculate as to plausible explanations, contrasting, perhaps, the hypotheses he formulates with those actually explored by practicing scientists.

Proceeding to another phase, the students are encouraged to trace the path whereby solutions to problems are established and conclusions stated. Questions are raised to determine how the end product is supported by evidence and whether it is consistent with and includes all of the available evidence.

During the final phase of a case analysis, new problems will be raised, those for which the answers are still unknown to the experts will emerge, and the students will begin to see how present knowledge in different areas of science is related.

With the completion of a case analysis, some instructors assume responsibility for and make overt effort to examine the changes in attitudes and behavior which should be the ultimate outcome of the study of the topic or block of subject matter. Pedagogically speaking, this is an area of teaching about which little is known for sure. "There is no evidence to indicate that an understanding of the meaning of scientific attitudes or even the practicing of them in the classroom or laboratory will insure their practice in situations outside the school or in other subject matter areas. It is probably true, however, that the more broadly and comprehensively they are dealt with in science courses, the more likely such carry-over will become possible."

Strengths and Weaknesses

One weakness of the case-analysis approach is its invitation to cause the instructor to impose a rigid pattern upon an episode in science. "Such an artificial procedure would be likely to destroy most of any advantages possessed by this particular approach and its avoidance is strongly recommended."

Because of the dogmatically compact nature of most textbook material, this approach requires supplementary and, sometimes, custom-written material. "A carefully selected popular article from the current literature has numerous advantages over textbook materials." For popular and semipopular journals, authors are permitted to devote many pages to a topic that must be treated in a paragraph in a text-book. In general, few instructors "would feel able to take the time to develop all our knowledge of the subject in this manner, even if adequate information for the purpose were available. But by a careful analysis of samples of the subject, some early and some contemporary, the students can gain an insight into how science operates that no other method provides."

Examples and Illustrations

Dressel and Mayhew provide well documented examples of the case analysis approach as used at the college level. The following example was developed and taught at the junior high school level by Nathaniel Hoff, Baltimore, Maryland.

HUBERTUS STRUGHOLD AND LIFE ON MARS

I. Introduction

Background of Hubertus Strughold

Hubertus Strughold, eminent aero-medical investigator and physiologist, has spent a lifetime of research in space medicine and related studies. Since 1949 he has been head of the Department of Space Medicine, USAF School of Aviation Medicine at Randolph Field, Texas. He was formerly Associate Professor of Physiology at the University of Berlin, Director of the Aeromedical Research Institute, Berlin, and Professor of Physiology at the University of Heidelberg. He is the author of some eighty scientific papers, and co-author of a textbook on the principles of aviation medicine.

Born at Westtuennen, Westfalen, Germany in 1898, Dr. Strughold studied at several German Universities, and served as a Research Assistant in the Department of Physiology at Western Reserve University, Cleveland, Ohio, and as a fellow of the Rockefeller Foundation at the University of Chicago. He received his Ph.D. at the University of Munster in 1922, and his M.D. at the University of Wurzburg in 1924.[12]

II. Origin and Statement of a Hypothesis

Man has been curious about his neighbors in space since time immemorial. Planets and heavenly bodies were worshipped as religious entities. The names of various gods were assigned to these heavenly bodies. Through the centuries man maintained many of these beliefs.

During the beginning of the seventeenth century, Galileo Galilei developed the first astronomical telescope. With the telescope at hand man again aroused his curiosity concerning the neighboring bodies in space. Extensive study of the heavens followed and from these studies man began to think of the possibility of life on other worlds.

Percival Lowell, an American astronomer, devoted his life to the attempt to prove that intelligent beings must exist on Mars. A number of books were written concerning his observations and beliefs.[13]

Other present day astronomers have devoted much of their work to the atmosphere, land and climatic conditions of the planet Mars. Outstanding among present day astronomers are: Japanese astronomer, Tsuneo Saheki; Dr. Earl C. Stephen of the Lowell Observatory; the Russian astronomer, Tikhoff; Estonian astronomer, E. J. Opik; Dr. Dean B. McLaughlin of the University of Michigan.[14]

Dr. Hubertus Strughold for the past twenty-five years has been examining life in the most complicated surroundings that support it on earth: in the high reaches of the atmosphere which have been made accessible to man only since the development of flight, less than a century ago.[15]

In studying Mars, man has noticed color changes on the planet throughout the year. Its colors range from red-yellow, green-blue to dark brown. In other words, the color system of the planet resembles the seasonal changes of the foliage on Earth. Man has noticed that the atmosphere of Mars lists nitrogen as the major component of the atmosphere, the atmosphere has very little water vapor, and the atmosphere is governed by extreme temperatures of 70°F to –95°F.

From his study of the Earth, man knows that lichens and bacteria are very hardy living material which can survive the most adverse conditions.[16]

Dr. Strughold probably juggled these thoughts around in his mind and then set up the hypothesis that *simple plant life such as lichens and bacteria on Earth possibly exist on the planet Mars.*

III. Investigation of His Hypothesis

In investigating his hypothesis of the possibility of the existence of simple plant life on Mars, Dr. Hubertus Strughold decided to begin an experiment based on some of the factual data pertaining to the atmosphere of Mars.

Dr. Strughold secured examples of simple plant life on Earth and attempted to have them survive under the conditions of a Martian atmosphere. Here is an account of this particular experiment:

"Bacteria have been made to grow and reproduce in a Mars-like atmosphere duplicated in a laboratory at the Air Force School of Aviation Medicine, Randolph Air Force Base near San Antonio, Texas.

"First results of the eight-month-old research project were reported to a symposium on Mars at Lowell Observatory, Flagstaff, Arizona. The living specimens, collected from desolate regions in the United States, are kept under conditions similar to those on Mars.

"The red planet has an atmosphere composed mostly of nitrogen and the pressure there is approximately equivalent to that in the earth's stratosphere some ten miles up.

"The water supply spreading from thin polar ice caps in the Martian spring is normally less than that found in earth's driest desert.

"Temperatures range from about 70 degrees Fahrenheit at noon on a summer day near the equator to 95 degrees below zero on a winter night.

"The bacteria-containing soils are kept in bottles filled with dry nitrogen. Organic materials in the soil are the bacteria's food, and their only water is a trace of moisture left in the soil. The Martian temperatures are simulated by keeping the samples overnight in a very cold refrigerator, then warming them up during the day."[17]

IV. State of Man's Knowledge

The state of man's knowledge concerning the planet Mars can be listed as follows.

1. The physical dimensions of the planet can easily be measured.
2. Markings of various colors have been observed via telescope.
3. The content of the Martian atmosphere has been partially determined. It is still under investigation.
4. Man's recent investigators have been unable to yield positive proof of the existence or non-existence of life on Mars though their studies tend to endorse the latter.

V. Impact of Strughold's Hypothesis

It is too early to conceive that Strughold's hypothesis concerning the possibility of simple plant life on Mars would launch a landslide of investigations concerning his work. However, since the publication of his book on the *Green and Red Planet* and the conduction of his experiments pertaining to his hypothesis, an independent study of Mars made by Dr. William M. Sinton has been brought into focus. Dr. Sinton in observing the wavelengths being absorbed by matter on Mars with those recorded for lichens on Earth, discovered through spectroscopic studies that their wavelengths are identical.

Since Dr. Strughold's experimental book, *The Green and Red Planet,* there has been an increase in the telescopic investigations of Mars, especially as to the water vapor and carbon dioxide content of the air.

For Discussion and Further Study

1. If total episodes in science have the educational value that is claimed for them in the quotations at the introduction of this section, why do textbooks contain so little of this kind of material?

2. How valid is the contention that today's students are interested only in today's explanations of natural phenomena?

3. Is there a significant hazard in the validity with which historians reconstruct the tactics and strategy that actually accompanied episodes in science? Perhaps the pursuit of science, in reality, is totally without pattern. Perhaps scholars "see" patterns because they look at science through a patterned perspective and, thus, impose an extrinsically derived pattern.

4. Is there an increasing tendency for the literature of science to report discoveries and inventions as complete episodes? Why do students report that it is easier to reconstruct an episode from the seventeenth or eighteenth centuries than it is to reconstruct a twentieth century episode?

5. Should science teachers defer to social science teachers' efforts to interpret the social and cultural implications of discoveries and inventions in science?

6. What assets and liabilities accompany use of the "block and gap" approach to designing courses in science?

7. How valid is the belief that students are turned away from the pursuit of science by courses that overemphasize the "calcified skeleton of fact" apart from the "sinew and muscle" provided by the history, logic, and philosophy of science?

References

1. Leo E. Klopfer and Fletcher G. Watson. "Historical Materials and High School Science Teaching," *The Science Teacher,* 24 (October 1957), pp. 264–65.

2. Auley A. McAuley. "Origin of the Cell Principle: An Example of the Growth of Scientific Knowledge," *Science Education,* 42 (February 1958), pp. 60–65.

3. James S. Perlman. "Scientific Thinking: A Basis of Organization for

Physical Science Laboratory Programs in College General Education," *Science Education,* **39** (October 1955), pp. 287–300.

4. Reprinted by permission of the publishers from Joseph J. Schwab and Paul F. Brandwein, *The Teaching of Science.* Cambridge, Mass.: Harvard University Press, Copyright 1962, by the President and Fellows of Harvard College. Pp. 73–78.

5. George Sarton. *A History of Science.* Cambridge, Mass.: Harvard University Press, 1952, p. xii.

6. Leonard K. Nash. *General Education in Science.* I. Bernard Cohen and Fletcher G. Watson, eds. Harvard University Press, 1952, pp. 106–110.

7. Philosophical Transactions of the Royal Society. *Account of a Comet.* London: The Royal Society, 1781, p. 492.

8. Constance Ann (Herschel) Lubbock, *The Herschel Chronicle, The Life Story of William Herschel and His Sister.* Cambridge University Press, 1933.

9. Philosophical Transactions of the Royal Society. *An Account of the Discovery of Two Satellites Revolving Round the Georgian Planet.* London: The Royal Society, 1787, p. 125.

10. Philosophical Transactions of the Royal Society. *On Discovery of Four Additional Satellites of the Gorgium Sidus.* London: The Royal Society, 1798, p. 47.

11. Paul L. Dressel and Lewis D. Mayhew. *General Education: Exploration in Evaluation, Report of Intercollege Committee on the Evaluation of Science Objectives.* Washington: American Council on Education, 1954, p. 102.

12. Hubertus Strughold. *The Green and Red Planet.* Albuquerque, N.M.: University of New Mexico Press, 1953.

13. Percival Lowell. *Mars and Its Canals.* New York: The Macmillan Company, 1908.

14. Willy Ley and Wernher von Braun. *The Exploration of Mars.* New York: The Viking Press, 1956.

15. Hubertus Strughold. *The Green and Red Planet.* Albuquerque, N.M.: University of New Mexico Press, 1953.

16. Willy Ley and Wernher von Braun. *The Exploration of Mars.* New York: The Viking Press, 1956.

17. "Bacteria Survive in Mars-Like Atmosphere," *Science News Letter,* **71** (June 29, 1957), p. 403.

22

The Lecture with Demonstration

Since we learn by doing, a good demonstration gathers the audience into vicarious participation with the experimenter. A good demonstration can be effective in maintaining student motivation and interest in the way in which physicists deal with natural phenomena.

A good lecture demonstration should (1) be carefully planned and tested beforehand, (2) be simple and clear (3) contain a minimum of "black box" components, (4) be constructed to a scale which will make it visible to every student in the audience or employ optical projection techniques for clear viewing, and (5) be skillfully presented. In addition, the experiment should not only give enjoyment to the audience but make the audience realize that the lecturer is enjoying himself.

. . . We must not abandon an instructional technique that, in skilled hands, offers to large groups of people a first-hand association with the rich content of physics.[1]

V. E. Eaton, C. J. Overbeck, and R. P. Winch   1960

. . . The "classroom demonstration" and the "laboratory experiment" have more in common than many science teachers suspect. Both can be contributory to much the same kinds of learning, they involve the same or similar kinds of materials, they involve nearly the same knowledge and skills on the part of the lecturer.[2]

Robert Stollberg   1955

. . . Lecture demonstrations provide unexcelled opportunities for students to watch physicists in action, to see how they think and operate (a) when they attempt to isolate particular phenomena for study, (b) when they try to identify causes, effects, and functional relationships, (c) when, confronted by puzzling situations, they make guesses, follow hunches and construct various hypotheses, and (d) when they have to choose among alternative theoretical possibilities.[3]

Harold K. Schilling   1960

When applied to groups of pupils of unequal mental capacity, the demonstration method is better suited for the presentation of information for relatively permanent retention than is the individual laboratory program. For the purpose of imparting to a group of pupils a scientific attitude and training in a method of attack on new problems, the demonstration method is equal, if not superior, to the laboratory method of instruction.[4]

W. W. Knox   1927

To win in the battle for interest, study the gentle techniques in the art of gaining attention. A part of the victory for the teacher rests in preparation—a professional attitude of working hard to bring interesting things, compelling experiments, and lucid demonstrations to the classroom.[5]

Elbert C. Weaver   1964

By definition, a demonstration is a planned manipulation of materials and equipment to the end that the students are able to observe all or at least some of the manifestations of one or more scientific

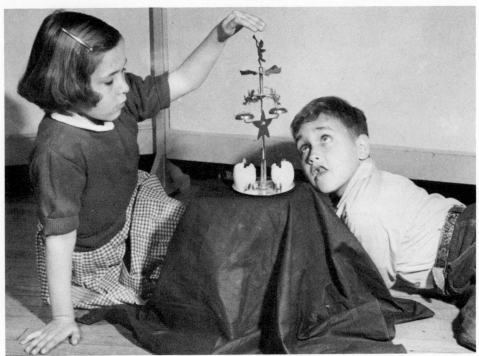

FIGURE 5. By choosing "apparatus" for classroom demonstrations wisely, concepts and principles developed in science classrooms will be inadvertently recalled or reviewed in the everyday activities of young people.

principles operating within a phenomenon. Within the limits of this definition, mere exhibits of things as illustrations of facts are not demonstrations. However, exhibiting an array of mineral specimens in order to show the relationship between cooling rate and crystal size can bring at least certain facets of one or more scientific principles before a class. The exhibit thus has some of the characteristics of a demonstration. The word as used in "the demonstration of a scientific skill" does not carry quite the same meaning as defined here.

Strengths and Weaknesses

In many instances, a demonstration can be the most efficient way to bring before a class the segment of the pursuit of science that is to be a day's lesson. Furthermore, if properly presented, a demonstration provides opportunities for the instructor to observe his students while they are performing many of the intellectual processes ordinarily held to be associated with the work of scientists.

Strictly speaking, the exercises many teachers carry out when they say, "Now we are going to do an experiment," can be properly identified as demonstrations. The term *experiment* should be reserved for procedures to obtain information not readily available otherwise.

The validity with which a phenomenon is revealed is the most important single criterion in establishing the value of a demonstration. If, for example, a lesson involved the movement of the pseudopods of amoeba, and the instructor chose to demonstrate the behavior of a drop of mercury upon being touched by a chromate crystal in a dilute solution of nitric acid, the instructor must be ready to contrast the similar behavior as observed in an organic versus inorganic system. If both instances hinge upon surface-tension phenomena, the demonstration would be a valid one.

Hazards are encountered whenever instructors attempt to demonstrate phenomena which are basically nonmaterialistic by using obviously materialistic models or other apparatus. The apparent repulsion of a bombarding neutron by an atomic nucleus provides a good example. A model using steel balls in a magnetic field can illustrate the concept, but can never bring before a class the actual phenomenon. Instructional efficiency in such cases demands that the students understand that a concept is being illustrated and not that a phenomenon is being demonstrated. This need not detract from the pedagogical efficiency associated with the use of models.

Those demonstrations are most efficient that cause students to encounter phenomena in such a way that the same intellectual processes are exercised as those that were used in the original identification and description of these phenomena. This assumes, of course, that these intellectual processes retain current relevancy within the pursuit of science. Any instructor during a demonstration should be ready to identify the process of inquiry that are to be exercised by the participation of his students.

Although different demonstrations suggest different sequences with which they will be accomplished, an ideal demonstration proceeds through several phases. It presents an array of observations that, if accurately made, suggest hypotheses that can be fed back into the demonstration to prove their consistency with observations. This process continues until it terminates in an accurate description of the scientific principles operating within the phenomenon being demonstrated.

Examples and Illustrations

The following example, in one form or another, has been a standard demonstration almost ever since Priestly used it to clarify some of the properties of his newly discovered "airs." Basically it consists of permitting something to burn in a limited volume of air under conditions such that the pressure of the confined volume of air is maintained approximately equal to atmospheric. The version cited here allows a candle to float on water until a bottle or flask is inverted over the candle.

This demonstration as presented in a junior high school general science class provides an example of the demonstration-centered lesson.

Teacher: Observe closely while I do a rather simple demonstration. *(Perform the demonstration.)*

Now, after drying the candle and shaking the water from the flask, I will repeat the demonstration. But this time write down in the order you see them happen, each thing that you think might be related to the up or down movement of the candle in the bottle. *(Repeat the demonstration.)*

Let us now compare our individual lists of observations to see if they are complete and accurately recorded. Jimmy, will you read your list.

Jimmy: 1. Bubbles.
       2. Why did the candle drop to the bottom of the dish when the flask was put over it?
       3. The candle started to rise.
       4. The water started to come up into the bottle.
       5. The candle began to grow dim and finally went out.
       6. Soon after going out, the candle and water stopped rising in the flask.

Teacher: Are there any additional observations which should be recorded?

Students: 1. The floating candle tended to move to the side of the dish while you were waiting to put the flask over it.
       2. Smoke formed in the flask when the candle went out.
       3. Fog collected on the inside of the flask.

Teacher: Now let's look at our observations one by one to see if they have been made accurately and recorded properly. How about No. 1, Bubbles? Jimmy, can you state that as an observation?

Jimmy: When the flask was put over the candle, bubbles, came out.

Teacher: Now about Observation No. 2. It is now a question. How should it be stated?

Jimmy: When the flask was put over the candle, the candle dropped to the bottom of the dish because the flask was full of air.

Teacher: Wait a minute. All we are doing now is recording our observations. The "because" part will come later. Now how about Observation No. 3?

Student: I think the water came into the bottle, Observation 4, before the candle began to rise.

Teacher: That's the way I saw it so unless there is disagreement, we will revise the order of these two observations. How about Observation 5?

Student: I think the candle quit rising immediately when it went out.

Teacher: How about this observation? Since there seems to be general uncertainty, I will repeat the demonstration once more so that you can recheck the accuracy of not only this but all of your observations. *(Repeats demonstration.)*

Jimmy: I was right. The candle started to rise, continued to rise while growing dim, and did so even after it had gone completely out.

Teacher: So it did. Now consider the three additional observations.

Student: I don't think the first of these had anything to do with the rise of the candle because the demonstration hadn't really started when that observation occurred.

Teacher: That is reasonable. How about the other two? So far as we know now, they may or may not be important.

Student: Why did the smoke and fog appear?

Teacher: I think you will see why later, but I have a definite plan for today's lesson and would like to stick to it. Now will each person write the best explanation or guess as to why the candle did what it did. (*Note: In actual practice, many illogical replies will come up which can be abandoned by using appropriate questions to show their lack of logic. Only the more logical responses appear here.*)

Student: The candle went down to the bottom of the dish because the air in the bottle did not allow the water on which the candle floated to come into the bottle.

Teacher: Can someone suggest an experiment that will strengthen or weaken this tentative explanation?

Student: If you repeat the demonstration but don't light the candle you can at least see whether the burning of the candle had anything to do with it.

Teacher: This we will do (*with obvious results*). Now what is the next observation to consider?

Student: I think we should consider the bubbles and they came out of the bottle because the heat from the candle raised the temperature of the air causing it to expand.

Teacher: Again, this sounds logical. Can someone suggest an experiment to strengthen or weaken this idea?

Student: Simply heat the sides of the inverted bottle with a Bunsen burner to see if more bubbles come out.

Teacher: This we will do (*with obvious results*).

Student: I think the candle began to rise, floating on water coming into the bottle to replace the oxygen consumed by the burning candle.

Student: But the burning of the candle produces carbon-dioxide and water, and I should think they would take up as much space as the oxygen did.

Student: But maybe the carbon dioxide was dissolved in the water, at least some of it, and the water vapor condensed into much less volume on the sides of the flask.

Teacher: We seem to have a logical hypothesis shaping up, but let me raise one more question. Why did the candle continue to rise after the candle stopped burning?

Student: First, the candle stopped burning because it consumed as much of the oxygen from the air as it could. It continued to rise after it went out because the air inside the bottle began to cool, thus diminishing its volume and allowing atmospheric pressure from outside the bottle to force more water up in the flask.

Teacher: To summarize, the level of the water inside the flask and hence the position of the floating candle is determined by the volume of air inside the flask. Two factors influence the volume of air. First, its temperature, and, second, the per cent of the oxygen consumed in the burning of the candle and the volume of gaseous combustion products. To increase the temperature of the air increases its apparent volume. To decrease its temperature would decrease its volume. Oxygen removed from the air would decrease the volume; carbon dioxide and water vapor added to the air would, assuming they were not removed by condensation or solution, increase the volume. In some cases, we find two or more things, sometimes with opposite effects, acting concurrently. How can we improve our tentative description of the behavior of the candle?

Student: We would need to make quantitative observations of each factor. We would also need to determine for sure exactly what gases are produced by the burning of the candle and find out whether or not they were soluble.

Thus we see how this demonstration leads into additional investigations. Up to this point, it has brought before the students phenomena in which such factors are operating as the relationship between temperature, volume, and pressure of gases; the composition of the atmosphere; and the nature of the combustion products of hydrocarbons.

In retrospect, because the demonstration was presented the way it was, the students were encouraged to make accurate observations, determine their relevancy, and to state them clearly. Tentative hypotheses were elicited from the students and the validity of these hypotheses estimated by projecting them against additional questioning based on their observations. The students were given experience in designing experiments, the results from which could be used to strengthen or abandon tentative hypotheses. Finally, the best explanation available upon the basis of information at hand was summarized and those students for whom it would be an appropriate exercise were encouraged to move ahead toward a more precise explanation of the phenomena.

A second example of the demonstration format illustrates the practice of encouraging the students to derive data from what the teacher does and then develop relationships and understanding from these data. The topic featured in this lesson is the relationship between the radius or diameter and volume of a sphere. The lesson begins by presenting two oranges and announcing that the radius of the larger is two inches and of the smaller, one inch. The teacher has asked the students to suggest how the quantities of juice that might be obtained from the two oranges would compare. Various suggestions were presented and the lesson begins.

Teacher: Let us now determine by calculation what is most probably the correct response. If we assume that both oranges are truly spherical and that the yield of juice is actually directly proportional to the volume of the oranges, can we not calculate the volumes of the two oranges?

Students: By substituting first 2 and then 1 for R in the formula $V = \frac{4}{3} \pi R^3$ the volumes of the two oranges can be calculated.

Teacher: How do the two calculated volumes compare?

Students: Approximately as 32.5 to 4.2, or 8 to 1.

Teacher: Now let's see if we can develop a general rule that will provide a more direct approach to the relationship between the volumes of two spheres of different radii. Let's designate the volume of the large orange by V and its radius by R. Similarly, designate the volume of the small orange by v and its radius by r. What would be an expression of the relationship between the volumes of the two oranges?

Students: $\frac{4}{3} \pi R^3$ divided by $\frac{4}{3} \pi r^3$ or $\frac{V}{v}$

Teacher: Since we have here two equal ratios, can we not express the relationship between them as a proportion and cancel equal factors in the numerator and demoninator? What is the result?

Students: $\frac{V}{v} = \frac{R^3}{r^3}$

Teacher: How does this proportion read?

Students: The volume of the large orange is to the volume of the small orange as the cubes of their respective radii.

Teacher: Keeping in mind that we used the generalized expression for the volume of a sphere, we now have a generalized expression for the relationship between the volumes of all spheres of designated radii.

For Discussion and Further Study

1. What is the significance of the observation that students in many schools refer to any activity in which laboratory equipment is used as being an "experiment?"

2. Although many science teachers believe that lecture demonstrations cannot accomplish some things that are accomplished by individual laboratory exercises, comparisons of the two instructional methods tend to reveal "no significant differences." Why?

3. Would it be possible or appropriate to devote an entire class period to using a lecture demonstration to nurture a single feature of the pursuit of science? For example, should a demonstration be used to see how many and what kinds of hypotheses a group of students can generate when confronted with a puzzling observation?

4. How significant is the hazard that a talkative teacher will destroy the value of a demonstration for nurturing observational skills, elaborating hypotheses, designing experiments, evaluating data, and similar elements of the pursuit of science?

5. Is there a place for the spectacular demonstration that mystifies or otherwise entertains students?

References

1. V. E. Eaton, C. J. Overbeck, and R. P. Winch (Editorial Committee). "AAPT Wesleyan Conference on Demonstration Lecures," *American Journal of Physics,* 28 (September 1960), pp. 539–41.
2. Robert Stollberg. "Science Demonstrations for Improved Learning," *The Science Teacher,* 22 (November 1955), pp. 277–79.
3. Harold K. Schilling. "On the Rationale of Lecture Demonstrations," *American Journal of Physics,* 28 (April, 1960), pp. 306–08.
4. W. W. Knox, in Francis D. Curtis. *Second Digest of Investigations in the Teaching of Science.* Philadelphia: P. Blakiston and Sons Publishing Co., 1931, p. 298. Used by permission of McGraw-Hill Book Company.
5. Elbert C. Weaver, "Demonstration IS Teaching," *The Science Teacher,* 31 (February 1964), pp. 34–35.

23

The Lecture with Films, Filmstrips, Slides, or Other Projected Materials

When good and generally supplementary sound motion pictures are introduced in connection with modern teaching methods in general-science instruction, we may expect the resulting increase in pupil learning to be an amount in excess of 20 per cent when measured in terms of permanent acquisitions.[1]

Phillip J. Rulon 1933

Films are used to bring to the classroom certain key experiments and a range of experiments that are likely to be too difficult, too time consuming, or too costly for students to perform or for teachers to demonstrate. For many experiments, films can bring the purposes, techniques, data, and analysis more directly within the students' purview than any other approach can. . . . The films are not impersonal, neither are they stylized in a personal sense. They present a number of real scientists, speaking in their individual ways to students, directing their attention to key points. In this quiet way, the films bring students into closer contact with a group of scientists as persons.[2]

Gilbert C. Finlay 1962

Even after reasonable discount, there are strong implications for the use of the micro-projector as an improved teaching device over the individual microscope for high-school pupils. A correct detailed observation with group discussion under the direction of the instructor prevails.[3]

Allan Strathers   1933

The problem was one of testing which method produced superior results in measured achievement during the one school year of instruction: the conventional method or the film method of instruction. . . . The data . . . seem to indicate that the students in the non-film classes achieved more in high school chemistry than did the students in the film classes. . . . The conclusion was not biased by the factor of sex nor influenced by an interaction between sex and method.[4]

**Kenneth E. Anderson, Fred S.
Montgomery, Sid F. Moore, and Dale P. Scannell   1961**

Too often the film "teaches" even preaches, conclusions not justified by the evidence presented in it. We consider the film as a means of presenting evidence, the conclusions should be reached by the students, through discussion and argument.[5]

**Paul E. Brandwein, Fletcher G.
Watson, and Paul E. Blackwood   1958**

Talking through a problem, with the use of the cut-out figures on the flannel board, has made the use of symbols clear to many students who have otherwise had difficulty in grasping the concept. Furthermore, permitting the student to think through a problem as he manipulates the figures himself has often turned on the light as far as the understanding of genetics is concerned.[6]

Edna Maki Kniskern   1960

The two treatments were (1) laboratory work with outline drawings provided in the laboratory guide and (2) laboratory work with outline drawings and labeled photomicrographs.

. . . Though none of the differences in means or variances were statistically significant, the difference was always in favor of the group receiving labeled photomicrographs.[7]

Joseph D. Novak   1961

The film was distinctly more effective than other forms of instruction in presenting items of the type dealing with action or activity; other forms of instruction were more effective than the film for items of the type dealing with objects. . . . The film was not more valuable for the children of one than for another of the three mental levels.[8]

Helen Caldwell Davis   1932

. . . To determine the relative values with respect to the acquisition and retention of factual knowledge of two methods of laboratory procedure: (1) Having the students make the drawings from their observations of the specimen under the microscope, and (2) having the students record their observations on photomicrographs of the specimens under the microscope.
. . . Students learned significantly more factual information in terms of total combined results for all units by the use of photomicrographs. [The photomicrographs were] made of the near-perfect section of tissue, or the section which most clearly illustrates the fact or principle to be learned.[9]

Lawrence J. Kiely   1958

[When using] overhead projection of chemical experiments . . . the teacher uses drops; the student sees them on the screen live, in color, as huge as baseballs in test tubes six feet tall and two feet wide. Invisible macro-reactions become clearly visible 100 ft. away. . . . First, we propose to project all of beginning chemistry demonstrations, not just a few special ones. Second, only 28 devices will be required to carry out at least 1,000 different experiments. . . . Any make or model of projector can be adapted to this technique, some more easily than others.[10]

Hubert N. Alyea   1962

Projected materials are used to supplement many different kinds of lesson formats. Certain lessons, however, take on unique characteristics from the use of projected materials as the principal means to bring the day's phenomenon before a class, to provide data bearing on a phenomenon, to test the consistency of tentative conclusions, or to facilitate achievement of some combination of these or other aspects of the pursuit of science.

Strengths and Weaknesses

The proliferation of motion picture theaters and, especially, home television receivers has reduced considerably the excitement and enthusiasm which once prevailed in classrooms when it was announced that the lesson for the day would feature projected pictures, either still or motion. But students continue to react favorably to this kind of teaching aid, and it can be used effectively. There is no unavoidable reason why disciplined learning cannot be comfortably pleasant but, more and more, students are turning to the projected picture solely for entertainment. When projected pictures are used to carry the principal pedagogical burden of a lesson or to supplement another format, classroom tactics and strategy must be sufficiently clever to establish and maintain a learning atmosphere rather than allowing the more passive entertainment atmosphere to settle down in the classroom.

The frantically blatant efforts of television to "educate" its viewers adds another hazard to the classroom use of projected materials, particularly motion pictures. It is becoming increasingly difficult for the home television program viewer to separate the "sales pitch" from the fictional, dramatic, or factual components of a televised program. If this trend continues, students will find it increasingly difficult to exploit the powerfully effective aids to learning that can be built into the classroom films, particularly so when the films are used to exercise the ability to determine whether or not data bear on a problem or to test the consistency of tentative conclusions.

Commercial producers of audio-visual materials are sensitive to the changing needs of classroom teachers. Time-lag between the need for and availability of commercially produced materials, however, causes the motion picture films that are available to teachers to differ markedly in the degree to which they complement rather than compromise a teacher's point of view and the kind of teaching he practices. Some films do and some do not try to create an inquiring, questioning attitude in the mind of the viewer. In some films, dogmatic statement of facts extends to the equaly dogmatic wording of opinions, attitudes, and beliefs despite the preference of many teachers to allow the latter to evolve gradually through weighing the pros and cons of an issue or generalization.

The pace of a film, the awkwardness of stopping, reversing, rearranging, and repeating, and trying to digest in a leisurely fashion the most significant pieces, combine to produce a problem that taxes the pedagogical inventiveness of even the most inspired teacher. In only the most modern films does the sound track invite the teacher to stop the projector at key points and supplement the viewers' efforts to assimilate the material being presented. Unfortunately, the most modern films are not the ones for which this pedagogical strategy is most needed.

Newer films are willing to sacrifice quantity of information presented to let the viewer see how the information was derived. Again, the more modern films take time to clarify the logic, rationale, and design of the experiments or investigations whereby the information that is presented by the film was achieved. Only rarely, however, is a film willing to explore any of the wrong avenues of approach, to entertain the fruitless hypothesis, or to include other indications of the halting, frustratingly meandering nature of the pursuit of science.

The overhead projector has encouraged teachers to invest much inventiveness and creativity in adapting this teaching aid to accomplish desired functions. Transparencies can be produced in color and overlays permit step-by-step build-up or breakdown of ideas. The separate slides are large enough to permit the instructor to write or sketch on them during projection. Light sources are strong enough to project clear, sharp pictures in rooms sufficiently illuminated to allow the students to take notes or consult supplementary materials. Additional adaptations of the overhead projector allow specially designed demonstration apparatus to be projected. Minature test tubes, gas generators, thermometers, burners, meters, and dozens of other pieces of apparatus can be mounted in the projector's slide holder and students see the reactions in the form of projected images. These accessories enable the instructor to bring many chemical and physical phenomena before a class with maximum visibility and with minimum quantities of reagents.

Adoption of 2×2 slide photography, particularly color, as a personal hobby, and individual possession of projector and screen, solves so many supply and scheduling problems that this teaching aid is attracting increased interest. The 2×2 projector is inexpensive, sturdy, and easy to operate. The slides are easily cataloged and stored. Individual pictures can be shown in any desired order and each slide leaves the teacher in complete control of the lesson.

Examples and Illustrations

The following lesson plan features the use of 2×2 color slides in teaching some of the introductory concepts of Mendelian genetics.

Topic: Transmission of traits wherein one or more pairs of alleles are associated with a single trait.

Prior Coverage: An adequate explanation of the transmission of a trait specifies (1) the number of different kinds of genes apparently distributed through the total population, (2) the number of pairs of genes most likely to be present within the cells of any one individual of the population, and (3) how unlike genes within the same individual react.

Nature of the 2 × 2 slides: The slides used in this sample lesson were made by photographing arrangements of four o'clock and snapdragon flowers. These arrangements permitted projecting first the phenotypes and then the results obtained by crossing various homozygous or heterozygous individuals.

Procedure: (Directions to students) "First, recall the three factors we have developed that seem to be required in a satisfactory explanation of the transmission of a genetic trait. Now you see here on the screen one specimen of every color of four o'clock flower that has ever been observed by gardeners the world over. During the next few minutes write the best hypothesis that you believe would be adequate to explain the transmission of flower color in four o'clocks."

The slide shows red, white, yellow, pink, lemon, and orange flowers. Hypotheses framed by students are likely to feature almost any number of genes and any kind of relationship between genes. The lesson evolves by having students read some of their hypotheses. Critical analysis of any one hypothesis is delayed until an array of possible hypotheses has been achieved.

"Now, the slide shows the kinds of offspring that are produced by crossing red with red four o'clocks, yellow with yellow, and white with white. Do these data square with your preferred hypotheses? Do these data suggest you modify your hypothesis in any way?"

Class discussion up to this point is likely to sift hypotheses down to involving either two or three different kinds of genes in the total population, one pair present in any individual, and a blending relationship existing between unlike genes when present in the same individual.

"Now, the slide shows the kinds of offspring that are produced by crossing pink with pink four o'clocks, lemon with lemon, and orange with orange. Examine these data to see if they square with your preferred hypothesis. Make any suggested modifications."

Class discussion will very likely eliminate all but the accepted explanation for flower color inheritance and a final hypothesis can be, in general agreed upon. The lesson will close by having the students individually apply their newly elaborated hypothesis by predicting the kinds and ratios of offspring to be expected from such crosses as pink with red, orange with lemon, etc. The next lesson can well involve a second slide in which a slightly more sophisticated explanation will be required, for example, one in which two kinds of genes are present in the population. Any one individual can possess two pairs, and a blending relationship exists between unlike genes when present in the same individual.

For Discussion and Further Study

1. Does the tendency for entertainment motion pictures to feature glamorized and fictitional situations create a significant hazard when the same medium is used to communicate the spirit and structure of science?

2. How can teachers determine whether or not the thought processes of students who are viewing a film are keeping pace with the logic that is reflected in the content of the film?

3. To what degree would the effectiveness of a motion picture be increased by (1) presenting to the students a list of questions to be answered while viewing the film, (2) asking the students to cast the film in the pattern of a representative episode in science, that is, a puzzling observation around which hypotheses are elaborated and experiments conducted to verify these hypotheses, (3) showing the film a second time, or (4) rescheduling the film as a review lesson near the end of the course?

4. What are the advantages and disadvantages of using slides to (1) "store" complex charts or diagrams, (2) facilitate demonstrations of complex dissections or set-ups of equipment, or (3) project unannounced quizzes or examinations?

5. Does the teaching profession really know how effectively motion pictures nurture learning, particularly learning the pursuit of science?

References

1. Phillip J. Rulon, in Francis D. Curtis. *A Third Digest of Investigations in the Teaching of Science.* Philadelphia: P. Blakiston and Sons Publishing Co., 1939, p. 336. Used by permission of McGraw-Hill Book Company.
2. Gilbert C. Finlay. "The Physical Science Study Committee," *The School Review,* **70** (Spring 1962), p. 68. Reprinted by permission of the University of Chicago Press.
3. Allan Strathers, in Curtis, *A Third Digest of Investigations in the Teaching of Science.* Philadelphia: P. Blakiston and Sons Publishing Co., 1939, p. 102. Used by permission of McGraw-Hill Book Company.
4. Kenneth E. Anderson *et al.* "An Evaluation of the Introductory Chemistry Course on Film," *Science Education,* **45** (April 1961), pp. 254–78.
5. Paul E. Brandwein, Fletcher G. Watson, and Paul E. Blackwood. *Teaching High School Science: A Book of Methods.* New York: Harcourt, Brace and World, 1958, p. 480.
6. Edna Maki Kniskern. "Teaching Genetics with a Flannel Board," *The American Biology Teacher,* **22** (December 1960), pp. 542–43.
7. Joseph D. Novak. "The Use of Labeled Photomicrographs in Teaching College General Botany," *Science Education,* **45** (March 1961), pp. 119–22.
8. Helen Caldwell Davis, in Curtis, *A Third Digest of Investigations in the Teaching of Science.* Philadelphia: P. Blakiston and Sons Publishing Co., 1939, p. 317. Used by permission of McGraw-Hill Book Company.
9. Lawrence J. Kiely. "Student Drawings vs. Photomicrographs," *Science Education,* **42** (February 1958), pp. 62–73.
10. Hubert N. Alyea. "TOPS in General Chemistry: Tested Overhead Projection Series," *Journal of Chemical Education,* **39** (January 1962), pp. 12 ff.

24

The Lecture with Natural History Specimen

Since the beginning of knowledge must be with the senses, the beginning of teaching should be made by dealing with actual things. The object must be a real, useful thing, capable of making an impression upon the senses. To this end it must be brought into communication with them [the pupils], if visible, with the eyes; if audible, with the ears; if tangible, with the touch; if odorous, with the nose; if sapid, with the taste. First the presentation of the thing itself and the real intuition of it, then the real explanation for further elucidation of it.[1]

Johann Amos Comenius 1657

. . . Pupils must always be encouraged to learn by means of direct sensory impressions gained by actually handling and manipulating the materials for study.[2] **Sam S. Blanc 1957**

Natural history is defined as "the study, description and classification of animals, plants, minerals and other natural objects." Thus, a lesson

336

which features the use of natural history specimens is one in which fresh or preserved plants or animals, their parts or products, or rock and mineral specimens are brought into the classroom.

Strengths and Weaknesses

Natural history specimens can bring into the classroom the actual observations that aroused the curiosity and captured the interest of the scientist who first identified and described many of the basic principles of science. Thus, this type of teaching aid can honestly and effectively bring before a class the phenomenon about which the lesson is concerned.

Natural history specimens provide opportunities for the teacher to sharpen the observational skills of his students. For example, an exhibit of minerals or of twigs in the winter condition, at first glance, can be easily passed by until the observer has had experience in noticing the variations which give individuality to each specimen.

After tentative hypotheses have been formulated, the teacher can redirect the attention of his students to the specimens in order to determine consistency or inconsistency of an hypothesis with the facts derived by observation.

Natural history specimens provide an effective link between the classroom and the students' continuing activities beyond the classroom. A mineral specimen, for example, studied in the classroom and encountered later on a summer vacation or in the foundation of a city building, can revive and review the student's appreciation of his natural environment. It is pedagogically axiomatic that things often reviewed stand less chance of being forgotten. If the interpretation of nature is one of the primary functions of science, natural history specimens can be exploited for their effectiveness in keeping students in touch with nature.

The tendency to become isolated museum pieces rather than representative fragments of nature is probably the greatest weakness inherent in the use of natural history specimens. Unless properly identified and labeled, plant and animal materials or mineral specimens that have been separated from their natural environment tend to become dust-catching, meaningless items on storeroom shelves or in classroom display cases. Unlabeled materials may have been meaningful to the student or teacher who originally collected them, but they cease to be so to the new generations in rapidly changing school situations.

Specimens too small to be viewed by the entire class or too scarce to be available in class quantities require special presentation techniques. It is almost impossible to conduct an effective natural-history-specimen-centered lesson if the specimen must be circulated among the students.

FIGURE 6. Apparent discrepancies of nature are often especially effective clues to the existence or action of scientific concepts, principles, and laws.

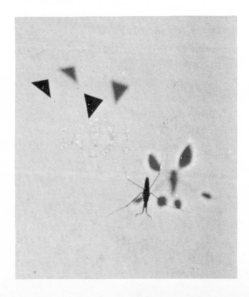

Again, the effectiveness of the natural history specimen in the classroom depends on how closely the specimen is or was involved in the
pursuit of one or more episodes of science. The more closely a specimen
is associated with the emergence of a scientific principle, the greater is
the probability that the specimen will be an effective teaching aid.
Similarly, the aid will be effective if it poses a puzzling event or circumstance, provides observations bearing on tentative explanations, or
serves as a reference standard for testing tentative conclusions. Finally,
if the natural history specimen is accompanied by an informative guide
sheet, informative in that it keeps the specimen associated with its
total niche in nature, the specimen can alternate between serving as a
museum and classroom specimen.

Examples and Illustrations

The first example to serve as an illustration of the natural history
specimen lesson format can be considered representative of many lessons
in the earth sciences.

THE SANDSTONE SPECIMEN. The natural history specimen selected for
this sample lesson is a block of sandstone approximately two feet long,
one foot wide, and three inches thick. The specimen shows definite
ripple marks on one surface and rippled banding on the sides. In addition, each student is provided with a smaller specimen of the sandstone.

The objectives for the lesson, in the mind of the teacher, are to develop the idea that rocks show characteristics which are directly related
to the environment in which they were formed and, by invoking the
principle of uniformitarianism, it is possible to study the characteristics
of rocks that were formed many, many years ago and reconstruct the
environment that existed during their formation. Specifically, the
teacher hopes that the students will recognize in the ripple marks on
this sandstone the same natural forces that produce comparable appearances along contemporary bodies of water.

Prior to this lesson, the students have dealt with the weathering and
erosive agents operating in the natural environment. The students are
in general familiar with the principle of uniformitarianism and how it
is applied in geology.

The teacher opened his lesson by such a request as, "Let's examine
both this large rock specimen and the small specimen you have as closely
as possible to see if we can find clues to its origin. Jim, will you please
list the observations on the chalk board as they come up." As the discussion developed, the teacher then interjected whatever questions he
felt necessary to bring the essential characteristics of the specimen before the students.

The second major phase of the lesson consisted of briefly summarizing environmental conditions operating today which produce deposits of sand. A significant feature of this phase was the identification of any characteristics of sand that are uniquely associated with formative agents. This information was available in an accompanying textbook assignment.

The lesson was brought to a conclusion by projecting the various circumstances accompanying the origin of sandstone against the evidence to be gained from observing the specimen at hand. Using this approach, the teacher was able to summarize his lesson by completing such a statement as: "To the extent that this specimen is representative of the total sandstone stratum from which it was collected and within the limitations of the whole principle of uniformitarianism, we can conclude that this sandstone must have originated. . . ."

THE SAND-DOLLAR SPECIMEN.   The second example used to illustrate the natural-history-specimen-centered lesson format leans heavily on a guide sheet to accompany the specimen. It differs from the previous example in that it provides a more vicarious excursion for the student in the pursuit of science. The primary function of the natural history specimen, in this case, is to add reality and clarity to the student's comprehension of a scientist and his work.

The opening phase of this lesson consisted of distributing copies of the guide sheet and specimens of fossil sand dollars to each student. Adequate time was provided to allow the student to observe the specimen in detail and to study the guide sheet. The objectives of the lesson can be gleaned from the various phases that follow.

The teacher used appropriate questions to bring out the basic problem underlying the research project in which these fossil sand dollars played a part. The teacher distinguished between the basic problem of reconstructing environmental conditions existing in the Kettleman Hills area ten million years ago and the immediate problem of associating environmental conditions existing today with the peculiar characteristics of living sand dollars.

In the next series of questions, the teacher intended to identify a scientist's working hypothesis. It was also necessary to clarify the assumptions which were woven into this hypothesis.

The next series of questions clarified the kinds of evidence brought to bear on the hypothesis. These questions led to the most tenable conclusions regarding the use of this natural history specimen as an aid in reconstructing a prior environment.

The guide sheet follows.

FOSSIL SAND DOLLARS (DENDRASTER GIBBSII, REMOND)

We are most likely to find the thin, usually chalky white shells or tests of sand dollars along the seashore. The waves and breaking surf may have washed away the spines and fleshy covering, exposing the delicate flower-like pattern on the upper surface. These fossil sand dollars, however, were collected high in California's Kettleman Hills, many miles from the Pacific Ocean's present-day shoreline and only a few miles from almost desert-like valleys.

Studies by several geologists suggest that the sandstone in which these fossils occur must have been deposited about 10,000,000 years ago. What can a detailed study of these fossil sand dollars tell us about environmental conditions which existed at that time in the area where we now find the Kettleman Hills?

One geologist who has studied these fossil sand dollars, David M. Raup of Johns Hopkins University, after a careful study of the research done in the area by other scientists, decided to study living sand dollars to see if the environmental conditions under which they live today leave any marks or characteristics on their shell—marks or characteristics which, if found on fossil sand dollars, would suggest that these same environmental conditions must have existed 10,000,000 years ago.

The most common living species of the genus Dendraster is called excentricus—so named because the center of the flower-like pattern (the apical system) is pushed to one side of the top surface of the shell. The eccentricity of this apical system varies considerably from specimen to specimen in the living species. Could this variation, hypothesized Dr. Raup, be related to a peculiarity of the living sand dollar's environment? But before he could test this hypothesis, other factors which might affect the placement of the apical system had to be investigated. Are the differences in eccentricity simply inherited traits causing a particular specimen to look the same no matter where it lived? Or do some sand dollars have a more eccentric apical system just because they are older than others? Study revealed that the answer to both these questions is No—and the way was clear to compare the eccentricity of sand dollars with differences in environmental conditions under which they live: such as water temperature, saltiness of the water, food supply, and the roughness of the water.

Dr. Raup collected about 10,000 sand dollars from living populations all the way from Mexico to British Columbia. Each specimen was carefully measured and the position of the flower pattern was noted. It turned out that sand dollars living in rough water had much more eccentric apical system (the center of the apical system was almost on the edge of the shell, like the fossil sand dollars) than those living in quiet, sheltered areas. This seemed reasonable because of the peculiar feeding habit of these sand dollars. In order to expose the mouth (which is on the under side) the feeding sand dollar tilts the shell up so that just one end is anchored in the sand. When the water is very rough, this tilted position is likely to be unstable and, if they were to be tumbled over and lie flat on the bottom, the continually moving sand on the bottom would foul their breathing system. Therefore, sand dollars living under conditions of turbulence are more likely to survive and produce offspring if the apical system is as close to the end of the shell as possible and, consequently, is well clear of the bottom when the animal is feeding.

Do you now see how the eccentricity-turbulence relationship might tell something about the environment of the Kettleman Hills 10,000,000 years ago? Fossil sand dollars of high eccentricity (like those included here) would indicate high turbulence and, furthermore, the exact amount of turbulence or roughness of the ancient sea could be calculated by comparing them with what we learn from our study of living sand dollars.

Often, in science, new problems may arise when we try to extend what we learn in one situation so that it will explain another situation. In our sand dollar problem evolution may be such a problem. It appears that although eccentricity probably varied with water turbulence in ancient seas as it does today, the eccentricities of fossil and living specimens can not be compared in absolute terms. The thousands of generations which have lived and died may also have undergone evolutionary changes. In other words, if changing environmental conditions cause species either to become extinct or to change, how can we know whether or not the changing characteristics are keeping up with or lagging behind the changing environment? The result of all this is that we can tell from fossil specimens that one type (like these sample specimens) lived in more turbulent water than other fossil sand dollars (of the same geological time) that have more nearly centered apical systems. We can not say just how much more turbulent the water was because evolution may have "warped" the scale which we have made by studying the living animals.

For Discussion and Further Study

1. How far can a teacher go in attempting to introduce a full-scale episode of science by directing attention to a single natural history specimen that is significantly related to the episode?

2. Is it overly idealistic to believe that rocks and stars or plants and trees with which students associate pleasant learnings become old friends to be "visited" repeatedly throughout adult life? Is this a case where familiarity breeds more familiarity?

3. What assets and liabilities are inherent in the class requirement to collect, mount, and identify natural history specimens?

4. Are photographs, particularly color slides, appropriate substitutes for natural history specimens?

5. Are there specific elements of the pursuit of science that can be uniquely nurtured by class formats featuring the use of natural history specimens?

References

1. Johann Amos Comenius. "The Great Didactic." Quoted by Philip G. Johnson in *Supervision for Quality Education in Science,* report of a conference arranged by U.S. Office of Education, June 25-29, 1962. Washington: Government Printing Office, Bulletin No. 3, OE-29039, 1963, pp. 122–23.
2. Sam S. Blanc. "Selecting Objects and Specimens for Biology." *The Science Teacher,* 24 (March 1957), pp. 71–73.

25

Textbook-Centered
Lesson Formats

. . . Although a textbook to be profitable publishing venture must be a compromise as to content, it should be clearly written and pitched to the level of the reader to whom it is addressed. It should be accurate; and that means consistent and up to date as to methodology, neither ahead of nor behind its time.[1]

Richard T. Wareham 1953

For the most part our textbooks have become encyclopedias of organized information. They abound with "essential data," tables of constants and specifications, and they recite seemingly endless facts and formulas—but they do little to encourage the student to think.[2]

J. Stanley Marshall 1962

Education is the acquisition of the art of utilisation of knowledge. This is an art very difficult to impart. Whenever a textbook is written of real educational worth, you may be quite certain that some reviewer will say that it will be difficult to teach from it. Of course it will be difficult to teach from it. If it were easy, the book ought to be burned; for it cannot be educational. In education, as elsewhere, the broad primrose path leads to a nasty place. This evil path is represented by a book or a set of lectures which will practically enable the student to learn by heart all the questions likely to be asked at the next external examination.[3]

Alfred North Whitehead 1916

The textbooks generally available for the course [biology] are encyclopedic, comprehensive, and uninspiring. There is too much color in the illustrations and not enough in the prose. The books repeat facts, give definitions, and fail to provide any of the excitement associated with exploration in science.[4]

Arnold B. Grobman 1962

My points of view are these: (1) There must be more analytical problems and less numerical exercises. (2) Limiting and special cases must be explored. (3) The habit of asking more penetrating questions must be cultivated. And finally, the absolutely necessary process of imagination must be stirred and aroused and awakened.[5]

Julius Summer Miller 1960

A textbook is, of course, more than a complex of words to be memorized. It consists of a pattern of illustrations, verbal explanations, questions and suggested activities. Every science educator should become intimately acquainted with the manner in which such materials are organized and the best ways to use them . . . not as a reading assignment but rather for the value its illustrations, questions, and activities can contribute to the science learnings.[7]

George G. Mallinson 1958

The average textbook of general science or biology is very poorly organized with respect to the topic of scientific method. Although many authors recognize the importance of the scientific method, as evidenced by statements in the preface, foreword, or in a separate chapter in the book, they have done little to organize the materials in their books

344

so that the scientific method may be readily understood and made to function in the daily affairs of the student.[7]

Victor L. Crowell   1936

There are few who would disagree with the statement that the textbook is one of the most important agents in our educational system. . . . a very potent potential medium for the stimulation of interest in science and the training of scientists of the future. . . . While textbooks should never attempt such a popularization, there is no reason why their contents cannot be presented in a manner which is interesting and understandable. There is no merit in a textbook style which is merely a dry catalogue of facts. . . . The potential textbook author must have sufficient interest and desire to write to furnish the drive to carry him through years of intensive, painstaking work. . . . If he is a highly sensitive person, easily disturbed and hurt by derogatory remarks as to his ability, he had better not begin textbook writing. . . . He is extending his range of useful instruction far beyond his own classroom to influence the minds of students in all sections of the nation.[8]

A. M. Winchester   1960

[A book for intellectually gifted students] provokes thinking and discussion, it develops interest in matters of science, it stimulates further reading, it helps to articulate and elucidate scientific concepts and principles, it suggests further problems, it gives insights into social implications and contributions of science.

It is accurate and authoritative, it is fair and sincere in its presentation of controversial subject matter, its enrichment material goes beyond that of secondary textbooks, it has good literary standards—clear style, grammatically correct, easy to read, its general theme and tone are wholesome, it is a book of lasting value—one worth owning and going back to.[9]

Cyrus W. Barnes, et al.   **1958**

. . . This paper involves an interplay between two theses. One, which has been explored by Barron, suggests that adult science fiction plays upon those human values and satisfactions which may be closely related to those which

motivate practicing scientists. The second thesis and the primary one developed in this paper, suggests that children's science fiction may be similarly related to whatever satisfactions keep young people interested in science.

Although the motivations for both practicing and would-be scientists are but dimly identified, science fiction may play a significant role in these motivations.[10]

Elizabeth H. Gross and John H. Woodburn   1959

A textbook can be any book containing a presentation of the principles of a subject and which is used as a basic tool of instruction. Usually, the textbook is the one book that is put into the hands of all of the students in the course. It represents the portion or sample of a subject that is to be the common denominator of a course and, if the instructor chooses to do so, it can be used to establish the sequence in which the segments of the course are considered.

Textbooks usually include learning exercises. The traditional problems and questions at the ends of the chapters and bibliographies of related works are often supplemented by suggestions for discussion techniques, examination or self-testing items, directions for lecture demonstrations, ideas for laboratory exercises or projects, sources of audio-visual materials, and other pedagogical aids.

Textbook-centered lessons are drawn from one or more pages of the text. These pages may be assigned for study prior to or during classtime. Class discussion of the assigned material may follow closely or range far from the ideas actually presented by the authors but, to one degree or another, the discussion becomes a recitation. Basically, a recitation is the citing or quoting of a passage or point of view. Many generations of teachers emphasized the "lesson hearing" concept of the recitation. The modern trend encourages the use of the recitation largely for interpretation of cited or quoted materials.

To draw any general conclusions on the worth and value of textbooks invites many conflicts of opinion. One point does seem to be verifiable. Textbooks are remarkably stable in format and content. In the paragraphs to follow are excerpts from textbooks that have been quite popular, one during the 1700's and the other during the 1800's. The reader is invited to compare their formats and this sample of their contents with any widely adopted textbook of the 1900's.

The older of these texts, the quoted edition of which was published in 1763, was written by J. T. Desaguliers and titled, *A Course of Experimental Philosophy.*[11] A quotation from the dedicatory statement is of special interest: "To contemplate the Works of God, to discover Causes from their Effects, and make Art and Nature subservient to the Necessities of Life by a Skill in joining proper Causes to produce the most useful Effects, is the Business of Science, the Grounds and Principles of which I have the Honour to lay at your Royal Highness's Feet." The preface of this book also makes reference to the author's concept of the nature of science and how he thinks it should be taught: "All of the Knowledge we have of Nature depends upon Facts; for without Observations and Experiments, our Natural Philosophy would only be a Science of Terms and an unintelligible Jargon."

EXPERIMENTAL PHILOSOPHY, VOL. 1
J. T. DESAGULIERS

It has been observed, that when a Body falls during one Second of Time, it goes thro' a Space equal to 16–1/2 English Feet, or one Rod, as we have already mentioned*: therefore the Force impressed by Gravity at the Beginning of its Fall (considering Gravity only as a Blow) is capable of making the Body go downwards at the rate of one Rod in a Second +, tho' it should act no longer upon it than during the first Second; that is, tho' the Body should for ever after cease to be heavy. For example, if the Body A falls thro' the Space AB during the first Second of its Fall; if then it should cease to be heavy, yet it would go through the Spaces equal to AB during all the succeeding Seconds of Time, viz. thro' the Spaces Bc, cD, De, ef, fG, Gh, hi, ik, kL, etc. But as the Body does not cease to be heavy, we must consider the Action of Gravity as an Impulse given by a new Force equal to the first, acting downwards when the Body is got to B at the Beginning of the 2d Second, and the Body during the 2d Second will go through the Space BD double the Space AB, or equal to the two Spaces Bc and cD. Then if the Body should cease to be heavy, it would go uniformly thro' the double Spaces Df, fh, etc. every Second; but Gravity acting upon it also at the Beginning of the 3d Second, when it is at D, superadds a Force able to make it go thro' a Space equal to the first AB in a Second: consequently it will go thro' 3 Spaces or Rods (or thro' a Space DG equal to 3 Rods) the 3d Second. At the Beginning of the fourth Second, Gravity acting by a fourth Impulse superadds a Force equal to the former, whereby it will go the Length GL, that is, four Rods or Spaces the fourth Second; and so on +; and this will be a Motion uniformly accelerated.

This Motion of a Body thus accelerated in its Descent would be the real Motion of falling Bodies, if Gravity acted by Intervals, as we have only suppos'd, to help Conception: But as Gravity never ceases to act, we must fill up the Intervals between the Beginning and End of every Second or small Part of Time.

---

* Bodies in reality only fall 16 English Feet and one Tenth of a Foot in a Second; but we call that Space here 16 and a half Feet; because one Rod (which is a Measure of 16 and a half Feet) gives us such a Number as to avoid fractions in the Examples of the Calculations that we give.

Thus, if we consider the Body falling thro' the Space AB* in the first Second, we must not only consider Gravity superadding a Force capable of making the Body fall one Rod farther at the Beginning of every Second; but also during the Time of every Second. For Example, at B at the Beginning of the 2d Second, the Body not only receives an additional Impulse to carry it to d instead of c, but also during the Time of the 2d Second another Impulse, which makes it go to E instead of d; so that the Body will fall 3 Rods during the 2d Second. Likewise at the Beginning of the 3d Second, when the Body is at E, it will again receive from Gravity one Impulse at the Beginning of that Second, and another during the Time of it; so that it will go thro' the five Spaces Ef, fg, gh, hi, and iK, during the Time of that 3d Second. So in the Time of the 4th Second, the Body will (for the same Reason) go thro' seven Spaces or Rods from K to R, and so on, the Number of Spaces describ'd increasing by two every Second; that is, according to the Series of the odd Numbers, 1, 3, 5, 7, 9, etc.

As a great Part of my Auditors, tho' very curious, are unacquainted with mathematical Studies; I always found it very difficult to make them understand the Effect of Gravity in accelerating Bodies in their Fall, by *Galileo's* Scheme of Triangles, till I had prepared them by what I have now said in the 14th Paragraph; but as that Account is not strictly true, I hope this following will satisfy every Body.

The Actions or Accelerations of any centripetal Force upon a Body, are (at the same, or equal Distances from the central Body) always proportionable to the Times; that is, equal in equal Times: And such are those of Gravity (as to Sense) near the Surface of the Earth.

The preface and a representative page of Paul Bert's *First Steps in Scientific Knowledge* follow. The quoted edition is from Madame Paul Bert's translation.[12]

FIRST STEPS IN SCIENTIFIC KNOWLEDGE
PAUL BERT

Preface

Before the English translation of the "First Steps in Scientific Knowledge" appeared, five hundred thousand copies of the original had been sold in France within three years. Immediately after the appearance of the first English edition a second was called for, and the American publishers feel confident that the success of the American edition will not be less than that of the foreign.

The American editor has made in the excellent translation of Madame Bert only such changes and additions as were necessary to Americanize the book, and adapt it to the requirements of public and private schools as well as to home instruction in this country.

The Natural History has been slightly enlarged by the introduction of several American species, omitted in the original and in the English edition, and a few inaccuracies concerning other species met with in the United States have been corrected.

61. Force of Gravity.—I hold in my hand a small stone and a sheet of paper. I let both go at the same time, and the stone falls straight to the ground, while the paper floats and oscillates an instant, but finally reaches the floor. What I have done with these two bodies I might have done with many others: *let go in the air, they would have fallen to the ground.*

I take the paper and the stone in my hand once more; but this time before I let go the paper I shall crush it up into a ball, as small and as tight as possible. There, look: this time the paper ball falls as rapidly as the stone, and both reach the floor at the same moment.

This is one demonstration of the fact that all bodies fall with equal rapidity: when differences exist they are caused solely by the resistance of the air, which is greater or less according to the extent of surface presented to it, the greater surface of course offering the greater resistance.

Stand forward and hold out your open hand (Fig. 97). Here is a small ball of lead. I shall let it fall into your hand from the height of about three inches. That does not hurt you, does it?—"No."—Well, this time I shall hold it a yard high before letting it fall.—"Ah! this time I felt it more smartly."— Well, let us try once more. This time I shall get upon the chair and let it drop from twice the former height.—"Ah! this time it makes my fingers tingle."—Then that is enough. Now, what should we conclude from this experiment? We must evidently conclude that *the longer the fall lasts, the greater is the force that the body acquires, or, in other words, the greater the distance through which a falling body has to pass, the greater is the rapidity attained.*

And this rapidity, when the body falls from a great height, is so considerable that one cannot see it pass. For instance, during the first second a falling body travels 16 feet 1 inch; the same body, in 2 seconds, passes through 64 feet 4 inches; during the 5th second, about 145 feet; and about 306 feet during the 10th second of its fall; and so on, always increasing its velocity more and more. Thus, were you to jump out of the school-room window, which is $3\frac{1}{2}$ feet above the level of the court-yard, you would do yourself no harm; but were you to fall from the church steeple, which is 50 feet high, your bones would be broken by striking the ground.

Strengths and Weaknesses

The textbook provides an element of stability for a course. The orderliness of its structure can be a constant suggestion of the order that exists in the various activities that add to the total course in which the textbook is being used. A teacher operating without a textbook may have his course laid out with supreme orderliness, but unforeseen difficulties can disrupt for some or all of the students the planned sequence of lectures, laboratory exercises, films, or other activities which require scheduling of materials or equipment. Students can always find in their textbooks an orderly presentation of at least one man's concept of the material normally included in the course.

The textbook is one feature of the teaching-learning process that permits each student to approach at his individual pace. Paragraphs once read can be reread, but only when the student deems necessary. Previews of the portions of the course yet to unfold can be gained merely by skimming ahead and material already covered can be equally easily reviewed.

Many teachers believe that learning is promoted through verbal repetition and by listening to the interpretations of other points of view. Although intellectual participation is preferred, participation of one kind or another is essential to the success of a student in any course. Talking about assigned text material is probably the most easily provoked kind of student participation.

The recitation format alerts the teacher to the rates at which his students, at least the ones who participate, are advancing in his course. There are always those students who are overly sensitive to the impression they may make on their classmates by their recitations. The "show-off" tends to upholster his contributions or divert his answer toward a topic on which he is better prepared. The student who feels he is gaining a reputation for being too brainy may adjust his recitation accordingly. Use of the recitation identifies these problem cases. Each teacher retains the option of either ignoring or attempting to eliminate student adjustment problems that are identified through use of the recitation format, but only rarely can the teacher ignore the problems which arise due to the different rates of advancement of his students.

Once a clear-cut phenomenon has been brought to the attention of the class, the recitation format is a logical procedure to bring out observations bearing on the phenomenon. To recite additional instances of the phenomenon about which they have read or to recall out-of-school circumstances in which the phenomenon may be involved, puts the students into position to frame or evaluate hypotheses regarding the phenomenon. When accomplished effectively, this preliminary discussion of observations associated with the phenomenon tends to create an atmosphere in which the puzzling features of the phenomenon become impregnated with facts which can be extended to create hypotheses. Actual creation of these hypotheses is likely to be the culminating feature of the lesson and, as such, the usual recitation format can well be modified to permit a maximum number of the students to experience it. One such modification consists of declaring a five-minute period during which each student will have an uninterrupted opportunity to compose and record his best tentative explanation of the phenomenon being considered. This modification, by providing time for each student to exercise his mind free from the disturbance of other students' recitations, extends and distributes to a larger number of students the satisfactions that come to an individual when his own thought processes allow him to sense order in apparent chaos, a satisfaction thought by many to be quite closely associated with the basic motivation of the pursuit of science.

Properly used, the recitation format can nurture an increasingly effective student attitude toward the whole business of school attendance. All too often, students reach the higher levels of the educational system before they come to think of going to school as an activity to be engaged in for their own welfare. All too many students think of their assignments as being something to be done for the teacher. The efficiency of the class and its activities is the concern of the teacher. Books, equipment, supplies, furnishings—all these are the weapons and the school itself is the arsenal of a hostile or, at best, a competing agency. Quite obviously, attitudes arise from exceedingly obtuse forces and can seldom be restructured by direct attack, but there are things a teacher can do to nurture the concept that schooling is intended to promote the welfare of the student and should be approached as an opportunity rather than a period of servitude or punishment.

Although seemingly trivial, the accumulative effect of differences in the manner of expressing the questions the teacher uses to conduct the recitation format can influence the students' concepts of why they are in school. These differences are illustrated in the following questions: "James, will you tell me the definition of osmosis?" "James, will you tell us the definition of osmosis?" "James, do the authors of the text provide a definition of osmosis that will help you move toward a laboratory investigation of the process?"

The artful teacher learns to avoid allowing class recitations to degenerate into a conversation among a small group. He invites all present to share in awarding commendation or criticism to the contributions made by the participants in the recitation. He avoids the frantic, last-minute preparation in which students engage as they count ahead to see when their turn will come if the teacher follows a fixed or identifiable order of questioning. The arts and skills of leading discussion through the recitation format cannot be prescribed by rules. They accumulate, however, through practiced sensitivity to the success or failure of daily lessons—sensitivity followed by modifying the obvious and subtle procedures and mannerisms employed by the teacher until a pattern is achieved that causes class recitations to take on as much as possible the character and spirit of the pursuit of science. No rules or magic formulas exist that can retrieve the teacher whose sensitivity to the success or failure of his tactics and procedures has been deadened by the disenchantment that comes from believing that he has drawn students who are either basically incapable of learning or are so caught up with competing interests as to ensure failure to advance satisfactorily in his course.

To use the class period for mere repetition of material presented clearly in the textbook can be a pernicious waste of student time. On the other hand, the teacher who can ask questions that provoke the kind of thinking done in the pursuit of science has no cause to apologize for his use of the recitation format. The recitation provides for quick discovery of inadequacy of preparation or lack of comprehension. This format can degenerate to nothing more than exercising a "ready and faithful memory," but there is equal potential for its use to exercise "comparison, criticism, analysis" and many of the other powers of the mind alleged to be exercised during the pursuit of science.

Inaccuracies and inconsistencies in the textbook, obviously, are potential liabilities in the textbook-centered recitation format. So may be the author's emphasis on or selection of topics. The textbook that emphasizes only the end products and ignores the procedures of the pursuit of science would fail to complement the instructor who chooses to accompany the exhibition of the products of science with analysis of their derivation. Few students lack the attitude that books, especially textbooks, possess an air of authority. This attitude ranges from sheer reverence toward what is in the book, to a subtle suspicion of the teacher who departs too drastically from the adopted textbook's approach to the subject and its treatment.

Inconsistency between teacher and author can be illustrated by allocation of space and emphasis on "pure" versus "applied" science. A teacher moving into a new school may inherit an adopted textbook in which the author's emphasis is quite inconsistent with his own. If this leads to superficial use of the textbook, inefficiency is quite likely to result. A textbook for which no assignments are given or for which assignments are given but not followed through by the teacher in one way or another breeds nonparticipation by the students—not only in assignment preparation but in all other features of the course.

Examples and Illustrations

Conducting class discussions draws on so many of the teacher's individual traits and abilities that examples and illustrations of the textbook-centered lesson format can do little beyond suggesting ideas for adaptation and modification. One such example provides a basic pattern around which many but not all of the class discussions are organized. In this pattern, class discussion is stimulated through use of a series of questions such as: What puzzling events or circumstances triggered development of the information presented in the pages of the textbook assigned for today? What observations led to the identification of these events? What hypotheses have been entertained regarding the relationships between these events and other natural phenomena? What experiments or other kinds of investigations have been conducted to verify these hypotheses? Within what limits can the conclusions to be drawn from these experiments be accepted? What was the ultimate impact of a newly verified or accepted concept on the beliefs of mankind or on the manner of solving technological problems?

Through experience, teachers can accumulate a repertory of questions that have special values. One type of question can evoke one kind of thought process whereas another type of question will arouse another mental exercise. Examples are: "Eric, will you comment on the logic that shows through Randy's interpretation of the question?" "Ronald, are Jim's comments consistent or inconsistent with the information provided by the authors of the textbook?" "Martha, whose point of view, Jane's or Susan's, appears to be the more logical?" When considered out of the perspective of the classroom, questions such as these may seem to be contrived and much too sophisticated for routine classroom operations. Boys and girls, however, rise to whatever level of intellectual participation is demanded and, although they may react negatively to questions or other instructional techniques that force them to exercise their intelligence, they soon come to accept such exercise and enjoy it.

For Discussion and Further Study

1. To what extent would science textbooks be improved by (1) decreasing the time lapse between the discovery of scientific principles and their appearance in textbooks, (2) decreasing attention to the technological aspects of science, or (3) increased application of the psychology of learning?

2. Are there situations in which teachers should use no textbooks or multiple texts rather than assigning a basic textbook for the course?

3. Is the tendency of textbooks to stabilize course content a significant hazard to teaching the pursuit of science?

4. How can teachers adapt their use of the textbooks that are generally available to encourage students to improve their abilities to observe, hypothesize, define assumptions, interpret and evaluate data, and delimit generalizations?

5. Are there significant trends in the nature of textbooks and the role they are expected to play in science teaching?

References

1. Richard T. Wareham. "The Preparation of School Science Textbook Manuscripts," *The Science Teacher,* 20 (April 1953), p. 119.
2. J. Stanley Marshall. "The New School Science." A Report to School Administrators on Regional Orientation Conferences in Science, AAAS Misc. Publ. 63–6. Washington: American Association for the Advancement of Science, 1963, p. 3.
3. Alfred North Whitehead. *Education in the Age of Science (The Aims of Education).* New York: The New American Library of World Literature, 1949. Originally published 1916.
4. Arnold B. Grobman. *Advances in Secondary-School Science Education.*

Taken from Proceedings of the Conference on Progress in Nuclear Education, Report TID-7638. Oak Ridge, Tennessee: United States Atomic Energy Commission, Division of Technical Information, 1962, p. 24.

5. Julius Sumner Miller. "It is Important to Know What Questions to Ask," *American Journal of Physics,* 28 (January 1960), pp. 38–42.

6. George G. Mallinson. "Textbook and Reading Difficulty in Science Teaching," *The Science Teacher,* 25 (December 1958), pp. 474–75.

7. Victor L. Crowell in Francis D. Curtis. *A Third Digest of Investigations in the Teaching of Science.* Philadelphia: P. Blakiston and Sons Publishing Co., 1939, p. 38. Used by permission of McGraw-Hill Book Company.

8. A. M. Winchester. "Tribulations of the Textbook Authors," *Science Education,* 44 (April 1960), pp. 194–98.

9. Cyrus W. Barnes *et al.* "Criteria for Selecting Supplementary Reading Science Books for Intellectually Gifted High School Students," *Science Education,* 42 (April 1958), pp. 215–18.

10. Elizabeth H. Gross and John H. Woodburn. "Science Fiction As a Factor in Science Education," *Science Education,* 43 (February 1959), pp. 28–31.

11. J. T. Desaguliers. *A Course of Experimental Philosophy,* 3rd ed., corrected. London: 1763, p. 328.

12. Paul Bert. *First Steps in Scientific Knowledge.* Philadelphia: J. B. Lippincott Co., 1887, p. 3.

26

Miscellaneous
Recitation
Lesson Formats

The art of questioning is related to teaching as the art of bowing is related to violin playing or as the art of casting is related to trout fishing. It is essential and fundamental. Properly worded questions put to the class at the psychological moment may stimulate curiosity, arouse interest, spur and guide thinking, encourage expression. Through sagacious questioning, the teacher can maintain attention, discover and diagnose weaknesses, and fix knowledge in the mind. On the other hand, poorly worded questions put to the class at the wrong time may make for discontinuous thinking and confusion. They may even lead the class entirely away from the topic under discussion.

The poor question. *Many of the so-called poor questions listed below are used occasionally by the best teachers. In fact, under certain conditions and for certain special purposes, these kinds of questions may prove to be the most effective. It is true, nevertheless, that such questions do not tend to stimulate good thinking. Nor do they give the student practice in thought expression. The work of beginning teachers, of below-average teachers, of nervous teachers, and of teachers with poor discipline seems to be characterized by extensive use of questions like these:*

The question that answers itself: *"Don't substances expand when they are heated?" "Isn't sodium hydroxide a base?"*

The leading question: *"Is the pole of a magnet the place where most of the magnetic strength is concentrated?" Is chlorine a halogen?"*

The tugging question: *"Density is mass divided by what?"*

The ambiguous question: *"What happens when there is a short circuit?" "What takes place when an acid touches a metal?"*

The double question: *"Who discovered what about the action of electric currents in solutions?"*

The indefinite question: *"What about the specific heat of water?"*

The guessing question: *"Is sodium bicarbonate an acid or a base?"*

The echo question: *"Acceleration is velocity divided by time. What is acceleration?"*

The elliptic question: *"The atomic weight of oxygen is. . . ." "The mechanical advantage of an inclined plane is the length of the incline divided by its. . . ."*

Good professional practice. *If you would improve yourself in the art of questioning, make it a practice to incorporate critical and strategic questions in your lesson plan. Write them down, together with the "target" answers. Scrutinize them in the light of this discussion, improve them (if necessary), and then use them. There is nothing wrong wih a teacher's pausing in the course of a lesson to look in his lesson plan. Look down into your plan book, read the question to yourself, then look up and put the question to the class with confidence. Above all, be enthusiastically interested in the answer. As you improve in the questioning art, you will find that your teaching improves.*[1]

Zachariah Subarsky 1959

Work-sheets will not overcome the defects of poor instruction but they may be helpful especially in directing teacher and pupil attention to the more important phases of the unit topic by calling for definite, individual reactions to these phases.[2]

Archer W. Hurd 1930

Specific training in finding the central thought of a paragraph, determining the questions one must be able to answer in order to obtain an adequate understanding of a topic, and reading an entire block of material through for its general plan, results in a more thorough comprehension of the subject-matter than undirected study on the same material. Specific training and practice in answering thought questions based on the application of some scientific principle are more efficient than incidental training in answering thought questions. Training the pupil to make various types of analyses of the subject-matter increases the ability of the pupil to interpret and reproduce what he reads.[3]

Wilbur L. Beauchamp   1923

The writing of a permanent notebook does not increase immediate or delayed retention of facts for an average class. . . . A written exercise, in which the student answers questions designed to emphasize the important parts of an experiment, is as effective as a permanent notebook.[4]

L. W. Applegarth   1935

As far as the outcomes of instruction that can be measured by written examinations are concerned, there seems to be little demonstrable difference in the relative efficiency of the workbook and the notebook as a device for teachers in general science. . . . If there is any relation between the intelligence of pupils and the relative efficiency of either method, the notebook is slightly better for pupils with lower intelligence quotients and the workbook for pupils with higher intelligence quotients.[5]

George W. Peterson and Harl R. Douglass   1935

Problems to solve, skills to be practiced, information to be drilled, and materials to be reviewed often constitute the basis for recurring lessons in many teaching situations. Each type of lesson falls into its peculiar format and the success of each lesson depends upon proper execution of the format. Even the most routine lesson can be administered with finesse—finesse derived from constant examination of the tactics and strategy employed in presenting the lesson and retaining those procedures which prove to be most efficient.

Strengths and Weaknesses

Problems to solve consist of sets of questions, usually requiring the use of mathematics, intended to engage the time and attention of students. Such problems provide an opportunity to stretch the students' abilities and to extend what they have been taught beyond the immediate dimensions within which they were taught. Problems can be framed in which the answer follows closely upon the information provided in the problem or the answer can be sufficiently remote to challenge even the most precocious student. By being confronted with sets of problems reflecting a range of difficulty, students can discover for themselves what degrees of mental exercise they are really capable of achieving.

The ability to call upon accumulated knowledge and bring it to bear on a new situation must be brought into play when students attempt to solve problems. When properly conceived, problems exercise students' abilities to analyze situations and provide opportunities to use insight, intuition, and other of the so-called higher mental processes. Students derive real satisfactions from solving problems and especially so if the problems cast the student in the role of discoverer. Ideally, students approach problems with heuristic attitudes. They are to discover knowledge for themselves rather than be passive recipients thereof. If a problem challenges curiosity and brings into play any of the inventive faculties, the student will experience the tension and enjoy the triumph of mastery.

Problems teach exactness and the appreciation of its importance. The "precising" of the plan for solution, the testing of a solution and its final proof indicate the importance of exactness. Although there are many interpretations in science wherein one person's point of view may be held to be as valid as any other, the problems to solve lesson format alerts the student to a disciplined concept of consistency and agreement with a common set of postulates.

Too many of the wrong kinds of problems clumsily assigned can kill students' interest in a course, hamper their intellectual development, and misdirect their educational resources. Good problems cause the student to feel that to invest his time in their solution will produce a worthwhile accomplishment. In general, students should possess the power to solve the problems assigned to them and the requisite mathematical skills should either be already in the background or freshly clarified. The teacher's role is not so much that of taskmaster as that of setting the problems and providing help and guidance, not only in the solution of the problems immediately assigned but also in the development of problem solving skills in general. For example, students must be taught to extricate from the language of the problem the specific relationships for which they are expected to derive quantitative descriptions. Once students sense how to analyze problems and array the information contained in them, they are well along the way to mastery of problem solving skills. Another very valuable element of strategy is to learn to estimate in advance of calculation the general dimensions of the solution to a problem.

Problems to solve, especially if the work is to be done outside the usual classtime, loom large in the complex of things that decide whether or not students feel comfortable in a course. When competition for their time by other interests prevents returning to the next day's class with homework completed, unsolved problems cannot be compensated for by any of the tactics by which students influence teachers. Resistance to the problems to solve lesson format may stem more from this factor than from the reasons usually cited by delinquent students.

Drill lessons have for their purposes the perfection of skills or strengthening of associations. Their intent is to fix newly gained learnings. Drill activities are essential supplement to many other instructional formats. Overlearning of some kinds of material seems to be essential to memorization and the establishment of desirable habits. The many citations against the drill format stem more from its abuse than from intrinsic inefficiency.

Effective and economical drill is carried on with understanding, interest, and the realization that the specific exercises being practiced are the ones the learner needs. The student should feel satisfaction rather than annoyance and accept repetition as an essential prerequisite to permanence of learning. The drill activity should be an integrating experience on the whole of a process rather than on isolated elements. Each element of the drill should be understood and appreciated. Practice should be in as real a setting as possible and distributed over a number of short sessions. Drill should not be attempted until the students have an accurate and vivid impression of the skill or concept to be practiced. Lapses into error must be corrected immediately and a period provided at the close of the drill session for reflection, self-criticism, and self-assessment. As many channels of impression and response as possible should be used. Contemplate the learning process as one in which no single pathway is worn smooth but rather the terrain is explored until the best pathway is discovered. Effort should be made to have drill become increasingly self-prescribed, self-planned, self-directed, and self-evaluated.

If the definition of science developed in the beginning pages of this book is valid, the phrase, "to describe with ever-increasing accuracy," suggests that review becomes an automatically dictated aspect of many lessons in the pursuit of science. Teachers often feel called upon to retrace materials already covered on days prior to term-end examinations or when other pedagogical reasons require looking back through work already covered. In general, however, teaching the pursuit of science emphasizes the cumulative nature of the pursuit and students should recognize that materials taught today are subject to recall for reuse as the course unfolds with the descriptions of phonomena constantly taking on increased sophistication. The question students so often ask when examinations are announced: "How much of the material we have had will be covered on the examination?" provides opportunities for the teacher to emphasize the cumulative nature of the scientific endeavor.

EXAMPLES AND ILLUSTRATIONS

One type of lesson that may illustrate the drill format involves the use of an identification key. Although this kind of learning exercise is not as commonly employed as it once was, there are valuable goals to be gained from it. By design, identification keys parallel many of the features of procedure and logic used in the pursuit of science. To identify the specimen at hand becomes the problem. The key provides two or more alternative "hypotheses." By resorting to observation, the student selects the more consistent of the alternatives but, lacking sufficient data to establish a conclusion, he must proceed through successive stages of increasingly precise "hypotheses." When a conclusion is reached, the student knows how it was obtained and he senses that the validity of the conclusion hinges on the uniqueness of the sets of alternative "hypotheses" and the accuracy of his observations of the specimen.

A streamlined version of a key to the commoner minerals that has been developed by A. G. Applegarth illustrates this type of drill lesson.

KEY TO COMMON ROCK-FORMING MINERALS

1. Can be scratched with thumb nail .... Go to 2
   Cannot be scratched with thumb nail .... Go to 5

2. Can be split into sheets (has shiny lustre) .... Go to 3
   Cannot be split (usually light colored, may be dull or
   shiny) .... Go to 4

3. Easily split with a knife: sheets elastic: may be black,
   brown, or transparent .... Mica
   Less easily split with a knife: sheets brittle:
   transparent .... Clear Gypsum

4. Chalky or claylike: Can be crumpled into dust with fingers: has odor of clay when breathed upon .... Kaolin
   Smooth with soapy feel: will mark light streak on
   cloth: may be white or greenish color .... Talc

Smooth or granular, but without soapy feel: does not
mark on cloth .... Gypsum

Can be scratched with a penny .... Go to 6
Cannot be scratched with a penny .... Go to 7

6. Effervesces when touched with dilute HCl or sometimes
stained by impurities: 3 good cleavage planes .... Calcite
Does not effervesce: often in cubical crystals:
soluble in water: salty taste .... Salt or Halite

7. Can be scratched with knife blade or file .... Go to 8
Cannot be scratched with knife .... Go to 10

8. Scrape some powder loose. If it effervesces with cold acid
go back to 6. If effervesces with warm acid .... Go to 9
Does not effervesce with acid. Two cleavage planes.
Blackish or greenish color. Planes nearly at right angles
and when found as a mineral in rocks forms short,
squarish crystal grains .... Augite

9. Cleavage planes oblique angles. In rocks forms long,
slender crystal grains .... Hornblende
Usually shiny: crystalline .... Dolomite
Seldom shiny: usually dull, like unglazed dish .... Magnesite

10. Two good cleavage planes present: light colored, white,
pink, or gray: shiny lustre .... Feldspar
No cleavage planes present: may be crystalline or granular: crystals may be six-sided and pyramid shaped
at end .... Quartz

For Discussion and Further Study

1. How can a teacher maintain the feeling that his science course has continuity and still devote time to review and drill?

2. When using the "problems to solve" lesson format, how can the teacher keep student attention on the principles that are involved rather than permitting the student to become preoccupied with the mathematics of the problems?

3. Is it impossible for teachers to adapt such tried and true instructional materials as identification keys to providing overt instruction in the pursuit of science?

4. What psychological functions are "problems to solve" actually intended to achieve?

5. What should a science teacher do if he senses that his students lack proficiency in the mathematical skills that are needed to solve the kinds of problems that ordinarily accompany the science course?

References

1. Zachariah Subarsky, "The Art of Questioning." *The Science Teacher's World* (February 10, 1959). Reprinted by permission from *Science Teacher's World*, © 1959 by Scholastic Magazines, Inc.

2. Archer W. Hurd, in Francis D. Curtis, *A Third Digest of Investigations in the Teaching of Science.* Philadelphia: P. Blakiston and Sons Publishing Co., 1939, p. 44. Used by permission of McGraw-Hill Book Company.
3. Wilbur L. Beauchamp, in Francis D. Curtis, *A Digest of Investigations in the Teaching of Science.* Philadelphia: P. Blakiston and Sons Publishing Co., 1926, p. 85. Used by permission of McGraw-Hill Book Company.
4. L. W. Applegarth, in Curtis, *A Third Digest of Investigation in the Teaching of Science.* Philadelphia: P. Blakiston and Sons Publishing Co., 1939, p. 279. Used by permission of McGraw-Hill Book Company.
5. George Peterson and Harl R. Douglass, in Curtis, *ibid.,* p. 81. Used by permission of McGraw-Hill Book Company.

27

The Laboratory Exercise

. . . The first function of the enquiring laboratory . . . is the replacement of illustrations only of conclusions by illustrations of problem situations. It displays the phenomena which give rise to problems, the circumstances surrounding the acquisition of data for solving these problems, and the difficulties of working with and among these circumstances. . . . The second function of the enquiring laboratory is to provide occasions for and invitations to the conduct of minature but exemplary programs of enquiry. . . . The enquiring laboratory is characterized by a third general feature: it erases the artificial distinction between classroom and the laboratory, between mind and hand.[1]

Joseph J. Schwab 1962

I want to plead for laboratory work for all, on a simple scale. How can the general citizen understand the scientists' experimenting if he does not himself experience some of its trials and delights? The emphasis needs to be on doing simple things and trying to extract results honestly—not following cookbook instructions with servile care or verifying "what the book says" come what may.[2]

Eric M. Rogers 1953

Changing conceptions of the values and purposes of science teaching have tended toward an increasing emphasis upon laboratory work. The nature of the scientific enterprise is found in the methods by which the problems are attacked. Therefore, more attention should be directed to the processes or methods of seeking answers in the laboratory rather than putting so much stress on finding exact answers.[3]

Paul DeH. Hurd and Philip G. Johnson 1960

It is a waste of time, in the interests of scientific thinking, to require pupils to spend extended periods of time at representative drawing. In fact, it is worse than a waste of time, for it encourages bad habits of analytical study which are opposed to the interests of scientific thinking and constructive research. The excessive use of representative drawing is a serious pedagogical formalism which produces copyists instead of scientists and which creates distaste instead of enthusiasm for science.[4]

Fred C. Ayer 1916

If ability to do experimentation or to solve perplexities of a chemical nature is a desirable goal, practice in this experimentation—not practice in watching some one else experiment—is necessary . . . practice in solving problems and in exercising judgment must be given and . . . neither demonstration nor individual laboratory work following printed or other directions does give the opportunity for such practice . . . to obtain such outcomes the evidence points to individual, self-directed experimentation in problematic situations as the method offering the best possibilities of success.[5]

Ralph E. Horton 1928

A mere copying of methods, which are given in print, or even recording these in the pupil's own words, does not appreciably aid him in grasping the main points of the exercise, and is largely a waste of time.[6]

Morris F. Stubbs 1926

Students with absolutely no laboratory experience showed no laboratory resourcefulness whatever; they refused to touch the apparatus. . . . Maturity does not develop resourcefulness spontaneously; men and women do not acquire resourcefulness by mere circumstance of growing older. Neither may it be deduced that the bold asurance of adolescence is resourcefulness.[7]

H. A. Webb 1922

Based on comparative marks, the oral laboratory lesson *was far superior to the laboratory manual lesson. Judge by the fatigue of the teacher, the* laboratory manual lesson *is much easier in every way.*[8]

George W. Hunter 1922

Carefully written note-book work and neatly drawn diagrams of scientific apparatus do not increase pupils' knowledge of elementary science.[9]

Jacob E. Mayman 1912

One of the important functions of the laboratory is the deepening of a student's understanding that scientific and technological concepts and applications are closely related to his own natural environment. The laboratory in a science course is concerned with a combination of facilities and techniques that will enable the student to observe natural phenomena with a discerning eye, to make measurements and analyze the data recorded, and to engage in free-ranging investigations that do not necessarily have a predetermined end.[10]

M. H. Trytten 1963

The actualities of scientific investigation are not going to become significant to pupils through the chanting of incantations or filling in any five-step laboratory report forms. Only direct experience with the factors, preferably even unnamed, involved in creating some tentative order in the complex world will provide the pupils with an internal awareness of what science is like. At the core of such efforts to create some understanding of scientific inquiry is the most important invention of the past four hundred years—experimentation.[11]

Fletcher G. Watson 1953

The procedure of labeling prepared drawings and the pro- dure of making original drawings are equally effective with regard to the student's ability to acquire and remember factual information from his laboratory observations. The two methods were equally effective at all levels of student ability.[12]

Morris L. Alpern 1936

Three or four periods a week can be of extreme value to high school students in the laboratory. However, many of us invalidate this time by providing improper written materials for their use. . . . The student is not required to write more than a word or phrase here and there. . . . The attention of the student is directed toward those observations that the author wants him to make. . . . The experiments offered do not follow any organized pattern. . . . Most of the directions listed either directly or indirectly imply the answers to the questions asked.[13]

Frederick B. Eiseman, Jr. 1953

Any science teacher could readily find reasons to abandon individual lab exercises: too many students . . . no money for supplies . . . makeshift facilities . . . no time to maintain what little equipment there is. But his conscience tells him that lab exercises probably contribute as much—or even more—to students' scientific understanding than any of his own most elaborate demonstrations. So most teachers find some way to give their students firsthand scientific experience, despite the extra time and work involved. . . . All the material for a single exercise is packaged in an ordinary shoebox. There is no need to hunt for, assemble, and test materials and equipment each time the exercise is performed. In addition, each of the boxes contains an inventory card, and a student guide sheet is pasted underneath the lid. A student report form completes the shoebox. On laboratory days, the students are called to the storage shelves in teams, receive a box, sign the inventory card, and return to their seats. . . . The teacher, being free, can provide help where needed.[14]

Darrel Tomer 1958

Basically, laboratory exercises are done or performed as a means of practice or training. Common usage often fails to distinguish between laboratory exercises and experiments. Experiments are tests or trials,

366

tentative procedures, acts or operations for the purpose of discovering something unknown or testing a principle or supposition. Obviously, laboratory exercises can provide practice or training in designing, operating, and interpreting experiments, but they are quite likely to be contrived pedagogical devices and, as such, should be clearly distinguished from experimentation as it exists in the pursuit of science. Well designed and conducted laboratory exercises, however, can incorporate much of the spirit and many of the skills of experimentation.

Strengths and Weaknesses

The laboratory exercise can be a very efficient way to (1) add reality to textbook material, (2) develop first-hand familiarity with the tools, materials, and/or techniques of the pursuit of science, (3) create an environment in which the student can prove for himself something he already knows to be true, (4) give the student an opportunity to pit his labor against "par" in seeking an experimental answer, and (5) create opportunities wherein the student can predict events or circumstances and then design experiments to test the accuracy of his predictions.

The greatest single criterion in determining the value of a laboratory exercise is the manner in which it is encountered by the student. Ideally, a laboratory exercise evolves from a gradually accumulating background of things that are known leading up to something that is unknown but that can be found out by experimentation in a laboratory period. In actual practice, however, guide sheets, manuals, or other printed instructions are used to confront the student with a laboratory exercise. It is these instructions that have been the brunt of much criticism.

If the instructions for students entering upon a laboratory exercise are too detailed, the epithet of "cookbook" will be hurled at the authors. At the other extreme, students who are given inadequate instruction before going into a science laboratory can create not only inefficient chaos, but dangerous and destructive results.

Laboratory exercises should be presented to the student with progressively diminishing detailed guidance as the student advances in the pursuit of science. Instruction in the use of a piece of equipment new to the student or precautions which must be exercised in handling a strange, new reagent can rightfully be quite "cookbookish." As these situations recur, however, to repeat detailed instructions will contribute to the "slow learning" delinquency of the students.

Sooner or later as a laboratory program unfolds, the students should gain experience in designing, operating, interpreting, and evaluating their own experiments. To do this requires, of course, an accumulating backlog of information and skill. There may be little opportunity for

FIGURE 7. Properly supervised laboratory assistants become extra hands whereby a teacher can make special materials available to larger numbers of students.

this type of laboratory exercise in the elementary grades and junior high school. Many students will want to do this sort of thing at the high school level, and there should be many opportunities for the self-designed experiment in college science laboratory programs.

Unless a teacher has equal access to classroom and laboratory facilities, he must be very adroit in programming the approach to a concept so as to reach the "experimentation" stage on the days his students are scheduled to use the laboratory. If it were not for scheduling difficulties, students should go into the laboratory only as, when, and if individual laboratory work holds promise of being the most efficient means to accomplish the day's work. How closely the laboratory exercise is meshed with textbook and other learning activities is an important criterion of the probable success of the exercise.

Although it reduces the utilization factor for often expensive installations, the ideal setting for the teaching of science combines laboratory, classroom, and library facilities at each teacher station. Some teachers will add that at least one corner of the laboratory must provide wood and metal shop facilities and that greenhouse and darkroom facilities must be included or be quite readily available. If all such facilities are equally available, the teacher can proceed through the problem-setting and hypothesis-elaborating stages, and then move into the laboratory at the most logical and opportune time.

Another facet of the "meshing" problem is the time lag which invariably exists between the development of appropriate laboratory exercises and the addition of new subject matter to science courses of study. Early in the history of science, a scientist's experiments involved equipment and procedures simple enough to become the laboratory exercises for the classroom presentation of the principles that the scientist clarified. This is not so today. Nor is there operating today a recognized agency to create appropriate laboratory exercises when a new discovery is made that deserves to be and is rather quickly caught up in school curricula. This lag becomes all the more significant when we realize that new principles and theories tend to be increasingly complex and that they are sometimes quite difficult to learn, especially in comparison with the concepts and principles for which the science teaching profession has gradually accumulated a broad repertory of laboratory exercises, lecture demonstrations, and other teaching aids.

Another criterion of the value of a laboratory exercise thus becomes whether the exercise is really needed to accomplish what it purports to teach. There is little efficiency to be gained by doing a time-honored laboratory exercise simply because it occupies a place in a pedagogical repertory. In a similar vein, teachers should exploit every resource that holds promise of reducing the time lag between the appearance of a concept in the textbooks and the development of appropriate laboratory exercises. If the teaching of the concept seems to call for a laboratory approach, there are, of course, definite and worthwhile values to be gained from sheer repetition of classic experiments. These values must be identified for what they are and time spent to achieve them justified accordingly.

In the pursuit of science, the effectiveness of the scientist is often determined at least partially by his ability to describe and publish his work. The final criterion for judging the value of a laboratory exercise involves the student's report of the exercise. A laboratory exercise inadequately reported by a student becomes less valuable than one which teaches a student how to report an experiment.

Unless students are being trained to fit into a specific, on-going organization, no single format for presenting a laboratory report should be held sacred. The report should take its format from the nature of the experiment, and experiments can vary not only in the nature of the hypothesis being tested but in the sequence of procedures. Just as laboratory directors sometimes standardize the format of their research reports, science teachers can establish a preferred style for reporting laboratory exercises. The emphasis, however, should be on the actual communication of information.

For those who comprehend the function of the laboratory and experimentation in the pursuit of science, there is no need to emphasize the role of laboratory exercises in teaching the pursuit of science. But laboratory facilities are expensive and exercises are time-consuming. Science teachers must use the laboratory efficiently to counter the inroads being made on the time and money budgets of science departments by other and, for the time being, more popular portions of the school curriculum.

Examples and Illustrations

Schools differ widely in the amounts of time, equipment, and supplies for individual laboratory experiments that are provided to science teachers. A variety of examples and illustrations will be cited here to suggest the ingenuity teachers must exercise in providing the best possible adaptation of or substitutes for individual laboratory work.

The first examples have been selected to illustrate a kind of laboratory exercise that has been found to be effective as the first step toward advancing students beyond simply following directions in the laboratory manual, a practice that seems to be particularly likely to develop in high school chemistry. A type of laboratory assignment can be quite easily developed by combining the goals sought in several exercises. For example, one widely used laboratory exercise involves the stoichiometric decomposition of cupric carbonate to yield cupric oxide. The goal of a second exercise is to show the reduction of cupric oxide by hydrogen. To combine these exercises yields the assignment: Begin with cupric carbonate, end with copper, and compare the actual yield of copper with the weight present in the original sample of cupric carbonate.

A second example combines the exercises in which tin is converted to an oxide to provide data for determining the empirical formula of a compound and the demonstration of the reducing property of hydrogen or of hot carbon. In this case the assignment can be: Begin with tin, practice as much chemistry as you can, end with metallic tin and compare the weight recovered with the weight with which you began your work.

A third example follows the assignment: Begin with this sample of white marble and show me some carbon obtained from it. This assignment assumes that the student will collect carbon dioxide by the usual action of acid on the marble and then free the carbon by the action of a burning strip of magnesium.

In actual laboratory practice, the responses of students to assignments such as those in the preceding paragraphs can be very thought provoking. Students who have become totally dependent upon detailed instruction are completely dazed. Other slightly more resourceful students will begin searching through the laboratory manuals, confident that adequate instructions are surely to be found somewhere. Although much of a laboratory period may go by before it happens, sooner or later, looks of confident anticipation will break out here and there, and word will quickly spread that the assignment can be accomplished by retrieving and combining procedures from past laboratory periods. Some assignments also require the student to substitute reagents or modify procedures beyond the suggestions in the laboratory manual but in keeping with information provided by the textbook or class discussions. The students who are frustrated by this type of laboratory assignment cause soul searching on the part of the instructor; not so much because they didn't learn what they were expected to learn from prior laboratory exercises as because they are dumbfounded when they realize that they are expected to retrieve, re-order, and otherwise apply the skills and knowledge from prior exercises.

Newly developed laboratory procedures within the total scientific endeavor often suggest valuable laboratory exercises or modifications of the standard laboratory activities. Radioisotopes, for example, hold promise of improving many standard laboratory exercises and spawning new ones. So-called tracer experiments can provide valuable information on the up-take and circulation of specific elements during the germination of seeds, the sprouting of bulbs and tubers, healing of wounds in plant tissues and organs, and the reaction of plants to weed killers or other abnormal or normal environmental factors. A whole new dimension of obervations can be gained from the usual chemistry laboratory exercises when exceedingly minute quantities of an unstable isotope are used to trace one or more of the elements that are involved in the exercise.

The physical characteristics of sub-atomic particles, especially beta particles, reveal themselves with spectacular clarity if they are studied first-hand in simple laboratory exercises. To combine the usual counting procedures with the very adaptable technique of autoradiography can yield audio-visual aids of much longer lasting use than is possible with the short-life isotopes available for use by classroom teachers. These ideas are illustrated in detail in "Low Level Radioisotope Techniques," *The Science Teacher,* November 1960, and in "Amateur Scientist," *Scientific American,* May 1960.

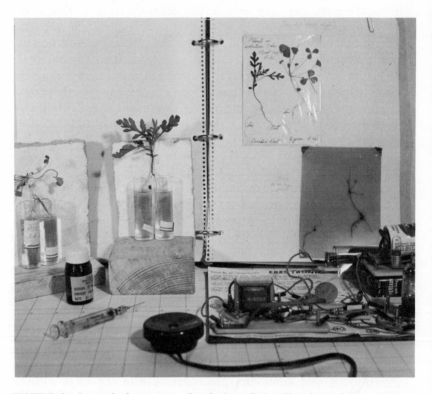

FIGURE 8. Increasingly accurate description of the directions of ion transport in root tissues was the outcome of this small dimension investigation using radioactive phosphorus.

Ion-exchange materials, cell and tissue culture, column and paper chromatography, polymerization, antigen-antibody reactions, and similar materials and procedures can be explored quite profitably by teachers and students who are looking for new and improved laboratory exercises.

For Discussion and Further Study

1. Are there elements of agreement reflected in all of the quotations used in the introduction to this section?

2. How important is the admonition to distinguish clearly between laboratory "experiments" and laboratory "exercises?"

3. Is it possible to develop laboratory exercises which provide overt training in the separate elements of the pursuit of science? Can an exercise, for example, train observational abilities or provide practice in the elaboration of hypotheses apart from the total complex of the procedures that are involved in the pursuit of science?

4. How can the directions as presented in typical school laboratory manuals be modified toward giving students more of the feel and spirit of exploration and discovery?

5. What precautions may cause students to look upon laboratory work as contributing to advancing their proficiency in the pursuit of science rather than being terminated by "handing in" a report at the end of the laboratory session?

References

1. Reprinted by permission of the publishers from Joseph J. Schwab and Paul F. Brandwein, *The Teaching of Science*. Cambridge, Mass.: Harvard University Press, Copyright 1962, by the President and Fellows of Harvard College. Pp. 52–56.

2. Eric M. Rogers, for Committee on Special Bulletins, N.S.T.A. "Science in Secondary Schools Today," *The Bulletin of the National Association of Secondary-School Principals*, NEA 37 (January 1953), p. 49. Reprinted by permission from the *Bulletin of the National Association of Secondary-School Principals*, January 1953. Copyright: Washington, D.C.

3. Paul DeH. Hurd and Phillip G. Johnson. *Rethinking Science Education*. The Fifty-ninth Yearbook of the National Society for the Study of Education. Chicago: University of Chicago Press, 1960, p. 334.

4. Fred C. Ayer, in Francis D. Curtis. *A Digest of Investigations in the Teaching of Science*. Philadelphia: P. Blakiston and Sons Publishing Co., 1926, p. 38. Used by permission of McGraw-Hill Book Company.

5. Ralph E. Horton, in Francis D. Curtis. *Second Digest of Investigations in the Teaching of Science*. Philadelphia: P. Blakiston Sons Publishing Co., 1931, p. 311. Used by permission of McGraw-Hill Book Company.

6. Morris F. Stubbs, in Curtis, *ibid.*, p. 320.

7. H. A. Webb, in Curtis, *A Digest of Investigations in the Teaching of Science*. Philadelphia: P. Blakiston and Sons Publishing Co., 1926, p. 67. Used by permission of McGraw-Hill Book Company.

8. George W. Hunter, in Curtis, *ibid.*, 1926, p. 62.

9. Jacob E. Mayman, in Curtis, *Second Digest of Investigations in the Teaching of Science*. Philadelphia: P. Blakiston and Sons Publishing Co., 1931, p. 320. Used by permission of McGraw-Hill Book Company.

10. M. H. Trytten. *Guidelines for Development of Programs in Science Instruction*. Washington: National Academy of Sciences–National Research Council, Office of Scientific Personnel, Publication 1093, 1963, p. 1.

11. Fletcher G. Watson. "Science in Secondary Schools Today," *Bulletin of National Association of Secondary-School Principals*, NEA (January 1953), p. 100. Reprinted by permission from the *Bulletin of the National Associa-*

tion of Secondary-School Principals, January 1953. Copyright: Washington, D.C.

12. Morris L. Alpern, in Curtis, *Third Digest of Investigations in the Teaching of Science.* Philadelphia: P. Blakiston and Sons Publishing Co., 1936, p. 379. Used by permission of McGraw-Hill Book Company.

13. Frederick B. Eiseman, Jr. "Laboratory Manuals and Workbooks," *The Science Teacher,* **20** (April 1953), pp. 116–117.

14. John H. Woodburn, reporting the work of Darrel Tomer. *Science Teacher's World,* Vol. III, No. 2 (February 20, 1958), p.1–T.

28

Small Group Formats

One of the most important ways a science teacher can create an abiding interest in science is through the use of student talent in the daily operations of the science classroom or laboratory. And one of the tried-and-true methods of doing this is the science squad. . . . It is wise to make the squad a formal organization so that students can receive service credit on their school record. . . . [Duties can include] daily preparation of apparatus . . . returning it to storage . . . service the bulletin board . . . general clean-up of the science room and the preparation room . . . operation of projectors . . . make charts, models, and slides . . . daily care of plants and feeding of animals . . . charge of the classroom science library . . . cutting stencils and running the mimeograph machine . . . tutoring . . . checking out and in of materials and equipment for laboratory work.

The time a teacher devotes to setting up a squad and training the members will be returned a hundredfold. A good squad makes classroom life less hectic, more pleasant, and considerably more efficient. Furthermore, squads can be self-perpetuating when senior members train younger members, thus insuring continuity from school year to school year.[1]

Alexander Joseph 1959

The planning and selection of activities should take into account the composition of the group, the competency of the teacher, and nature of the learning that is in progress. Encouraging pupil participation in decision-making, planning, and evaluation will make the activity more purposeful and the attainment of desired goals more probable.[2]

Glenn O. Blough   1960

Good leaders are needed for groupings of three or more. Haphazard assignment of leadership responsibilities may give difficulty, especially if a "clown" or "slave" is put in charge of a group; many pupils will refuse to work under unacceptable individuals and many pupils will not know how to accept leadership responsibilities. . . . A teacher should not be discouraged if grouping procedures do not come up to expectations. For one thing, he is dealing with individuals who have minds of their own; no group activities will go exactly as the teacher has planned. For another thing, secondary school pupils are just learning group processes; in many systems they have been given no practice within curricular boundaries. Failures are inevitable. But failures should not end grouping; the pupils probably need more experiences in simpler situations.[3]

Walter A. Thurber and Alfred T. Collette   1959

The characteristic feature of these formats is that the students work in groups containing approximately four individuals. Almost any lesson format can be adapted to small group administration but it is most often used for projects, laboratory exercises, student demonstrations, panel discussions, and similar activities. Any one of the usual systems can be used to organize the group and the organization can either be established by the instructor while the groups are forming or the members can designate their own chairman, recorder, or other "officers."

Strengths and Weaknesses

To the extent that the pursuit of science has or will become a pursuit requiring group effort, young people need experience in performing as effective members of groups. There are few things to be done in the classroom or laboratory that can be done by small groups under circumstances requiring less effort on the teacher's part than if these things were to be assigned to the individual students. In fact, many teachers become quite impatient with the apparent inefficiency of the small group format and are quick to abandon it. Furthermore, any improvement in group participation is so difficult to observe or measure that few teachers will recognize when the values inherent in the group format are being attained.

For one reason or another, many students have picked up experience in working in small groups and bring to any new situation the behavior they developed in these prior experiences. The member of the group who "learned" how to dominate the group will tend to dominate another group, just as the less forward person who found a haven within the group format will be difficult to bring out and be made to become a productive member of the group. Unless corrective measures are taken, the self-confident person tends to become overconfident, and the reticent or shy member of the group becomes increasingly so. The alert teacher acquires a repertory of techniques whereby these weaknesses of the group format can be at least partially avoided, but such weaknesses seem to be inherent in the format.

Properly administered, the small group format furnishes opportunities to discover and nurture talents that might not show through while the students are functioning in the usual class organization. Many young people will create the impression of being not at all given to examining ideas critically when doing so requires them to "speak up" in class. These people, however, take a very active part in the discussion whereby a small group arrives at a decision to do or not to do something. Conversely, those people who seem to dominate class discussion in large groups may show completely different behavior patterns while functioning in small groups.

It is the principle of synergism that requires the teacher to keep the small group format within his repertory. Whenever the goal set for a lesson may be attained more effectively by exploiting the synergistic effect, use of the small group format should be considered. If young people gain practice in coalescing their individual efforts so that the total effect is greater than the individual effects taken separately, they will have gained something that is held to be quite valuable by the people who are sold on the "team" approach to the pursuit of science.

Behavior patterns already acquired by students may not only reverse the synergistic principle but also create negative synergism. There are always those students who are quick to exploit any opportunity to socialize or promote the achievement of goals thought to be more immediately valuable than those inherent in the assigned objective. Unless the teacher can be confident that his students lack these negative behavior patterns, he must include in his plans for the group format adequate disciplinary precautions. When such precautions loom larger than the values unique to the small group format, the values are quite likely to be sacrificed.

The small group format places additional stress on availability of apparatus and supplies. To delay progress of four or five people, obviously, is less efficient than delay involving an individual. Thus, planning for group work must anticipate needed supplies, references, and equipment, and ensure availability.

For Discussion and Further Study

1. Is it valid to argue that inasmuch as science is becoming increasingly a "team" enterprise, teachers should give science students experience in working as members of teams?

2. What types of course content might be approached most profitably through a team format? Least profitably?

3. How much time should a science teacher be willing to invest in improving the abilities of his students to work as team members: As team leaders?

4. Does Joseph's estimate of the return from time invested in setting up and training a squad of laboratory assistants reflect familiarity with typical students in typical teaching situations?

5. Is there a professional ethical hazard in the exploitation of student assistants? Is it valid to argue that the added instruction they receive is adequate compensation for their labor?

References

1. Alexander Joseph. "Student Science Squads," *Science Teacher's World*, Vol. V, No. 5 (April 7, 1959), p. 1–T. Reprinted by permission from *Science Teacher's World,* © 1959 by Scholastic Magazines, Inc.
2. Glenn O. Blough. *Rethinking Science Education.* The Fifty-ninth Yearbook of the National Society for the Study of Education. Chicago: University of Chicago Press, 1960, p. 143.
3. Walter A. Thurber and Alfred T. Collette, *Teaching Science in Today's Secondary Schools.* Boston: Allyn & Bacon, 1959, p. 434.

29

The Term Paper
or
Special Report

The research report is never anything but the description of
an actual study *which has been carried to completion by
the scholar. The essay, on the other hand, is a* discussion
*of some subject or problem, usually expressing the writer's
opinion, interpretation, or point of view. . . . In the essay
the writer may simply show that he has thought about the
problem, or he may describe his personal observations and
experiences with it, or he may analyze and classify the
opinions and the scholarly discoveries of others regarding it.*[1]

Tyrus Hillway 1956

*First should come a clear statement of motive—of what
is to be attempted, what it is desired to find out. This should
be followed by an explanation or justification of the particular form given to the experiment. The why and wherefore
being thus made clear, an exact account of what is done
should follow; then would come the observations made and
the results obtained. The conclusions to be drawn and
their bearing on the question under discussion having been*

most carefully pointed out, the next experiment should be led up to. Throughout, the language should be such as to make the account a personal one, leaving no doubt that something which had been done and witnessed by the writer was described.[2]

Henry E. Armstrong   1910

The first few paragraphs should orient the reader and connect the new work with the current situation in the field. . . . It is important that enough is said so that an uninformed reader can acquire a correct picture of where the new fits in with the old. Sufficient references should always be given to enable the history of past work to be traced. . . . Usually the next part will deal with the method used in the research. . . . If new procedures or new variants of old procedures have been employed, these should be described. Ideally, sufficient detail should be given to enable a research worker on another continent to duplicate the method. . . . It is vital to publish the actual data on which the conclusions are based. . . . Mathematical derivations should start from elementary principles or from equations for whose origin a reference is given. . . . The final conclusions should be supported by a clear argument leading directly from the experimental results. . . . It is extremely important that proper credit be given, usually at the end of the paper, for assistance from other scientists.[3]

E. Bright Wilson, Jr.   1952

A student report is an account brought back or presented, an announcement of some matter specially investigated, or an announcement of what has been discovered by a student who was sent to examine, explore, or investigate. "Specially" is the word in this definition that distinguishes the student report lesson format from the ordinary textbook assignment or recitation.

Strengths and Weaknesses

Not only can the student report increase the amount of information brought to bear on a subject but this format also helps the teacher transfer some of the responsibility for the information gathering process to the students. According to some teachers, the best student reports grow out of problems actually encountered by the class and in which the members of the class are actively interested.

The student report is a natural data-gathering technique and thus can find many appropriate incidences for employment in the pursuit of many topics. This is especially true if the teacher encourages consideration of topics beyond the limits of his own remembered experiences. Asking students to seek additional information beyond that immediately at hand should be done by the teacher neither apologetically nor to cover up what he might feel was an uncalled for shortcoming on his part. The pursuit of science is becoming more and more a team effort and no one individual is expected to command the whole of it.

Use of the student-report format carries with it the additional value of teaching students the skills of abstracting material and presenting oral reports. Unfortunately, these skills must be taught and the teaching of these skills often becomes a part of the science teacher's prerequisites if he really hopes to capitalize upon the advantages of the student-report format. A student report ineptly presented frequently turns out to be boring and confusing if it is audible and sometimes it is not even that.

Because the student-report format is widely used at many grade levels and in many different subjects, students are likely to have predetermined attitudes and habits about how a report should be prepared and presented. Too often, these attitudes lead to verbatim copied material with a minimum of analysis, criticism, or composition. Sharply structured assignments must be given if these weaknesses are to be overcome. Finally, student reports tend to be ineffective if the class has the traditional attitude of expecting to be held responsible for only that material presented in the textbook or by the teacher.

Examples and Illustrations

The examples that follow are intended to illustrate how the student-report format can be so used as to exploit its strengths and diminish its weaknesses. In the first example, the six questions were assigned to serve as the structuring of the report and as a mechanical safeguard against verbatim copying, and the students were advised to cast the report in the first person.

CHEMIST: *Sir Humphry Davy*   DATES: *1778–1829*   HOME: *England*

1. What event, circumstance, or process did this chemist's work enable us to describe more accurately, understand more clearly, or reproduce more effectively?

My work enabled people to describe more accurately and to understand more clearly the action of electric current on solutions, electrochemical phenomena, and the composition and state of the caustic alkalies, specifically caustic soda and caustic potash. My experiments also led to the discovery of several new elements, sodium and potassium among others. These discoveries, of course, explained many circumstances and events with which these elements were connected.

2. What prevailing point of view or manner of doing something did this chemist's work improve upon?

Until my experiments, caustic alkalies were thought to be simple indivisible substances. They were known to combine with all kinds of other substances, but it was thought utterly impossible to break them down into simpler substances. They were therefore considered to be elements. In 1807, I subjected caustic potash and later caustic soda to electrolysis, and showed that these caustic alkalies were compounds of electrochemical action. This strengthened the connection between chemistry and electricity as shown by Anthony and Nicholson Carlisle's experiments on the decomposition of water by electrolysis.

3. What things in the early life, training, and work of this chemist probably contributed most to his ultimate success?

I was the eldest of five children born into a middle-class English household. I went to the local grammar school, where my intelligence was manifest in mischief and day-dreaming, until I reached the age of sixteen. At that time my father died, consequently I was apprenticed to the local doctor, one Bingham Borlas. It was in the doctor's apothecary that I had my first contact with chemistry, after having set myself a rigorous course of self-instruction in the arts and sciences. From preparing pills and medicines, I went on to more complicated chemical experiments. These experiments included disproving Lavoisier's theory that the "caloric," an imponderable fluid of heat, was responsible for the heat and light given off during combustion. I supported Nicholson's theory (heat was not a fluid but the motion of the constituent particles of matter) and proved it to be correct by an experiment involving the rubbing together of two pieces of wax enclosed by ice. If caloric were pumped in, it would have melted the ice through which it passed. Only the wax melted, however, confirming my theory.

About this time, I made the acquaintance of Davies Giddy, afterwards Gilbert, who was president of the Royal Society. Giddy recommended me to Dr. Thomas Diddoes, who in 1798 was establishing a Medical Pneumatic institution at Bristol for investigating the medical properties of various gases. I was released from my indenture and installed as superintendent of this institution towards the end of 1798. Here I carried on experiments to provide information on the physiological properties of gases, and discovered "laughing gas." This discovery made me known throughout England and led to an invitation by the Royal Institution to be assistant lecturer in chemistry and director of the laboratory. It was at the Royal Institution that I became interested in electrolysis and electrochemistry, and developed the theory of electrochemical action which led to my experiments with casutic alkalies.

My theory was based on the hypothesis that chemical and electrical attraction were produced by the same cause.

4. What hypothesis led this chemist to his discovery or invention?

My hypothesis was this: If an electric current is passed through molten solutions of sodium hydroxide and potassium hydroxide (caustic soda and caustic potash respectively), then, a disintegrating effect will take place resulting in the decomposition of these fixed alkalies, whose chemical affinity is electrical and a property of their constituent particles.

5. What observations or circumstances most probably triggered his hypothesis?

While at the Royal Institution, I became so interested in electrochemistry that this became my specialty. Previous experiments and discoveries by four chemists influenced my work. Alessandro Volta set up the ground work for the electrochemical field with his discovery that electric current could be generated in a pile consisting of discs of copper, zinc, and paper. Soon afterwards, Berzelius decomposed compounds by means of voltaic electricity, and Nicholson and Anthony Carlisle showed that this current could decompose water into hydrogen and oxygen. I performed many studies to clarify three major problems concerning the Carlisles' experiments. These problems were "(1) If electricity did tear the water particles into these two components, what accounted for the fact that gases bubbled up at widely separated points? (2) Why did the gases not appear at the center of a vessel of water rather than near the electric wires? (3) When the terminal wires of a voltaic battery were immersed in 'pure' water, acid could be detected at the negative pole and alkali at the positive. How could this be reconciled with the accepted theory of the composition of water?"

I first proved that the foreign ingredients found in the electrolysis of water were merely contaminants, and by using vessels made of agate or gold with connecting wires of platinum, excluded them. I finally clarified the mechanism of the electrolytic process by disproving Ritter's theory that the failure of bubbles to appear in the middle of the electrolytic cell indicated action took place at the poles: at the positive pole water gained positive electricity to become oxygen; at the negative pole it gained negative electricity to become hydrogen.

To show that electrolysis occurred within solution and to show that substances could migrate through a solution, I "placed the solution in three vessels, connected by asbestos wicks and placed the leads from the poles of a voltaic battery to the two outer vessels. In each vessel I dropped some powdered litmus; a change in its color would indicate the breakdown of any compounds the vessels contained. I found that if I dissolved a neutral salt in the end vessels and closed the circuit, the litmus in these vessels changed color, but the litmus in the middle did not. Moreover, I showed that the constituents of the salt were migrating, by placing a solution of sodium sulfate in one of the end vessels and a solution of barium nitrate in the other. When the circuit was closed, a precipitate of insoluble barium sulfate formed in the middle vessel, indicating the passage of the barium in one direction and the sulfate in the other."[4] From these results I formulated a theory of electrochemical action. This theory stated that the force of combination between constituents of electrically decomposed compounds was electrical and was a property of the constituent particles. Chemical combination was a union of oppositely charged particles. The poles of a battery forced the particles to move in opposite directions. "As each particle moved toward one of the poles, it was grasped . . . by a particle of opposite charge moving in the opposite direction. Such a scheme very nicely explained all the observed results: Gases and other substances were deposited at the poles, particles migrated toward their respective attractive poles, but at any point between the poles the electronegative and electropositive particles combined with each other to render the solution electrically neutral."[5] In order to verify this theory, I began experimentation with caustic alkalies.

6. What was the basic design and steps of the procedure by which he conducted his investigation(s) and/or experiments?

"A small piece of pure potash, which had been exposed for a few seconds to the atmosphere, so as to give conducting powers to the surface, was placed upon an insulated disc of platina, connected with the negative side of the battery of the power of 250 of 6 and 4, in the state of intense activity; and a platina wire, communicating with the positive side was brought into contact with the upper surface of the alkali. The whole apparatus was in the open atmosphere.

"Under these circumstances I soon observed a vivid action to take place. The potash began to fuse at both its points of electrization. There was a violent effervescence at the upper surface; at the lower or negative surface there was no liberation of elastic fluid; but small globules having a high metallic lustre, and being precisely similar in visible characters to quicksilver, appeared, some of which burnt with explosion and bright flame, as soon as they were formed, and others remained, and were merely tarnished, and finally covered by a white film which formed on their surfaces.

"These globules, numerous experiments soon showed to be the substance I was in search of, and a peculiar inflammable principle the basis of potash. I found that platina was in no way connected with the result, except as the medium for exhibiting the electrical powers of decomposition; and a substance of the same kind was produced when pieces of copper, silver, gold, plumbago, or even charcoal were employed for completing the circuit. . . .

"Soda, when acted upon in the same manner as potash, exhibited an analogous result, but the decomposition demanded greater intensity of action in the batteries, or the alkali was required to be in much thinner or smaller pieces. . . .

"The substance produced from potash remained fluid at the temperature of the atmosphere at the time of its production, that from soda, which was fluid in the degree of heat of the alkali during its formation became solid on cooling, and appeared having the lustre of silver."[6]

—Jane Levine

The second illustration of the term paper or special-report format shows how a student's response can be correlated with other aspects of the pursuit of science. Reference has been made in Chapter 16 to the subject and setting of the following term paper.

AUTUMNAL COLORATION IN TREES

Of all the physiological changes exhibited by deciduous trees, the most dramatic is that of autumnal coloration. Poets and artists have long rhapsodized over the dazzling hues of the fall foliage. Magnificent as this spectacle is, its beauty is matched by its complexity. Scientists are still attempting to describe accurately the interplay of factors responsible for autumn pigmenta-

CHLOROPHYLL

tion. It is the purpose of this paper to review briefly some of the more significant studies that have sought to identify the factors that are related to and influence autumnal coloration and to pay special attention to disparities associated with it.

Perhaps it is best to begin with those studies which have identified the pigments that are involved. These pigments fall into three main categories:

BETA - CAROTENE

the chlorophylls, the carotenoids, and the anthocyanins and anthoxanthins. Our knowledge of these pigments can be traced largely to the research of Richard Willstatter who isolated and worked out their basic structures.

The best known plant pigment is chlorophyll, the green substance that plays the well known role in photosynthesis. Willstatter demonstrated that chlorophyll is not homogeneous and several types have now been distinguished.

Two varieties, chlorophyll *a* and chlorophyll *b,* constitute the green pigments of the higher plants. These two compounds differ only slightly; both have a central magnesium atom surrounded by four pyrrhole rings, but chlorophyll *b* differs from chlorophyll *a* by the substitution of a CHO group for a methyl radical. Thus, chlorophyll *a* has the empirical formula, $C_{55}H_{72}O_5N_4Mg$ as compared to $C_{55}H_{70}O_6N_4Mg$ for chlorophyll *b.*[7]

In close association with chlorophyll are the yellow pigments, the carotenoids. These are found in water-soluble protein complexes and/or dissolved in lipid droplets.[8] The carotenoids have been described as "yellow to red pigments of aliphatic or acyclic structure, composed of isoprene units (usually eight) linked together." They are commonly divided into two classes: the carotenes, which are very soluble in hydrocarbons and the xanthophylls which are more soluble in ethanol.[9]

Of the four types of carotenes—α, β–, and γ–carotene and lycopene, β–carotene is the most common, occurring in all green tissues of the higher plants. It is often, but not always, associated with α–carotene.[10] Xanthophylls are about the same as carotenes, but they have oxygen atoms in addition to the usual carotene components. Luteol $(C_{40}H_{56}O_2)$ is the most common xanthophyll.

It has been postulated that carotenoids are used to form the long phytol chain of the chlorophyll molecule. This is indicated by experiments performed on etiolated seedlings. In the absence of light, these plants produce carotenoids, but no chlorophyll. When the seedlings were transferred to the light, however, the quantity of carotenoids decreased just as chlorophyll was being formed. In addition, it was discovered that wavelengths of light most efficient in bringing about carotenoid destruction were also the most efficient in promoting chlorophyll synthesis.[11] Other recent research shows that carotenoids may also absorb light to be used photosynthetically.[12]

The next large group of pigments under consideration, the anthocyanins, are responsible for the reds and violet-reds of autumn foliage. The anthocyanins are glycosides which have been formed by the combination of a sugar and a complex cyclic compound called an *anthocyanidin.* Known sugar components of the anthocyanins are glucose, galactose, rhamnose, and gentiobiose. The anthocyanins are water-soluble and are found dissolved in the cell sap, the cytoplasmic membranes being impermeable to them. Anthocyanins are sometimes found in plant cells as crystals or as amorphous solid bodies.[13]

The basic constituent of the anthocyanins is the flavone molecule, which has the following structure:[14]

The pH of the cell fluid influences the color of the pigment. Acids cause it to turn red; bases cause it to turn blue. The blue and purple shades, however, are restricted to flower petals.[15]

Anthoxanthins are glycosides which are very similar to anthocyanins. Anthoxanthins, however, produce only pale yellow colors; often they are entirely colorless.[16] Anthoxanthins can be converted to anthocyanins in chemical experiments and it is believed that such a transformation occurs naturally in living plants.[17] The biochemical function of the anthocyanins and anthoxanthins in the plant is unknown.

Toward the end of the growing season, the plant pigments undergo successive changes which bring about the phenomenon of autumnal coloration. First there is, by some unknown process, a preferential destruction of chlorophyll in the leaf. This unmasks the carotenoids, which have been present throughout the growing season, and the leaf turns yellow. The carotenoids themselves are undergoing changes. Zeaxanthol, an isomer of luteol, becomes the most abundant xanthophyll constituent.[18]

Meanwhile, in certain species, the anthocyanin pigments are being formed. The exact mechanism which effects their formation is still a mystery, but it has been observed that several factors influence anthocyanin concentration.

Production of anthocyanins seems to be dependent on the sugar accumulation in plant tissues. Environmental factors such as high light intensity, low temperature, shortage of water, and low nitrogen supply, which favor an increase in sugar content, often favor the synthesis of anthocyanins. Conditions which check sugar increase usually check anthocyanin increase, too.[19] This probably accounts for the observations that autumn foliage is brightest after a period of cool, bright weather, and that the trees at the top of a mountain seem to display brighter reds than the trees in the valley. Contrary to popular belief, frost does not cause leaves to turn; frost will reduce brilliance of colors by severely injuring leaves before pigments reach their maximum development.

Non-environmental conditions which affect pigmentation are: the genetic make-up of the plant, the pH of the cell sap, the physical state of the anthocyanins (in solution or absorbed), and the modifying effects on color of such compounds as tannins and anthoxanthins.[20] Also, a phosphate deficiency or the withdrawal of phosphate and nitrogen during senescence can cause an increase in the amount of anthocyanins.

Various disparities of autumnal coloration challenge the theories of biochemists. For example, it has been observed that the coloration of sumac leaves proceeds from the lowest and innermost leaves to the highest and outermost; in sugar maples the process is exactly the reverse. It would seem that the outer leaves should color first, since they get the most light and have a greater sugar content because of their higher metabolic rate. On the other hand, the lower leaves are older than the others, and might, therefore, be expected to senesce and color first. No satisfactory explanation has yet been given for this phenomenon, mainly because such an explanation requires a more detailed description of the leaf processes than is now available.

A more striking abnormality and one that seems to suggest explanations rather easily is the early coloration of certain isolated sections of a tree. In one instance, a sugar maple showed several limbs on which the leaves began autumnal coloration well in advance of the total foliage. To note that asphalt pavement had been laid beneath the affected portion of the tree would suggest that root injury might be responsible for this discrepancy. To observe, however, that there are many other instances of this disparity that occur in the absence of apparent root injury demands that a more sophisticated hypothesis be entertained.

There are other instances in which premature coloration is apparently precipitated by injury. Oak leaves that have been creased sharply tend to color beyond the crease well in advance of coloration of those portions closer to the stem. Trees have been observed in which those limbs above a supporting device that constricted the stem colored before those limbs below the mechanical constriction. In one instance, the same tree was observed to exhibit this disparity two years in a row.

Several entire trees have been observed to color in advance of other members of the same species in practically identical habitats. Two instances of this observation, upon closer examination, were found to have had soil spread several inches deep about the base of the tree. One of the trees died during the following winter and the second was observed to repeat exhibition of the disparity. It was interesting to note that the thickness of the soil layer in the latter instance was not as great as in the former. Each of these disparities involving injury, constriction, or impairment of metabolic function in any way points sharply toward heavy involvement of premature coloration with the total metabolism of the tree.

In the case of the trees whose roots were covered with extra soil, the action probably leads to "smothering" the young roots. Many studies[21] have shown that an adequate circulation of air in the soil is essential to the proper functioning of a plant's root system. Similarly, studies have proved that oxygen is necessary for the respiratory activity of the phloem and its role in maintaining translocation.

Another irregularity in pigmentation occurs in certain trees during the ripening of fruit. In the horse chestnut, for example, those twigs which bear fruits have been observed to turn to deep yellow well before any tinge of coloration appears in nearby, non-fruit bearing twigs. The most obvious inference is that the transportation of nutrients uniquely associated with the formation and ripening of the fruit disturbs in one way or another the total metabolism of the fruit bearing twig.

Finally, disparities in the coloration schedule of trees often occur where they receive abnormally extended periods of illumination. Quite often trees closest to street lights retain their green color several days, even weeks, after the trees farther from the lights have begun autumnal coloration. Equally often, the leaves surrounding a street light will remain green after other leaves on the same tree farther from or shielded from the light have not only colored but been shed.

Adequate though they are to capture the admiration of anyone who sees the brilliant colors of trees in their autumn foliage, the complexity of the physio-chemical reactions that accompany these changing colors is equally adequate to delay their accurate description. And it is not only the beauty of this phenomenon that drives one to seek a description that is sufficiently accurate and detailed to facilitate prediction, management, or control. In effect, the unfolding, maturing, and ultimate shedding of leaves parallels the total birth, growth, senescence, and ultimate death of an individual. Who knows, perhaps an hypothesis that is adequate to encompass the many disparities to be observed in autumnal leaf coloration might also shed light on the singularly significant phenomenon of senescence.

Obviously, it is entirely beyond expectations to be able to close this paper with such an hypothesis. The best that can be done is to suggest the probable general nature that this hypothesis might reflect—a suggestion that includes three elements together with the assumption that all manner of interaction might occur. First, if there is a degradation of transport efficiency within the tissues of a pigment-prone leaf, then the abnormal concentrations of metabolates will lead to abnormal pigment changes. Second, if environmental factors undergo changes adequate to create metabolates within the tissues of leaves in excess of the transport potential of normally functioning transport tissues, then the abnormal pigment changes in a pigment-prone leaf. Third, action of either of the previous factors may precipitate the formation of a "senescence" substance which, if it reaches the concentration that is attained during normal autumnal changes, then premature coloration will occur.

Each of these factors lends itself to experimental investigation. It is the author's hopes that she will be able to continue her study of the data revealed by experiments already conducted that bear on these factors and, if appropriate to do so, attempt to design additional experiments whereby increased accuracy will be reflected in the effort to describe the spectacularly beautiful and thought-provoking phenomenon of autumnal leaf coloration.

—Mary Lynn Hendrix

For Discussion and Further Study

1. Should special reports and term papers be generally assigned or should these formats be limited to a carefully selected portion of a teacher's class members?

2. What precautions might prevent student reports from becoming imitations of encyclopedic material?

3. How can a teacher structure the special report or term paper assignment to encourage students to gain desired information?

4. Are there safeguards against students postponing work on such major assignments as term papers until the end of the allotted time?

5. What aspects of the pursuit of science are likely to be especially nurtured by completion of term papers or special reports?

References

1. Tyrus Hillway. *Introduction to Research.* Boston: Houghton Mifflin, 1956, pp. 234–35.
2. Henry E. Armstrong. *The Teaching of Scientific Method and Other Papers on Education.* London: The Macmillan Company, 1910, p. 266.
3. E. Bright Wilson, Jr. *An Introduction to Scientific Research.* New York: McGraw-Hill, 1952, pp. 359–63. Used by permission of McGraw-Hill Book Company.

4. L. Pearce Williams. "Humphry Davy," *Scientific American,* **202** (June 1960), pp. 106–16.

5. *Ibid.,* p. 111.

6. Adapted from Sir Humphry Davy's writings by Jane Levine, a student at Walter Johnson High School, Bethesda, Maryland.

7. Erston V. Miller. *The Chemistry of Plants.* New York: Reinhold Publishing Corporation, 1957, p. 50.

8. Goodwin Trevor. *Carotenoids, Their Comparative Biochemistry.* New York: Chemical Publishing Company, 1924, p. 6.

9. *Ibid.,* p. 1.

10. *Ibid.,* p. 6.

11. Erston V. Miller. *The Chemistry of Plants.* New York: Reinhold Publishing Corporation, 1957, p. 53.

12. Jacob Levitt. *Plant Physiology.* New York: Prentice-Hall, 1954, p. 126.

13. Donald Anderson and Bernard Meyer. *Plant Physiology.* Princeton, N.J.: D. Van Nostrand Company, 1952, p. 388.

14. "Anthocyanins and Anthoxanthins." *Encyclopedia Britannica,* 1960, Vol. II, p. 27.

15. Donald Anderson and Bernard Meyer. *Plant Physiology.* Princeton, N.J.: D. Van Nostrand Company, 1952, p. 388.

16. Erston V. Miller. *The Chemistry of Plants.* New York: Reinhold Publishing Corporation, 1957, p. 59.

17. *Ibid.,* p. 60.

18. Robert Hill and C. P. Whittingham. *Photosynthesis,* New York: John Wiley & Sons, 1958, p. 30.

19. Donald Anderson and Bernard Meyer. *Plant Physiology.* Princeton, N.J.: D. Van Nostrand Company, 1952, p. 389.

20. *Ibid.,* p. 388.

21. James Bonner and Frederick Galston. *Principles of Plant Physiology.* San Francisco: W. H. Freeman & Company, 1952, p. 226.

30

Panels, Interviews, and Debates

It has been a typical experience in schools that many resource visitors fail to come up to expectations and to interest young people. This is usually because they have been formally invited to speak to a group and have consequently prepared a formal, and sometimes highly academic, discourse in advance. When they are invited simply to answer questions the situation itself precludes a stodgy and uninteresting talk and promises, by its very nature, a highlighting of those aspects in which young people are especially interested.[1]

M. L. Story   1957

The individual participating in debate . . . (1) learns what good clear, straight thinking is, has his reasoning sharpened, and learns about logic; (2) gains poise and self-control, learns how to think on his feet before people; (3) learns to argue effectively in a controlled manner.[2]

Wesley P. Callender, Jr.   1957

Young people are assisted in improving their effectiveness
in thinking with the help of language when those with whom
they are in contact, and especially their teachers, have a high
standard of discipline in thought and communication. Lack
of definiteness in a student's discourse or lack of recognition
of indefiniteness in that of others is a sign that his education
is being mishandled in an important way.[3]

The Committee on the Function of
Science in General Education   1937

The panel format features a discussion by a select number of informed persons of vital, interesting, and, usually, controversial subjects. Its proper audience are those who are interested in informed bias, and the panelists are permitted to use rhetorical persuasion. To debate is to argue or dispute, hence, to discuss or examine a question or issue by considering evidence on both sides. Debaters in their resort to rhetorical persuasion are expected to be limited by the usual discipline of logic and reasoning.

Strengths and Weaknesses

These formats exercise skill in dialectical techniques and discipline and their use can develop certain degrees of social poise. In the minds of many science teachers, however, these goals are scarcely those of science, and can better be left as the responsibility of other facets of the educational enterprise. Assuming, however, that a class enrolls students who possess the skills required for panel members and debaters, the efficient teacher may find occasion to use these formats. They provide one of the few means whereby controversial issues can be brought up for classroom discussion and those teachers who are quite sensitive to the spirit of science, if they lack an appropriate format, tend to yield discussion of controversial issues to the social sciences or some other part of the total school program. In some instances, however, the information required to produce an intelligent airing of controversial issues is truly within the domain of science and, all too often, exclusively so.

At first glance, these formats appear to be completely out of place in the science classroom. In the pursuit of science, for example, conclusions arise from objectively verified hypotheses, not from rhetorical supremacy. Biased opinions, regardless of how persuasively they are presented, supposedly have no place in science. In reality, many episodes in science go through sensitive, controversial stages and the teacher who chooses to teach the whole of the scientific endeavor finds need for classroom formats that are suited to controversial issues.

Other weaknesses arise from the general tendency of students not to listen or not to take seriously the information or points of view expressed by other students. Rarely do students present information more efficiently than does the experienced teacher. To be successful, these formats assume that the students have adopted fairly mature degrees of self-discipline and are accustomed to take full advantage of whatever information-gathering opportunities confront them.

In contrast to the usually much more subtle instances of illogical reasoning one finds in selected episodes in science, the student debater or panel member is quite likely to provide glaring examples of faulty reasoning. Even the most naive student can participate in the analysis of these examples, and the experience gained thereby may gradually mature sufficiently to be useful in attacking the subtle instances of illogic that occur even among the reasoning that appears in the reports written by practicing scientists.

Examples and Illustrations

Very little ingenuity is needed to adapt these formats to the usual classroom situation. For this reason, only two examples are presented: one involving students who have yet to gain any concept of how to take part in panels or debates, and the other involving students who were already familiar with one or another version of these formats in action.

PROBLEM APPEARING IN COURSE OF STUDY: IS THERE LIFE ON OTHER PLANETS?

Objectives

1. To examine whatever information can be gathered that bears on the possibility of life on other planets.
2. To introduce some of the skills and rules of formal discussion.

Procedure

ASSIGNMENT: In addition to the information included in the textbook, each student will become as familiar as possible with the information in the following references: Hubertus Strughold, "The Green and Red Planet," *Science Digest,* p. 37, January 1955, and p. 32, August 1952; and *Science Newsletter,* p. 244, April 16, 1955, p. 222, April 7, 1956, p. 165, September 15, 1956, p. 403, June 29, 1957, p. 275, November 2, 1957, and p. 121, February 1, 1958.

PRELIMINARY DISCUSSION: You recall our assignment for today: A discussion of the possibility of life on other planets. During the next eight minutes, write some of the ideas you have on this question. Now, what kinds of ideas have you been writing? During the reading of these ideas, I have noticed six or so of you people who seem to be quite interested in this question. Furthermore, three of you seem to believe that there is very little possibility of life on the other planets whereas the other three tend to disagree. Will the students to my left pass their papers to Robert, who will serve as chairman of a group who will present tomorrow as many reasons as they can for our believing that there is life on other planets. The people on my right should pass their papers to Pablo, who will be chairman of his group who will present the opposite point of view.

Robert, you and Pablo meet with Susan, who will be the chairman of our panel discussion for tomorrow. Decide the order in which each member of your groups will speak. Remember that no one on the panel or in the class can speak unless he has been recognized by the chairman. Try to have each thing you say be worth saying. You may argue, of course, but respect what your classmates have to say.

PANEL DISCUSSION: (*The chairman recognized alternately members of the two groups with each person presenting his or her information and point of view. Class members were encouraged to enter into the rebuttal. At the close of the panel discussion, recognizing that no general agreement had been reached, a debate between four members of the class seemed to be in order. Two students were selected to represent the two opposing points of view.*) In keeping with the general rules of debating, the team representing the affirmative will speak first and will state clearly the question that is to be debated. Following four-minute presentations by each member of the two teams, each is to be allowed a two-minute rebuttal speech. To help us decide which team should be declared the winner, copy this evaluation form and we will use it tomorrow during the debate.

Debate Score Card

Place a check mark in the column that best describes the work of each of the debaters. *I*—Inferior, *F*—Fair, *G*—Good, *E*—Excellent, and *S*—Superior.

	I	F	G	E	S
Analysis	——	——	——	——	——
Argument	——	——	——	——	——
Evidence	——	——	——	——	——
Organization	——	——	——	——	——
Extempore Ability	——	——	——	——	——
Adaptation	——	——	——	——	——
Refutation	——	——	——	——	——
Speaking Ability	——	——	——	——	——

Prepare columns of blanks for each speaker. If there are questions about what any of the words mean, I will be glad to answer them.

THE DEBATE: (*Following the actual debate, three students were selected to collect the score cards and judge which team was to be declared the winner. While the score cards were being tallied, the class discussed not only the skills of the debaters but also the issues debated.*)

The second example is limited to the debate format and is drawn from observations in a senior high school chemistry class. The assigned topic was: In light of the threat of an expanding world population, and keeping in mind that the world's supply of the metallic elements is limited, a program should be launched dedicated to enforced recycling of all metals already extracted from their natural ores. In making the assignment, the teacher suggested that the following points might be touched on: Is there a real threat to the world's supply of the metallic elements? Does the continuation of our way of living depend upon the availability of adequate supplies of iron, copper, tin, uranium, silver, etc? At what rate are these metals being taken from the earth's crust? Can we rely on the development of new plastics or other substitutes for metals? Does not the law of conservation of matter automatically take care of this question? What are the chances of tapping the untold quantities of metals that supposedly exist in the oceans?

At the conclusion of the debate, the students were asked to identify what they thought might have been instances of inaccurate information or of illogical reasoning in the presentations of the speakers. In addition, they were invited to express opinions on the overall value of the debate format in high school science classes. Representative replies follow.

I noted many instances of sheer inaccuracies in the debate. The conflicting statistics must mean that some of the reference sources were either out of date or were being misinterpreted.

There were many things said in the heat of the argument that were either slips of the tongue or evidence of confusion. For example, silicon and sand are two different things, diamonds are scarcely metals, etc.

Some of the argument was, to say the least, scarcely logical. To say, for example, that the success in conservation of forests and wild life could be analogous to the restoration of the world's supply of metals, is surely stretching a point. Or to argue that since inventors have found substitutes for some kinds of metals in some kinds of applications they can be relied upon to find substitutes for all kinds of metals in all kinds of applications, is definitely not the kind of logic we are being taught to use in setting up hypotheses to be tested in the laboratory.

I think it was worthwhile despite the fact that the debaters weren't thinking like scientists part of the time. It was interesting and provided some variety in the class period. Also, the fact that we could criticize their logic, indicates that we might have some idea of how a scientist should think.

The two sides caught each other's mistakes valiantly.

As for those in the audience, it gives them a little mental exercise; trying to decide if either side is making sense.

For Discussion and Further Study

1. Do the positive features of the panel format for science lessons outweigh the negative features?

2. To what elements of scientific inquiry does the panel format promise to make unique contributions?

3. How does the subject matter to be brought by an interview influence the agenda or techniques of the interview?

4. Under what circumstances might an interview yield greater values than to invite the person being interviewed into the classroom as a guest lecturer?

5. What precautions might prevent a lesson using the debate format from degenerating into a free-for-all argument?

References

1. M. L. Story. "The Press Conference Technique with Resource Visitors," *School Activities,* **28** (January 1957), p. 157.
2. Wesley P. Callender, Jr. "Thoughts *With* Expression—The Values of Debate in Schools," *Education,* **78** (October 1957), p. 117.
3. Committee on the Function of Science in General Education, Commission on Secondary School Curriculum, Progressive Education Association. *Science in General Education.* New York: Appleton-Century-Crofts, 1938, p. 326.

31

Dramatization

Children learn factual information only slightly, if any, more rapidly when taught by the dramatic rather than by the non-dramatic method. . . . A sizable increase in factual learnings was observed from the use of plays partly written by the children themselves in contrast with the conventional adult-written play. [Children] are much more interested in the average dramatic lesson than in the non-dramatic presentation [and] feel well repaid for their extra time and energy spent.[1]

Robert A. Greene 1937

In the broadest interpretation, teachers employ dramatic procedures whenever they portray the life of a scientist or an episode in science by means of dialogue and action. In a narrower sense, a lesson format, in order to be labeled dramatization, must revolve around the portrayal of a series of real events having dramatic value and interest.

Authors are likely to select dramatic forms when their purposes include deeply stirring the imagination or emotions. Dramatization suggests gestures, movements, costumes, staging, and all of the paraphernalia of theatrical performances together with the rather specialized skill of script writing or adaptation.

In practice, dramatization in the classroom exists in many forms. At the simplest level, teachers or students may read "dramatically" from a scientist's writings or from things said about a scientist. At a higher level, these writings can be broken into dialogue and read or recited. Finally, since the pursuit of science is replete with "series of real events having dramatic value and interest," supposedly even the most advanced dramatic form could be used to arouse the imagination and increase the emotional involvement of students in an episode in science.

Strengths and Weaknesses

The question of whether dramatization is or is not the appropriate format for a science lesson brings sharply into play the most important criterion for choosing a lesson format. Dramatization can accomplish a specialized purpose with supreme efficiency.

To pass up dramatization when the primary "target for the day" is to stir the imagination or emotions, or to force dramatization to accomplish objectives other than this, is to invite inefficiency.

The spirit of science supports the argument that the stirring of imagination is a worthy, yet all too often neglected goal in teaching the pursuit of science. Perhaps valuable contributions toward accomplishing this objective await those teachers or students who can combine the flair for doing dramatic writing with the ability to comprehend how a scientist's imagination becomes involved in the pursuit of his investigations.

In contrast to stirring the imagination, the use of dramatization to arouse the emotions of students must be approached with greater calculation. There are many instances in the pursuit of science in which scientists' emotions contribute sharply to the success or failure of their pursuits. How much of their emotional involvement is intrinsic in the pursuit and therefore subject to recurrence for those who would pursue science is very difficult to determine. Emotional involvement that is entirely extrinsic to the pursuit of science, although of great concern to those who would comprehend the scientific enterprise, has less immediate urgency for those young people who are beginning their pursuit of science.

For example, religious groups who sensed in the discoveries of science a weakening of their status often created sharp emotional impact on the authors of these discoveries. This impact lends itself to, in fact, invites dramatization. But does such involvement have currency in the twentieth century?

Some scientific pursuits intrinsically invite emotional involvement, and to attempt to present unemotional versions of these pursuits in the classroom invites distortion or censorship. Although such topics change frequently, examples that were widely "dramatized" in the popular press midway in the twentieth century include the fluoridation of drinking water to prevent dental caries and peacetime testing of nuclear weapons with subsequent pollution of the atmosphere with radioactive wastes. Examples of perennial topics that draw emotional reactions sometimes within and always outside the scientific fraternity are vivisection, the origin of species, and the physico-chemical concept of the life process.

The use of dramatization to increase the authenticity of the presentation of an episode in science would be good. Fostering prejudiced or biased emotional involvement would be a weakness. Allowing emotional stimulation under the supposedly controlled conditions of the classroom would appear to be more courageous than abandoning it to the locker rooms and student hangouts where it will surely flourish.

To schedule the dramatization lesson format to coincide with public relation events and without regard to the appropriateness of the topic that would have been up for consideration is, at best, a questionable practice. On the other hand, shunning this format because it appears to be too progressive or soft-minded may be short-sighted. Participation in a dramatized episode in the pursuit of science could easily be the key event in attracting new creative, artistic, and imaginative recruits into an endeavor which has too often been pictured as stultifying, pragmatic, and emotionless.

Examples and Illustrations

The first illustration of the dramatization type of lesson follows somewhat the "man-in-the-street" interview. The examples have been developed by students of Fred Moore in his science classes at the high school in Owosso, Michigan. In his instruction to his students, Moore emphasized the value of using direct quotations from scientists' writings to answer the questions the students would like to have answered.

Moderator: Approaching now is the ever-popular teacher, English-American preacher, and member of the Royal Society, John Dalton.
Student: Mr. Dalton, may I ask you a few questions about your scientific work.
Dalton: Yes, certainly.
Student: I have heard it said that you have discovered the smallest particle of matter. Would you comment on this?

Dalton: Only theoretically have I discovered it. It seems probable to me that in the beginning God formed matter in solid, massive, hard, impenetrable, movable particles—so very hard as never to wear or break into pieces; no ordinary power being able to divide what God made in the first creation. My atomic theory came to me all at once. It seemed so simple that I was amazed that no one had discovered it before. The particles are infinitely small; and, therefore, cannot be seen. To explain my atomic theory to my students, I devised a chart with symbols to represent the different elements. The atoms are so small that they cannot be divided.

Student: Are all atoms alike in size and weight?

Dalton: No, precisely not. Atoms of the same element are alike, but each element's atoms are different in size and weight. As Mr. Proust has discovered, the composition of every true compound never varies. Atoms themselves are very concrete particles which will join with another but never will a single atom break apart.

Student: Is it true that you have developed a table of relative atomic weights?

Dalton: Yes, that is correct. Again, to clarify the study of the atoms I have devised a standard of weights. As a standard, I have used hydrogen atoms equal to 1. A hydrogen atom and an oxygen atom unite to form a unit which is 7 to 1 by weight. Therefore, the relative weight of oxygen is 7. This table that I have constructed consists of the 14 elements known at this time. In a series of compounds made up of the same elements, a simple ratio exists between the weights of one and the fixed weight of the other element.

Student: Thank you very much, Mr. Dalton, for your concise views. We know that you have contributed much to the field of science, and we hope you will continue the good work. Now, have you anything else you would like to say concerning your study?

Dalton: I have nothing that is basic. It is all highly technical from here on in. If you would like to have me explain it to you, I would be glad to, at a later date. However, I must be on my way.

Moderator: Thank you, and good-bye John Dalton.

* * *

Moderator: Another of the famous men we are going to interview is the Italian scientist, Amadeo Avogadro.

Student: Would you like to tell us something about your discovery?

Avogadro: Yes, I would be delighted to.

Student: Is there a difference between atoms and molecules?

Avogadro: Yes, there is a difference. Many experiments have shown this. However, no distinction has been made between molecules of an atom and molecules of a compound. I believe there to be three kinds of molecules:

1. *Molecule elementaires*=atoms of elements
2. *Molecule constituantes*=molecules of elements
3. *Molecule integrantes*=molecules of compounds.

Student: I understand you have developed a principle along this line of atoms, if so, just what is it?

Avogadro: I have developed a principle not based on scientific experiments, but on sound logical reason. The principle is that equal volumes of all gases under the same conditions of temperature and pressure contain equal numbers of molecules.

Student: A principle like this would solve all chemical problems. It was probably accepted over the entire scientific world.

Avogadro: On the contrary, the only people that had faith in my theory were my students. I received no immediate credit for this discovery.

Student: How did it become known to the world?

Avogadro: I owe the credit of the widespread publishing of this theory to my faithful student Canizzaro. He is responsible for getting people to accept my theory. Almost a century later, a statue was unveiled and scientists from all over the world paid tribute to me and the theory I had developed. My idea was that scientists would resort to my theory in due time, and now the time is come.

Moderator: You have made remarkable discoveries in chemistry. Thank you, Amadeo Avogadro, for your contribution.

*   *   *

Moderator: And now, we have an Englishman, Mr. Electron himself. Mr. Thomson, we would like to have our reporter ask you a few questions to help us understand some things about nuclear electrons.

Student: What have been your conclusions concerning the nature of Cathode Rays?

Thomson: Through my experiments using a magnetic field and an electric field, I have proved that cathode rays are actually a stream of particles carrying negative electrical charges. The reason for this conclusion is that the ray can be deflected by both electrical and magnetic fields.

Student: Where do these cathode rays or "streams of particles" as you call them, originate?

Thomson: They originate from, or in the vicinity of, the negative electrode which is the cathode of an evacuated discharge tube.

Student: Have you arrived at any definite speed for these particles?

Thomson: Yes, and the speed seems to be about one-tenth the speed of light.

Student: Are the cathode rays always the same?

Thomson: The carriers of the electric charges in the cathode rays are the same whatever the gas through which the discharge passes.

Student: What, then, do you think is a logical explanation of these rays or particles?

Thomson: The explanation which seems to me to account in the most simple and straight-forward manner for the facts is founded on the view of the constitution of the chemical elements which has been favorably entertained by many chemists: this view is that the atoms of the different chemical elements are different aggregations of or ultimate particles of the same kind. If, in the very intense field of the neighborhood of the cathode, the molecules of the gas are split up, not into ordinary chemical atoms, but into these primordial atoms which we shall call for brevity corpuscles; and, if these corpuscles are charged with electricity and projected from the cathodes by the electric field, they would behave exactly like the cathode rays. Their electromagnetic value is independent of the nature of the gas because they are the same whatever the gas may be. Thus we have in the Cathode rays matter in a new state, a state in which the subdivision of matter is carried much further than is the ordinary gaseous state; a state in which all matter—that is, matter derived from different sources such as hydrogen, oxygen, and carbon—is one and the same kind; this matter being the substances from which all the chemical elements are built up.

Student: Aren't these particles called electrons now?

Thomson: Yes, they are. The reason for the name, electron, is probably due to Stoney. He named the particles electrons because the charge on the particles is identical to the elementary electronic charges. I still call them "corpuscles" though just because I am more used to the name.

Moderator: Thank you, Mr. J. J. Thomson, for clearing up this matter of the electron.

* * *

Moderator: Our final interview is with a contemporary Englishman, Dr. F. W. Aston, a contributor to the discovery of radioisotopes.

Student: Who are some of the men who contributed to the discovery of radioactive isotopes?

Dr. Aston: Among the early contributors to the discovery of radioactive isotopes were H. N. McCoy and B. B. Boltwood, who were United States scientists, W. Marckwald, a German scientist, and F. Soddy, a British scientist. These early contributors to the discovery of isotopes competed in the early progress of chemical identity of isotopes.

Student: What evidence led to the discovery of isotopes?

Dr. Aston: It was found that the periodic classification of these atoms could be broken down within a weight region of several radio species. The discovery of this fact led to the investigation of the possibility of having certain groups of elements within the region but having quite distinct radioactive properties. By 1911 nearly 40 species with different radioactive properties were known, but only 12 positions were available to accommodate them in the periodic table.

Student: What are some of the methods of separating radioactive isotopes within an element?

Dr. Aston: There are many methods including a centrifugal method in which the gravitational force acting on a particle is varied to partially separate and rearrange various particles within an atom. The thermal-diffusion method uses heat to separate lighter molecules which tend to concentrate in the regions of higher temperature and gaseous mixtures. The distillation method was my first attempt to separate the isotopes of neon by fractional distillation. This attempt was a failure; but, in general, the separating of isotopic species by fractional distillation was made possible when the vapor pressure or boiling points were found to be appreciably different. The electrolytic method was based on a theory involving continuous decomposition of a compound by an electric current. The chemical exchange method was not dependent on differences in physical properties and, therefore, was quite successful.

Student: What is the main use today for radioactive isotopes?

Dr. Aston: Radioactive isotopes are mainly used for experimental purposes. They are a powerful tool when in solution for the tracing and solving of numerous problems in biology, physiology, chemistry, physics, and other sciences. When radioactive isotopes are dissolved in solutions and taken up by plants and admitted into systems of animals, their paths can be traced by geiger counters and other means of radioactive determination. For this reason, they are helpful in cures, study, and location of physical defects, diseases, and abnormalities within the bodies of plants and animals. Isotopes of phosphorus and iodine are most commonly used for medical purposes. Also, isotopes of cobalt have been found to be useful in the treatment of cancer.

Student: Can isotopes achieve other purposes, Dr. Aston?

Dr. Aston: Isotopes of hydrogen, carbon, nitrogen, and other common elements used by plants in the photosynthesis process and their cell structure may be traced to determine the usefulness and benefits of various compounds used as plant food in agriculture. By following the progress of these radioactive isotopes within a plant structure, the growth and development of plants by application of these various food compounds may be determined and evaluated.

Student: In general, what is the future of radioactive isotopes?

Dr. Aston: Scientists today are just entering a vast field of study. We have achieved only a few of the possible benefits from these wonder elements. With continued progress, the future of radioactive isotopes is unlimited. The fields of medicine, biology, agriculture, and sociology stand to benefit immensely from further study of radioactive isotopes.

Moderator: Thank you, Dr. Aston. This concludes our special reports on the people who have contributed to our present day knowledge of nuclear energy.

The second illustration has been developed by Loretta Olver of Bethlehem, Pennsylvania. Miss Olver describes this dramatization as being particularly adaptable to tape recording.

HARVEY AND THE CIRCULATION OF BLOOD

Two boys have just watched a movie, showing how blood is pumped through a live turtle's heart.[2] Since they have become very much interested in the history of physiology, and John, at least is familiar with the work of Galen and Vesalius, they start a conversation.

John: Those ancients had some queer ideas about the blood, didn't they? Galen thought that the liver continuously manufactured blood from the food we eat. Then it was sent to the heart where the ventricles stored it like a cistern. Oozing through pores to the left side of the heart, it was revived with "vital spirits" from the lungs. Afterwards it flowed out into the body by both veins and arteries, occasionally coming back to the heart to be freshened by the lungs. Just how the blood could travel in opposite directions at the same time, going through the same vessels, I don't know. Something like two trains on a single track, going opposite directions and trying to pass, I'd say.

Dan: Harvey stopped all that, didn't he?

John: Harvey didn't exactly take the story from Galen. You remember reading about Vesalius, don't you? You know, the man who revived the lost art of dissection, stealing his bodies from hangmen's gallows and cemeteries at night, and who so many times proved Galen wrong! Vesalius had already shown that blood makes a circuit from the right ventricle through the lungs where it is replenished, and then comes back to the heart through the left ventricle.

Dan: Did this circulation of blood through the lungs suggest to Harvey that the blood might also make a circuit through the body?

John: You are traveling too fast for me, and too fast for Dr. Harvey too, I think. You see when he was twenty years old, Harvey went to the University of Padua in Italy, which was then a famous medical center. This was a strange college, probably one you would like, where the students hired the professors and could drive them out of town too, if they wished. So the teachers were on their toes! There Harvey became very friendly with one of his professors, Fabricius by name, who had discovered that veins have valves or, as he expressed it, little doors. "What do you suppose they are for," he would say to Harvey. "Do you think they keep the blood from moving too fast when it travels out to the extremities?" Neither of the men could find a satisfactory explanation then, but Harvey spent years trying to find the answer. Eventually it was the presence of the valves in the veins, there to keep the blood from back-tracking, that suggested to Harvey that the blood makes a complete circuit through the body. He just couldn't see why "so provident a cause as Nature had placed so many valves without design,"—if they were there, they must have some use.[3]

In the end, there was only one step which eluded Harvey, and that was how the blood got from the arteries to the veins. He thought that blood on leaving the arteries simply formed a pool, and was sucked up by some attraction the veins have for it. Thirty-three years after Harvey published his famous book *De Motu Cordis,* written in Latin, an Italian, Malphigi, found a third type of vessel, the capillaries.

Dan: Seems as though it took Harvey a long time to get anywhere!

John: Don't be too hard on him! Takes you a while to do things, too. You say you are going into nuclear research. When? Tomorrow? Besides Harvey was afraid of what people might say. Folks don't always like new ideas. They starve famous painters, an author like Poe had to live in an attic, and Dr. Semmelweiss died in an insane asylum because nobody would listen to him! Anyway, Harvey had been thinking, had made many experiments, but was afraid to publish his results. He said that "what he had to tell about the blood was so strange and undreamed of, that not only do I fear danger to myself from the malice of a few, but I dread lest I have all men as enemies, so much does doctrine . . . once absorbed . . . become second nature."[4]

Dan: Didn't Harvey test his results? Nowadays when a scientist makes a discovery, he always tries it out—on animals first, then on people. Of course, I know Harvey was afraid. They were very quick with the hangman's noose in those days and Harvey, no doubt, wanted to keep his own blood in circulation.

John: Yes, Harvey used a human subject for a demonstration of two sets of experiments which proved that blood makes a complete circuit through the body. They are very simple experiments. So simple that you can and will do them yourselves, if you are thin enough so that your veins come close to the surface of your skin. The only equipment you need is a tourniquet. In the first set by tying a bandage in such a way as to stop flow in the veins but leave the arteries open, he demonstrated that blood enters the extremities through the arteries; in the second set, experiments which concern the valves, he showed that the blood flows in the veins towards the heart, not away from it, as had previously been believed. When he put these ideas together with some calculations as to the amount of blood which goes through the heart in a given time, he knew that the same blood must circulate through the body repeatedly.

Harvey put on a demonstration for King Charles I, who was very much impressed, using the King's Chamberlain as the subject. The poor man shivered and shook, and probably *his* blood turned to water, but what could he do about it? He thought Harvey was going to nick his arteries and let the blood flow out, maybe to find out how much of it he had, just as he had been doing with the snakes.

Many other experiments were carried out on animals, particularly reptiles because, being cold-blooded, their blood moves slowly. Harvey also watched animals like dogs and pigs which were dying, for their bloodstream would be going slower and slower.

Dan: But you haven't told me yet just why Harvey was so interested in snakes, eels and nearly dead dogs! What was he trying to learn?

John: One thing Harvey proved with his animals was that it was the beating of the heart, especially the contraction of the ventricles, which sent the blood out through the arteries. It seems simple to us now, but people didn't understand it then! He would watch the heart contract and then nick the artery and see the blood come out in spurts!

He also used animals to get some idea of the amount of blood in the body, making all sorts of calculations and observations. One especially interesting experiment was carried out on the heart of a dead sheep, which is the same size as that of a man.[5] He filled a ventricle with water, finding that it held two ounces. But by his calculations in an hour that same ventricle would expel nearly twenty pounds of blood, although the whole sheep's body only held four pounds, drained to the last drop! How could the heart of the sheep in an hour pump out more blood than the body held, unless it was the same blood, going out by the arteries and coming back by the veins?

Dan: All very interesting! You told me that the king was impressed by Harvey's reasoning and experiments. How did other people feel about it? Did they believe him?

John: As usual, they thought he was a madman, and the doctors gave him especially violent opposition. Practically the only friends he had were at court; other doctors were jealous of him for that! Finally, just before he died, he received a little recognition.

Dan: This morning we learned. From the right ventricle to the pulmonary artery, to the lungs, and all the rest of it. You know, it makes sense to me now; it didn't before.

For Discussion and Further Study

1. How can dramatized lessons make unique contributions to student understanding and appreciation of the pursuit of science?

2. How might improper use of the dramatization format compromise the true spirit and function of science?

3. What kinds of episodes lend themselves to development as dramatized lessons?

4. Are the conclusions reported by Greene applicable to modern day students? Do these conclusions apply equally to all kinds of students?

5. Should teachers attempt to use "role-playing" techniques to introduce students to controversial topics?

References

1. Robert A. Greene, in Francis D. Curtis. *A Third Digest of Investigations in the Teaching of Science.* Philadelphia: P. Blakiston and Sons Publishing Co., 1939, p. 39. Used by permission of McGraw-Hill Book Company.
2. Encyclopedia Britannica Films. (B&W) *Heart and Circulation.*
3. Thomas S. Hall. *A Source Book in Animal Biology.* New York: McGraw-Hill, 1951, pp. 113–27.
4. Ruth Fox. *Great Men of Medicine.* New York: Random House, 1947, pp. 60–78.
5. Frederick G. Kilgour. "Galen," *Scientific American,* **196** (March 1957), p. 105.

32

Tests and Examinations

The course objectives, goals, or outcomes are designed to give direction to all aspects of the course, including course design, teaching techniques, instructional materials, and equipment, as well as the evaluation procedures, that will be employed. After the objectives have been formulated all the course activities should be planned in such a way that the objectives can be implemented with some prospect that they will be attainable. . . . A still more condensed version of these objectives constitute one axis on the chart of specifications for [constructing] examinations. . . . The other axis includes the major topics of course content. Such a chart of specifications should be prepared with great care before any item writing is undertaken. The chart is the blue print for the test or examination and should be followed as closely as the workmen follow the architect's plans when constructing a fine building. . . . As each item is subsequently completed a tally mark or identifying symbol is entered in the appropriate cell on the chart. The item writing and tallying continues until the predetermined number of items for each cell on the chart has been completed.[1]

Clarence H. Nelson 1958

. . . *Abilities to evaluate could include: the ability to in-terpret tables, graphs, and the like . . . the ability to analyze an experiment critically; the ability to test a whole situation whose solution requires the application of several theories or principles; the ability to carry out the solution of certain equations and other operations and perhaps to use principles and theories in abstract situations.*[2]

Alexander Joseph 1958

Designing a good physics achievement test quite logically involves combining the principles of good physics instruc-tion with the principles of good test construction. . . . Physi-cists seem agreed that process, or methodology, is fully as fundamental an aspect of physics education as is subject-matter content. This being the case, both dimensions should be represented in the test. This means defining explicitly not only the subject-matter content, but also the various kinds of abilities or ways of applying knowledge, that are to be expected of the students.[3]

Frederick L. Ferris, Jr. 1960

[Research projects require the investigator to design] exami-nations in the ability to formulate hypotheses, to test hy-potheses, to draw conclusions, and to recognize degrees of cause and effect relationship. . . . Most of the testing tech-niques developed in these studies can be adapted for in-formal use by the classroom teacher for testing purposes, for review materials, or as summarizing devices. Teachers can do this by studying the tests, and then writing their own test items to fit the course of study being used for their own classes. . . . Teachers can develop excellent test or exercise items by selecting situations that apply to everyday experiences of the pupils, by selecting items related to objec-tives contained in or germane to their course of study, and by careful editing of the items for clarity and proper vocab-ulary difficulty levels. . . . What is important is that the teacher recognize the value of reasoning as an objective, and that he attempt to appraise it in his classroom instruction.[4]

William B. Reiner 1958

409

*Remedial instruction, based upon a study of pupil responses
to items in a preliminary test is a valuable plan of teaching.*[5]

Archer W. Hurd   1933

*It is not difficult to sense a feeling of uneasiness about any
particular method of examining. After any type of examination has been given for several years, the person or persons
actually setting the examination find themselves, for example, forced into devising trickier and trickier questions
of the same type, in order to avoid duplicating past examinations. In the search for new examination questions the
examiner then tends to shift the emphasis from problems of
general interest to problems of specialized interest.*[6]

M. W. P. Strandberg and B. V. Gokhale   1959

*The students [college freshmen in biological science] in
group A were given short weekly tests for four consecutive
weeks with the students in group B taking objective tests
during the same period. The testing procedure was then
reversed. . . . Short essay testing can be one means for the
improvement of writing skills. . . . Students favored the use
of both essay and objective tests. . . . It should be emphasized
that a great deal of time and energy is required to adequately grade essays and therefore due cognizance of this
should be taken into consideration with respect to teacher
load whenever such a method is employed for the purpose
of improving writing skills.*[7]

Walter S. Lundahl and John M. Mason   1956

*When new-type examinations are made a teaching device
. . . the method of correction which requires the least of
the teacher's time and energy, namely, that under which the
pupils check the incorrect items on their own papers during
a discussion of the test items, is the most profitable for the
pupils. . . . The laborious method by which the teacher
corrects all errors on each paper seems not only wasteful of
the teacher's time and energy but also unjustified in the
light of subsequent benefit to the pupil.*[8]

Francis D. Curtis and Gerald G. Woods   1929

A test is a series of questions or exercises that can be used to measure the skills, knowledge, abilities, or aptitudes of a student. An examination is a careful inspection with a view to discover the real character or state of or, at least, obtaining fuller knowledge concerning a student's grasp of knowledge or his ability to perform certain skills. Tests and examinations may be loosely or tightly structured. At the former extreme would be: "Tell all you know about . . ." whereas various objective or "short answer" items restrict the student to revealing a precise bit of knowledge or to perform in a precisely assigned manner.

Nearly all teaching situations require the instructor to devote some part of his time to composing, administering, and interpreting tests and examinations. Data derived therefrom inform the instructor about the achievement of his students and can be used to determine marks or grades. Such achievement can be compared with standards either informally derived by remembering how former generations of students performed on similar tests or by carefully controlled administration of equivalent tests to standardizing groups. It is assumed that the performance of the standardizing group was not influenced by any factors absent among the groups whose performance is being compared. The probability of the tested group's performance actually exceeding, equaling, or falling short of that of the standardizing group should be predictable by statistical techniques.

Test and examination data are used for grade placement of students or for assigning them to special instructional groups. These data are also used to compare the relative effectiveness of teaching procedures or as measuring devices in various kinds of educational experimentation.

Strengths and Weaknesses

How well a test or examination measures skills and knowledge or reveals the true state of a student's achievement depends upon how effectively it is prepared, administered, and interpreted. The preparation of an examination begins with a careful ordering of the subject-matter upon which the examination is to be based, and precisely reviewing the objectives toward which instruction has been directed. To insure coverage and balance between content and objectives, various professional examiners recommend the use of a two-axis chart of specifications with the major objectives arranged on the horizontal axis and the subject-matter content topics on the vertical axis. By indicating the number of items budgeted to each cell, such a chart becomes a blueprint that, if followed, guarantees assigning proper emphasis to each item of content covered in the course and to each objective claimed for the course. There seems to be no better insurance against the often-expressed argument by students: "The examination did not include what I thought the course was all about."

Choice of format for the individual items is a second step in the preparation of an examination. No hard and fast rules dictate this choice. Each instructor tends to adopt whatever test-item formats he feels are most consistent with his instruction. The important thing seems to be that the instructor be familiar with a wide variety of test item formats and recognize what subject matter content and what

FIGURE 9. To rely on black marks made on test answer forms to judge a student's proficency in the pursuit of science creates a challenge to the ingenuity of examination writers.

PHOTO BY HARRY LUTTERMOSER

objectives can be best examined by a specific format. About the same amount of time is required to examine students regardless of the format of the examination. Constructing a good, objective item examination such as the multiple-choice or key-list format, requires much more time than is needed to prepare an examination composed primarily of essay questions. Grading the students' responses, however, requires much more time in the essay examination. Similarly, student responses to objective items can be more easily analyzed to reveal patterns of error. Composing objective-type examinations forces the examiner to make subjective judgments regarding the interdependence between the hoped-for response of the student and actual states of the student's knowledge or skill. It is while reading the students' responses to essay questions, however, that the examiner must make similar subjective judgments regarding the correlation between what he thinks the student has said and what the student actually knows about the subject matter being discussed. Hence the choice of test item format, especially as to objective versus essay, boils down to deciding whether the major expenditure of time will be for preparing the examination or grading it, and whether the hazard of subjectivity had best be faced in designing structured responses that allegedly reveal identifiable skill or knowledge or in judging whether or not students' responses do or do not say what the reader thinks they should.

Among the factors that determine the "goodness" of educational tests and examinations are validity, reliability, economy, discriminatory power, and objectivity. A test must measure what the person who interprets the results thinks it measures, else no valid conclusions can follow. The same test should produce consistent results when used to measure the same kind of achievement and the reliability of these results should not be subject to the examiner's judgment. In general, the test that requires the least time to prepare, administer, grade, and interpret is to be preferred over a less economical but no more valid or reliable test. Except in specialized training programs where tests are used to separate those trainees who have from those who haven't reached a level of achievement that advances them to a new phase of training, tests are intended to rank an array of students. On this basis, any test item answered correctly by all or none of the examinees is a wasted item. Such items, of course, do have the value of providing information regarding the status of achievement of the total group. Wherein the results from a test become a part of the student's recorded credentials, the test should be sufficiently objective to allow the examiner to be reasonably confident that the student's response to the test would have received the same ranking when read and evaluated by any other equally qualified examiner.

Assuming they remain sensitive to and study the performance of their tests and examinations, teachers rapidly develop the ability to construct very effective instruments. Too difficult or too easy items are adjusted. Loosely worded items are reframed and suggestive words or phrases are eliminated from the "give aways." Tests that are too long are shortened. Discrepancies in grading diminish with experience, especially so if the instructor adopts the practice during the writing of examinations of preparing a rough draft and then making the scoring key before producing the final draft. Much information is obtained by comparing the performance of individual items against the performance of the total test. At a very informal level, this kind of comparison consists of comparing, item by item, the responses of the students whose scores were among the top ten in total score, with the students whose papers were among the bottom ten. Such a comparison is, of course, merely a test of internal consistency, and infers that the student who masters one aspect of the subject matter or becomes proficient in one objective will be equally successful on all aspects of the examination. Item analysis identifies the items wherein the good student reads something into the item which the teacher did not expect him to, a reaction for which the student should not ordinarily be penalized.

Tests and examinations should complement the total instruction in the course, and the general nature of examination items should be consistent with the instructor's philosophy. It would be incongruous, for example, for an instructor to strive to develop creative and thought stimulating teaching procedures only to retain purely dogmatic and arbitrary recall examination and testing procedures. As the instructor strives to develop classroom procedures that will truly launch his students on the pursuit of science, he must devote a fraction of his effort to creating valid and reliable measures of student achievement in all of the intellectual abilities that seem to be peculiarly associated with success in the scientific endeavor.

Examples and Illustrations

The examples and illustrations that follow have been gleaned from the work of many examiners. Each example is particularly adaptable to the measurement either of a specific bit of subject matter or achievement of a separate objective.

(a) Which of the following five terms shares the least significant relationship with the other four?
    1. a. Cytoplasm b. Chromosome c. Gene d. Nucleus e. Neuron
    2. a. Elephantiasis b. Bubonic plague c. Typhoid d. Tuberculosis e. Malaria
    3. a. Avogadro b. Hall c. Charles d. Gay-Lussac e. Henry

(b) For items _____ through _____, choose the pair of terms that does NOT share the relationship shared by the other four pairs.
    1. a. Metabolism–Catabolism b. Respiration–Photosynthesis c. Ingestion–Excretion d. Excretion–Secretion e. Diurnal–Nocturnal

(c) For items _____ through _____, if the five events were listed in the order in which they occur, which event would occupy the middle position?
    1. a. Separation of halves of chromosomes b. Equatorial arrangement of chromosomes c. Formation of spindles d. Formation of daughter cells e. Development of matrices about the chromosomes

(d) Mark items _____ through _____ according to the following key:

KEY

I. Original statement and reason are both true

II. Original statement is true

but not for the reason given

III. Original statement is false

1. When zinc and sulfur react to form zinc sulfide, the zinc is oxidized and the sulfur reduced *because* the zinc gains electrons and the sulfur loses electrons.

2. Sulfur dioxide decolors a solution of potassium permanganate because the permanganate is more soluble in the SO_2 solution.

3. Continued absorption of heat by a solid at its melting temperature causes a rise in temperature of the solid because energy can be transformed but not destroyed.

(e) For items _____ through _____, mark the pairs of events according to the following key:

KEY

I. The first tends to precede the second

II. The second tends to precede the first

III. The two events occur simultaneously

IV. The two events occur independently

1. Prothrombin changes to thrombin–Fibrinogen changes to fibrin

2. A uranium atom undergoes fission–A neutron lodges in the nucleus of a uranium atom

3. Hydrogen collects at the cathode during electrolysis of water–Oxygen collects at the anode during electrolysis of water

(f) For items _____ through _____, evaluate the following definitions by selecting from the key list the most appropriate statement:

KEY

I. The definition states the essential characteristics of that which is defined

II. The definition is stated in terms of what the concept is not

III. The definition is expressed in uncommon and nondescriptive language

IV. The definition doubles back to repeat itself

V. The definition provides only a limited number of the essential characteristics of that which is defined

1. Environment: the kind of atmosphere in which an organism flourishes

2. Acquired character: a trait not possessed by the ancestors of an organism

3. Caudal: of or near the tail

4. Freezing point: the temperature at which a liquid freezes

(g) For items _____ through _____, mark the statements according to the following key:

KEY

I. Directly related to a solution to the problem

II. Unrelated to a solution to the problem

III. A false statement

Problem: Determine the molecular formula of a compound that is 39.95%

carbon, 6.69% hydrogen, and 53.36% oxygen. The molecular weight of the compound is 60.1.

1. An empirical formula consists of one or a group of symbols to show the kind of elements and the number of gram-atoms of each that is contained in one gram-molecular weight of the compound.
2. The atomic weight of carbon is 12.
3. 0.333 divided by 0.0699 equals approximately 5.

(h) For items _____ through _____, choose from the key list the concept or principle of greatest significance to the statement.

KEY

I. Variation
II. Mutation
III. Natural selection
IV. Inbreeding
V. Differentiation

1. A changing environment is invariably accompanied by a changing flora and fauna.
2. Closed populations show greater variability than do populations permitted a wider range.

(i) Identify items _____ through _____ as being most appropriately assigned to one of the categories provided by the key.

KEY

I. Generalization
II. Deduction
III. Experimental observation
IV. Analogy
V. None of the above

1. The color change accompanying the action of Fehling's solution on glucose is due to the reduction of copper ions.
2. Illumination varies inversely as the square of the distance from the source.
3. Movements of the earth's crust are related to the transfer of mass from one to another crustal segment.

(j) Items _____ through _____ involve the accompanying graph. The graph shows the relationship between the pressure and temperature of a confined body consisting of two gases that mix without chemical reaction. Mark the statements that follow according to the key:

KEY

1. Consistent with the data in the graph
2. Inconsistent with the data in the graph
3. Neither confirmed nor contradicted
   by the data in the graph

1. One of the gases condenses to a liquid at a higher temperature than the other.
2. The pressures exerted by the gases have a straight-line relationship to temperature.
3. If both gases remained in the gaseous state during the cooling process,

their pressures would be reduced to zero at a temperature of approximately −270°C.

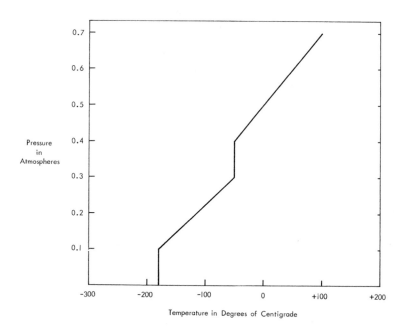

These examples suggest that one or another modification of the key-list type of objective item can easily be adapted to enable the examiner to observe or measure an almost unlimited number of specific learning events. Obviously, the examiner must comprehend that which he wishes to measure and be able to translate desired achievement into exercises that a student can do with pencil and paper—exercises, however, that provide valid evidence that the student does or does not possess the desired achievement. Although such items may find only occasional use during ordinary classroom instruction, elaborate key-list items may be quite effective in connection with measurement during experimental or exploratory studies. Almost any learning event can be analyzed and the steps of which it is composed converted into the elements of a key list. Two examples of the more complex types of key lists follow:

(k) For items _____ through _____, mark space according to the key:

KEY
  I. If the item is true according to the data
     and tends to support Hypothesis 1
 II. If the item is true according to the data
     but tends to refute Hypothesis 1

III. If the item is false according to the data,
but if true, would tend to support
Hypothesis 1

IV. If the item is false according to the data,
but if true, would tend to refute
Hypothesis 1

V. If the item is irrevelant to Hypothesis 1,
regardless of its truth or falsity
according to the data

(l) Evaluate each of the statements in items _____ through _____ by using the following key:

KEY

I. The thing to be found as the answer to the problem
II. Is given and is needed to solve the problem
III. Is given but is not needed to solve the problem
IV. Is not given, is needed, but is deducible
V. Is not given, is needed, but is not deducible
VI. Is not given, is not needed, but is deducible
VII. Is not given, is not needed, and is not deducible

Tradition and established evaluation practices tend to retain heavy emphasis on recall of the facts, laws, and principles of science. Only a reasonably minor portion of many examinations is devoted to measuring the examinee's ability to apply the information he can recall in novel and unrehearsed situations. There is even greater challenge awaiting those examinees who attempt to design valid instruments that will truly chart a student's progress toward gaining the skills and attitudes requisite to the pursuit of science.

Steps in this direction have been taken, especially with respect to exercising and improving observational abilities. The illustrations that follow were used in conjunction with a chemistry demonstration in which white phosphorus was dissolved in carbon disulfide and a small portion of the solution allowed to evaporate on filter paper atop a large graduated cylinder.

(m) The same key list as for illustration (e):
1. There is an explosion–The phosphorus ignites
2. The carbon disulfide evaporates–Carbon disulfide vapors collect in the cylinder
3. The phosphorus ignites–The carbon disulfide ignites
4. The gases in the cylinder expand–The gases in the cylinder are heated
5. The filter paper becomes blackened–The filter paper becomes yellow

(n) For items _____ through _____, mark the pairs of factors according to the following key:

KEY

I. An increase in the first would increase the second
II. An increase of the first would decrease the second

III. An increase or decrease of the first need not
change the dimensions of the second
1. Quantity of phosphorus in the solution–Time needed for the solution to evaporate
2. Quantity of carbon disulfide in the solution–Time needed for the phosphorus to ignite
3. Quantity of phosphorus on the filter paper–Loudness of the ultimate explosion
4. Volume of gases in the cylinder–Loudness of the explosion

For Discussion and Further Study

1. If the objectives of a course are not clearly evident, how can a teacher use the two-axis chart described by Nelson to insure coverage in designing an examination?

2. What kinds of test item formats lend themselves to testing the processes of inquiry, the so-called intangible or attitudinal objectives of instruction in science?

3. What objectives are tested for in currently available professionally prepared and standardized examinations?

4. How often should teachers devote major blocks of time to tests and examinations?

5. Have there been marked changes in the abilities of students to respond to examination items during the past few decades?

6. Prepare several examples of examination items that purport to test for the functional understanding of a concept or principle, for mastery of facts, for laboratory resourcefulness, for the ability to hypothesize, and other specific objectives of instruction in science. How would you prove that the items are valid measures of what they purport to measure?

7. Should a teacher match the format of his examinations with the kind of teaching he does, that is, are separate kinds of examinations needed for demonstration centered lessons, laboratory exercises, films, and so forth?

References

1. Clarence H. Nelson. "Let's Build Quality into Our Science Tests." Washington: National Science Teachers Association, 1958, p. 25.
2. Alexander Joseph. "Putting Thought Behind Science Tests," *Science Teacher's World* (November 25, 1958). Reprinted by permission from *Science Teacher's World,* © 1958 by Scholastic Magazines, Inc.
3. Frederick L. Ferris, Jr. "Testing for Physics Achievement," *American Journal of Physics,* **28** (March 1960), pp. 269–78.
4. William B. Reiner, "Testing and Evaluation in the Teaching of Science," *The Science Teacher,* **25** (October 1958), pp. 324–27.
5. Archer W. Hurd, in Francis D. Curtis. *A Third Digest of Investigations in the Teaching of Science.* Philadelphia: P. Blakiston and Sons Publishing Co., 1939, p. 129. Used by permission of McGraw-Hill Book Company.
6. M. W. P. Strandberg and B. V. Gokhale. "Graduate Examinations in Physics," *American Journal of Physics,* **27** (November 1959), pp. 539–955.
7. Walter S. Lundahl and John M. Mason. "Essay Testing in Biological

Science As a Means for Supplementing Training in Writing Skills," *Science Education,* **40** (October 1956), pp. 261–67.

8. Francis D. Curtis and Gerald G. Woods in Francis D. Curtis. *Second Digest of Investigations in the Teaching of Science.* Philadelphia: P. Blakiston and Sons Publishing Co., 1931, p. 366. Used by permission of McGraw-Hill Book Company.

33

The Field Trip

The sine qua non *of any successful excursion is the preview trip made by the teacher.*[1]

George E. Pitluga   1947

Although a field trip can yield so much if it is well conducted and prepared for, it is a difficult thing to carry out. A field trip takes more time than a class period; it disrupts administrative procedures; there is danger of accidents; and, above all, the field trip takes careful, even arduous, preparation.[2]

Paul F. Brandwein, Fletcher G. Watson, and Paul E. Blackwood   1958

"Going to see" is an important part of any effective science program. Potentially it is one of the most enjoyable and instructive ways to learn.[3]

Glenn O. Blough, Julius Schwartz, and Albert J. Huggett   1951

421

Once a child appreciates an animal, can respect it as a living thing with a life and interest all its own . . . if he can view a snake or a moth, a fish or a toad, with interest and compassion, he will want to learn more about it and the world it lives in.[4]

Robert M. McClung 1962

The real value . . . comes when the members of a class can discuss their findings and discover for themselves the inter-relationships that exist between organisms and their environment.[5]

Leonard G. Scheel 1961

True learning is the result of many sensations interacting and merging with one another. If one or more sensations is omitted during the learning process, the final impression is weakened, not only by the absence of the missing sensations, but also by the absence of their effect on each other.[6]

Walter A. Thurber and Alfred T. Collette 1959

The field trip takes students from the classroom to wherever they need to be to observe and gather data regarding the segment of science that is involved in the day's lesson. The destination of a field trip may be a locale that promises to nurture hypotheses regarding a phenomenon or to improve the design of experiments being planned to investigate these hypotheses. Sometimes field trips are taken to enable students to see and appreciate the significance of man's pursuit of one or more episodes in science.

Strengths and Weaknesses

In many cases, the field trip is the only lesson format that can give students first-hand acquaintance with phenomena and the true relationships among phenomena. This format provides opportunities to sharpen the keenness of observational abilities and to nurture habits of enjoying the beauty, intricacy, and orderliness of naturally occurring events and circumstances. Lessons taught outside the classroom enjoy the advantage of being reviewed repeatedly by the students. The scene of a field trip revisited or repeated serves to recall and strengthen a student's memory of what was taught at the scene.

Field trips can add reality to and verify classroom instruction, library reading, or laboratory exercises. While on a field trip, the student is automatically urged to take an active part in the lesson. Assuming that the format is administered wisely and well, the student will gain practice in being a responsible member of a group.

Field trips offer the teacher an opportunity to arouse, encourage, or exploit the out-of-school teaching resources of a community. In almost every community there are people who have specialized in the pursuit of one or more episodes in science. To fail to call on these people or to wait for them to approach the school may lead to or be interpreted as poor school-community relations. When the teacher takes the initiative, resource people can be asked to provide precisely what is needed to accomplish the day's lesson. When the teacher fails to take this initiative, he may find that his class is simply shown around or given a standard tour of the host's facility.

Many teachers improve the subtly intangible student-teacher relations during field trips. Usually, resource people in a community show high regard and respect for teachers. Students are likely to catch some of this spirit when they see that their teacher knows what is going on in the community and has established working relationships with its scientific and technical leaders. Furthermore, while taking students on field trips, closer relationships are invited than are usually adhered to in formal classrooms and laboratories. This does not mean that field trips should be looked upon as rewards for good behavior or socializing functions, but they do provide opportunities for teachers to dispel reputations for undue aloofness.

The weaknesses of the field-trip format stem primarily from the difficulties of its administration. These difficulties range all the way from the complex legal responsibilities of a school for its pupils to the annoying distractions that compete for student attention in almost any nonclassroom setting. To comply with the regulations that have been adopted by the school authorities and to arrange waivers of injury claims or certification of citizenship status that are required by many industrial or research facilities takes time. Time is also needed to brief the host agency or to mark out the trail to be followed on a field trip, and a trip not adequately planned is an open invitation to clumsiness that can approach dangerous chaos.

Field trips often involve unscheduled costs for transportation, meals, and "pocket money." The easiest solution is simply to assess each student for these costs, but many parents and students resent this practice. Where field-trip expenses are not included in the recognized operating budget of the school, parent-teacher groups or other service organizations can be asked for the needed money.

The sheer mechanics of hearing and being heard and seeing and being seen impose additional weaknesses on the field-trip format. It is difficult to keep a group in the preferred "horse-shoe" and to prevent the long, straggly lines which are so likely to develop. Trips to some kinds of facilities can be managed only by dividing the total group into smaller units and providing opportunities for exchanging notes among the groups.

If students feel a sudden release from arbitrarily imposed classroom discipline, student behavior can create another weakness of the field-trip format. Students who resist conforming to acceptable behavior find many and sometimes glorious opportunities to exhibit their resistance. After the teacher has clearly established the behavior to be expected from his students, equally clear arrangements should be made to exclude any student who chooses not to limit himself to such behavior. In general, however, more discipline problems are prevented, ameliorated, or corrected than are initiated while on field trips.

The field trip is very time-consuming. In addition to classtime used for planning and follow-up, sometimes it is necessary to give up additional time to compensate the teachers whose classes were missed. This and all other weaknesses must be weighed against the advantages in arriving at a decision to use or not use the field-trip format. In general, since solutions of one kind or another can be found to the problems and difficulties, as the example which follows shows, appropriate versions of a field trip are available to all teachers.

TOPIC: Overproduction, variations among species, and survival of the fittest as factors in the origin of species. This topic appears in the final chapters of a textbook being used in a Tenth Grade biology class.

PLANNING: Since this field trip involved only the usual class period and no travel arrangements, the only administrative planning consisted of leaving word at the school office that Miss Fellow's classes would be walking to the nearby park on the scheduled day. Teacher planning began with the decision that overpopulation, variation, and survival could be approached and appreciated by students through the field trip better than through any other lesson format. Thus, this format was chosen as an appropriate way to introduce the new unit of their textbook.

A brief scouting trip to a nearby park produced four stops. The teacher marked these spots in her mind and decided "to put the students in the role of discoverers. This I tried to do by taking them step by step from their own observations. To do this, I set up a series of questions."

Before leaving the classroom the students were told: "Today we are ready for a new unit in our textbooks. I believe we can approach this unit best by a field trip. Please bring only your notebooks and pens or pencils. We will be gone from rest room facilities for the hour. When I dismiss you, leave the building quietly and assemble at the tennis courts. While on the field trip there will be four main stops. At each of these stops, please form a horse-shoe-shaped group so we can all see and hear each other: in fact, it is each person's responsibility to make sure we can *all* see and hear each other. Let's assemble at the tennis courts in four minutes."

First Stop: Beneath an Eastern Red-Bud Tree. "I trust you can all see and recognize the seed pods on this red-bud tree. Use your head and pencil to estimate the total number of seeds on this tree. I will call for your individual estimates in five minutes." "Now as we move along to the next stop, look around and decide whether or not red-bud trees differ from other plants in regard to the number of seeds they produce."

Second Stop: Lily Pond. "Notice that the lily pads here are not all the same color. Find out why. (Some lily pads were practically covered with tiny sap-sucking insects.) If an insect-covered leaf were to die, what would happen to the insects? What would be the state of affairs when all lily pads save one were dead?"

Third Stop: Open Area in Mature Woods Near the Top of a Hill. "Note the kinds and numbers of plants growing here. Soon we will be moving to the small stream at the bottom of the hill. For now, record the factors of the environment here that you believe are most closely related to the kinds and numbers of plants here."

Fourth Stop: Open Area in Mature Woods Along a Small Stream. "Do the same thing here we did at stop three. We have about ten minutes before returning to our classroom. For tomorrow, think about what we have seen on this trip and bring to class your notes from today and have ready to hand in a copy of what you think are your best notes at any one stop. Are there any questions? Be at the tennis courts in eight minutes."

On the following day, class discussion drew upon the observations of the previous day to establish the general concepts of overproduction, variation, and survival of the fittest.

For Discussion and Further Study

1. What are the advantages and disadvantages that accompany efforts to confront students with phenomena in their natural settings?

2. Can attention and discipline problems be avoided by appointing student leaders to assist the field-trip guide?

3. Are there specific features of the pursuit of science that can be uniquely nurtured through the field-trip type of science lesson?

4. Under what conditions would the success of a field trip be improved by the teacher (1) reconnoitering the area, (2) preparing a fill-in-the-blanks type of student guide sheet, or (3) basing student grades on the report submitted at the conclusion of the field trip?

5. What are a teacher's professional and legal responsibilities for his students when a class is being conducted away from school property?

References

1. George E. Pitluga. "The Science Excursions and Teaching Technique," *School Science and Mathematics,* 47 (May 1947), pp. 460–69. Reprinted by permission of the editor.

2. Paul F. Brandwein, Fletcher G. Watson, and Paul E. Blackwood. *Teaching High School Science: A Book of Methods*. New York: Harcourt, Brace and World, 1958, p. 1958.
3. Glenn O. Blough, Julius Schwartz and Albert J. Huggett. *Elementary School Science and How to Teach It*. New York: The Dryden Press, 1958, p. 34.
4. Robert M. McClung. "An Author Looks to the Future," *The American Biology Teacher*, 24 (February 1962), pp. 108–12.
5. Leonard G. Scheel. "Why Follow the Leader," *The American Biology Teacher*, 23 (May 1961), pp. 276–78.
6. Walter A. Thurber and Alfred T. Collette. *Teaching Science in Today's Secondary Schools*. Boston: Allyn and Bacon, 1964, p. 156.

34

Teaching by Television

Television is a powerful means of communication. In and of itself it will do nothing to amuse, to entertain, or to educate. The sole value of the instrument depends upon the resourcefulness and abilities of the people who use it.[1]

T. Wilson Cahall   1961

Two years' experience using the best TV camera facilities available for the teaching of physics has led the author to the conviction that, while TV cannot take the place of laboratory practice in which individual students personally perform experiments, it can do a superior job in the lecture room teaching and demonstrating phase of instruction. . . . While certain aspects of the learning process may require close personal contacts between teacher and student, a great deal of factual knowledge has previously been imparted through the printed word, our books. To this static mode of the dissemination of knowledge, with all of its capabilities and refinements, we can now add the dynamic modes

of dissemination made possible through films and television. . . . One [plan for a TV classroom] is an auditorium with three complete lecture room fronts, mounted on a turntable, and a suitable number of TV monitors suspended from the ceiling. The other plan involves a group of several TV studios surrounded by suitable shop and preparation areas, and a number of average-sized classrooms, each equipped with a TV viewing screen.[2]

Harvey E. White   1960

The Science Corner telecast series was very effective in improving . . . pupils' interest in their environment [and] the children's fund of science information. [It was] rated as extremely useful in introducing science content and demonstration materials of the new Science Course of Study to teachers [and] in showing [teachers] activities useful in their teaching programs.[3]

William B. Reiner   1961

In the TV-centered lesson, all or the major portion of the instruction in a course comes into the classroom by way of TV receivers. The teacher in the televising studio and the teachers in the various classrooms in which the lesson is being received share responsibility for the total instruction in the course.

Strengths and Weaknesses

Although cooperation between the telecasting and classroom teacher is probably the factor which contributes most to the success or failure of the TV-centered lesson, the two phases will be taken up separately here. First, consider the strengths and weaknesses of the televised portion of TV-centered lesson.

The most obvious advantage of this type of lesson is the great return one gains from time and money invested in arranging the occurrence or demonstration of the phenomena or principles which are scheduled for the day's lesson. If the day's lesson, for example, involves the relationship between the physical factors of an environment and the characteristics of the plants and animals of that environment, a teacher may need to spend a whole Saturday or Sunday collecting the specimens needed to confront his students with the evidence of this relationship.

FIGURE 10. Behind the televised lesson are extensive supporting services and effective communication between classroom teachers, supervisory and administrative people, and the television teacher.

The TV-centered lesson enables hundreds of students to benefit from this investment of one teacher's time.

A second and equally obvious advantage of the TV-centered lesson is the ease with which observational problems are solved. To have students "come to the front of the room" better to observe the intricate details of a phenomenon, as all teachers know, is a completely inefficient and discipline-disturbing arrangement. There is no problem in having the TV camera come in for close-up observation; in fact, views through a microscope can also be televised.

Now that television programs can be efficiently recorded on magnetic tape, additional advantages of the TV-centered lesson are becoming apparent. Lessons can be easily reviewed and analyzed at the convenience of the telecast teacher. He can, thereby, improve the effectiveness of his presentation. In those cases where there may be duplication of material in the separate courses of a curriculum, the recorded televised lessons become indisputable evidence of duplication. Furthermore, students will know that there can be no arguments about what was included in prior courses for which they are responsible.

The extrinsically controlled pace of a televised lesson permits a lesson to unfold with predictable timing. Students realize that the lesson must be followed exactly as it is designed, and they soon learn to forego prior habits of relying on the considerate but less efficient practice of having the teacher repeat explanations that were presented when other things occupied the students' minds.

An additional advantage of the TV-centered lesson exploits the private and personal nature of the learning process. There are many instances in learning the pursuit of science where the individual must have an uninterrupted opportunity to think. For example, after a puzzling event or circumstance has been brought to the attention of a class, each student deserves the opportunity to wrestle a bit with his curiosity and attempt to frame a satisfactory explanation. It is easier for the television teacher to avoid the awkwardness of having to suppress the more precocious students who want to blurt out their thoughts immediately as "flashes of insight" occur. By metering additional evidence and data, the teacher can ensure that a much greater fraction of his students will enjoy the personal satisfaction of making "inductive leaps."

To gain maximum efficiency from the TV-centered lesson, it must be made clear from the beginning just which functions can be performed better by the studio teacher and which ones by the teachers in the classrooms. Generally speaking, the studio teacher is in the better position to stimulate interest, to inform by word and demonstration, to show applications of general concepts, to raise questions, and to challenge pupils to assume more responsibility for their own learning. The classroom teacher, on the other hand, may be better able to handle classroom discussion, to care for the individual differences in pupils, clear up immediate misunderstandings, supervise drill and problem-solving sessions, provide remedial teaching, help the pupil establish relationships between things learned and his daily activities, provide opportunities for pupils to exercise critical judgments, interpret the testing program, and give attention to the establishment of desirable habits and traits.

A synergistic effect derives from having a group of classroom teachers work with the telecast teacher in the development of a course. The classroom teachers can observe their suggestions being put into practice by the television teacher and adapt, into their own repertory of techniques, those that work well. Similarly, the natural processes of "feedback" will help the telecast teacher avoid continued use of inefficient or clumsy procedures.

There is little doubt that the new medium of television makes possible a much broader, deeper, and richer curriculum than is possible under conventional methods of instruction. When devotees of the status quo, and zealous guardians of "the good old way" of doing things, restrict the television teachers to purely rote memory or pronouncement patterns of teaching, the television concept of teaching becomes grossly incongruous with the uses being made of it. Television is essentially neutral as a conveyer of ideas, concepts, and information. Furthermore, it does not improve upon the teaching methods to which the cameras are directed.

Probably the greatest weakness of the TV-centered lesson derives from the patterns of behavior toward television broadcasts that are learned by students through frequently long periods of watching commercial television programs. Students must learn that exhortations to do homework arise from different motives than do other usually much more persuasive and earnest pleas of the commercial announcer to use a particular brand of cigarette or cosmetic.

In what would appear to be trivial respects, the telecast teacher will find himself in conflict with commercial television. The tactics and strategy of teaching are not necessarily those of a well-executed commercial television program. When the science teacher, for example, comes to a point in his lesson that requires the students to think uninterruptedly for five minutes or so, he will encounter almost overwhelming resistance from the commercial program manager for whom a "dead screen" is completely unthinkable. Furthermore, there are some things that in the commercial program simply must have a background of soft, mood music. This may be complete nonsense from the point of view of the spirit of the pursuit of science, and if the telecast teacher is overruled, his lessons will suffer.

Scheduling and room facilities may cause real problems for the TV-centered lesson. To be economically sound, telecast lessons require a much higher teacher-pupil ratio than do traditional lessons. In large schools with many sections of students studying the same subject, all will receive the televised lesson at the same hour. No longer can the geometry teacher, for example, spend his entire day teaching geometry, and, similarly, there will be as many geometry teachers needed during the telecast lesson as there are rooms full of geometry students. These problems will limit the effectiveness of TV-centered lessons unless the telecast teacher carries the full responsibility for the specialized aspects of his subject, and the classroom teachers have a liberal education broad enough to serve as classroom teachers in a variety of subjects.

Whereas the TV-centered lesson requires the telecast teacher to be a true scholar of his subject and provides adequate time for him to be an encyclopedia of knowledge, the classroom teacher must assume a different repertory of proficiencies. He must be adept at directing a logical analysis of data and evidence. He must be able to help his students frame hypotheses regarding the problems left unsolved by the telecast teacher and to test the validity of solutions to these problems. In short, the strength of those portions of the TV-centered lesson for which the classroom teacher is responsible will depend upon his mastery of the learning process more than his ability to purvey subject matter. He must know the spirit, structure, and function of the subject, but he can hold the telecast teacher responsible for the "right answers."

An example of the television format in action in the form of segments of the scripts for two lessons follows. The lessons were prepared and televised by M. Eugene Mittel, Washington County Schools, Hagerstown, Maryland.

TV SCRIPT OUTLINE

SUBJECT: *Science* GRADE: *9* DATE: *February 23, 1960*
TEACHER: *E. Mittel* LESSON # *Review* DIRECTOR: *Grove*

Camera	Shot	Cues
1	System	
2	Title	
1	Subtitle	
2	Teacher	What is sound? (form of energy)
		Created by vibrations
1	CU's	(tuning fork, paper, water, pp ball)
2	Teacher	Has a speed
		1. depends on temperature.
		(ea 1° rise in temp. = 2 ft/sec.)
1	PR	(? speed at − 20 C, 15 F, O C)
2	Teacher	2. depends on substance
		(solid, liquid, gas)
1	CU	(hold ruler against mike)
2	Teacher	What are the parts of a sound wave?
1	model	(look at magnet model)
2	Teacher	Let's put this on the paper roll

1	PR	
2	Teacher	Sound travels in waves in all direction from its source
1	Oscilloscope	(Show wave on oscilloscope)
2	Teacher	Reflected sound—echo—desirable and undesirable sonar radar
1	Oscillo-	How sounds differ from each other (Show with bells and oscilloscope) Intensity—force needed to produce sound Amplitude—loudness Frequency—wave lengths per second Pitch—highness or lowness Resonance—reenforcement, enrichment
2	Teacher	Let's see these things on the paper roll

TV SCRIPT OUTLINE

SUBJECT: *General Science* GRADE: *9* DATE: *November 13, 1959*
TEACHER: *E. Mittel* LESSON# *Enrich.* DIRECTOR: *Grove*

Camera	Shot	Cues
1	System	
2	Title Card	
Film Chair	Film	Yes, this is the F-27, designed by Fokker in Holland, modified and built by Fairchild Aircraft here in Hagerstown. This aircraft is powered by two Rolls Royce Turboprop engines which operate more economically than piston type engines. Here is the main plant in Hagerstown. Let's drop in and visit with Mr. John Catlin, F-27 project coordinator, and learn a little more about the F-27 and the airplane industry in general.
1		(TEACHER ENTERS—SHAKES HANDS—SAYS GOOD MORNING—SITS DOWN)
	Wide—to include entry of teacher and desk set Dolly in	The purpose of my visit this morning is to seek information that will help my students understand more about the airplane industry, and to realize that it is an industry which makes use of scientific discoveries and developments. A great many students and indeed a large part of the public, assume that it is a relatively easy thing to build an airplane, when in actuality it is a very time consuming, and money consuming venture. Would you give me some information that would help them understand this?

TV SCRIPT OUTLINE *(continued)*

SUBJECT: *General Science*   GRADE: *9*   DATE: *November 13, 1959*
TEACHER: *E. Mittel*   LESSON# *Enrich.*   DIRECTOR: *Grove*

Camera	Shot	Cues
1	Catlin—points out window at plane	I'd be very glad to Mr. Mittel. Perhaps if we use the development of the F-27 as an illustration, we'll accomplish what you ask.
2	Picture	This picture will explain. . . .
1	Catlin Dolly back Wide	Why don't we take a tour through the plant and see some of the work that goes on, and perhaps that will help you also.
2	Picture: 1	Here is the engineering department. . . .
1	2	smoke testing
2	3	wind tunnel
1	4	data collecting
2	5	data processing
1	6	die making

For Discussion and Further Study

1. What are the advantages and disadvantages of having a "master" teacher present televised lessons to multiple classes rather than having classes instructed individually by "average" teachers?

2. What satisfactions and frustrations accompany an attempt to produce the television script for a representative science lesson?

3. When new communicaton media are developed, radio, motion pictures, television, for example, is there a tendency for the educational profession to embrace them with undue hope? What factors accompany the finding of its "rightful" place by a new medium in the teaching profession?

4. What were the immediate and long-term effects of nationally televised secondary school science courses?

5. How can televised lessons be integrated with a classroom teacher's established way of presenting his course?

References

1. T. Wilson Cahall. "Closed-Circuit Television Instruction." Paper presented at symposium, "Tomorrow's Teaching," January 13–15, 1961. Oklahoma City: Frontiers of Science Foundation, 1962, p. 88.
2. Harvey E. White. "More Effective Teaching of Physics Through Television," *American Journal of Physics,* 28 (April 1960), pp. 368–74.
3. William B. Reiner. "The Effectiveness of Television in Improving the Science Program of Kindergarten to Grade 4 Classes in New York City Public Schools," *Science Education,* 45 (February 1961), pp. 43–54.

35

The Programmed
or
"Teaching Machine"
Format

*How does this new form of writing books proceed? The
basic principle we learned in the laboratory was that the
material must be decomposed into its atomic constituents.
If we want to teach a complicated thing, we first have to
discover what its parts are. . . . The biggest problem of the
programmer is to understand the subject matter so well
himself that he can write in this way. . . . One of the most
important consequences of the entire programming effort
is the education that it provides for the teacher who, faced
with a child who knows nothing, without any intervention
on the teacher's part, provides that child with information
that will produce a child who knows something.*[1]

Eugene Galanter 1961

*A student who answers all questions correctly proceeds
from one question to the next. In the scrambled book, however, the progression from question to question does not
follow any particular page sequence. The student who
selects an erroneous response is usually directed to a page*

which corrects the error by explaining the reason for the error. *The student is then directed to return to the question and select another answer.*[2]

Chester A. Lawson, Mary Alice Burmester, and Clarence H. Nelson 1960

Instructions: *Cover the items below with a piece of paper, lowering the paper item by item as you read. For each item fill in the blank spaces. The words in parentheses that preface the next item give the correct response. Use reasonable judgment in deciding whether your response is synonymous with the printed response. Now, read the items.*

To determine whether a student has understood a point, a teacher may _____ him a question.
(ask) if the student gives an incorrect answer, the teacher may tell him the _____ answer.
(correct) Sometimes a teacher will _____ a student a question and then, if necessary, tell him the _____ answer.
(ask, correct) Confirmation of success is also a part of pedagogy. If the student gives the correct answer, then he receives _____ of success.
(confirmation) If the student answers correctly, his success is _____; if he answers incorrectly, the teacher tells him the _____ answer.
(confirmed, correct) A fast learner likes to advance rapidly, while a slower learner is happier at a slower rate, each student advancing best at his own_____.
(rate) It would require an individual tutor for each student to insure that each student advanced exactly at his _____ rate.
(own) The teacher of a classroom is not able to insure that each student advances exactly at his _____ _____.
(own rate) A teaching machine presents a sequence of statements, one at a time, to the student. The student writes his responses on a strip of paper accessible through an opening in the machine. Each statement, in effect, _____ the student a question.
(asks) The student then operates the machine to make his written response inaccessible, but visible through a window, and to reveal the correct response for comparison. If the student is correct, his success is _____; if he is incorrect he is told the _____ answer.
(confirmed, correct) A teaching machine is like a teacher in that the student is _____ questions, his successes are _____, and his mistakes are _____.

436

*(asked, confirmed, corrected)   A teaching machine has the
advantage of an individual tutor in that each student proceeds at exactly his_____.
(own rate)   An ordinary textbook also allows each student
to proceed at his _____ _____ insofar as he is able to
proceed by himself.
(own rate)   But in an ordinary textbook the student is not
_____ questions, nor are his successes _____, nor are
his mistakes _____.
(asked, confirmed, corrected)   James G. Holland and B. F.
Skinner in their* The Analysis of Behavior, *published by
McGraw-Hill, now offer a new kind of textbook that does
offer these features. The book is, in effect, a machineless*

_____ _____.

*(teaching machine)   The sequence of items that you are
now reading is an example of the technique used in either
a real teaching machine or in a _____ teaching machine.
(machineless)   The new book makes for truly unforgettable
reading, and we recommend that you _____ it.
(read).*[3]

Joseph Turner   1961

*The teaching machine . . . displays one item of information
at a time and makes salient the critical cues. Also, if the
learner fails to understand a point, he can repeat it before
going on. The machine also requires or makes almost mandatory some form of response before correct answers are sup-
plied. With a teaching machine, the learner is in control,
in that his responses determine what he does next within
the preplanned limits of the program; thus there is feed-
back and adjustment of the learning situation to the needs
of the individual.*[4]

Lawrence M. Stolurow   1961

The programmed lesson is achieved when the instructor has examined
an episode in the pursuit of science and prepared a series of steps by
which a student may be expected to proceed from a state of almost
ignorance to one of comprehension of the episode. The steps, called
frames, incorporate the kinds of behavior expected of the student,
stimuli to prompt this behavior, and a means of rewarding the student
immediately upon achieving this behavior.

To construct a programmed lesson, the teacher begins by arranging
the terms, facts, laws, circumstances, and events that add up to the

total episode to be taught. From among this array of details, the teacher selects those with which the student is most likely to have had prior contact. The first steps of the program lead a student to launch himself on the pathway to new learning by rewarding him with the satisfaction he gains from knowing he can proceed satisfactorily through the initial frames. Wherein the teacher predicts that his students will have absolutely no prior contact with the material in the new lesson, the initial steps must include information of such low difficulty that the student can gain it by reading as he goes. Sheer trial and error is kept to an absolute minimum by including clues to the desired response to each frame, clues that nudge the student in the direction that he is expected to follow.

Strengths and Weaknesses

The outstanding strength of the programmed lesson format is the opportunity it provides for the teacher to exploit everything that is known about the nature of the learning process. Each facet of insight accumulated by educational psychologists can be applied and exploited in the preparation and arrangement of the individual frames of the lesson. In turn, the development of frames, their testing, revision, and re-testing contributes to the investigation of the learning process and to the design of new educational techniques. Proponents of the use of programmed lessons look forward to the day when much more precise and specific classroom procedures will replace the generalized "shotgun" procedures that have been inherited from prior generations of teachers.

A second clearly recognized value of the programmed lesson is the stimulus it provides toward complete mastery of a lesson by those who would teach it. Not only does the preparation of a program require the programmer to be familiar with each detail of the episode being taught, he must also give thought to the precise order in which the student is to confront each detail. Furthermore, the programmer must comprehend the episodes of science that form logical boundaries of the one being programmed. This comprehension permits him to construct frames that allow the student to make exploratory excursions into closely related domains and still be brought back to the main pathway of the lesson.

A student can approach a properly programmed lesson with confidence, certain that he will be able to proceed through the lesson successfully. The pleasure of being right replaces the fear of being wrong. Even the occasional errors that are made while working through the program are known only to the individual student. Each student proceeds through the program at his own best pace. Since he controls the administration of the lesson, it never needs move too slowly for him, nor does it threaten to leave him behind.

Again, proponents of the machine programmed lesson argue that this format enjoys quite favorable psychological acceptance by the student. The student remains alert, busy, and continuously involved in his study material. Since the learner is asked to answer questions about each new segment of information as he encounters it, his continuing participation in the learning process is ensured. When students stumble over a frame, the programmer does not censure the student. He assumes there is something wrong with that particular step and reworks the material to eliminate causes of student frustration.

The greatest single weakness of this format stems from the almost unlimited number of the facets of behavior prerequisite to a student's becoming familiar with even a reasonably simple episode in the pursuit of science. To anticipate the numerous channels of thought in which the student might engage and to design subtle reinforcements adequate to retrieve the student from the "wrong" and return him to the "right" pathway may overtax the skill of the programmer. "Feed-back" arising from use of a programmed lesson, however, automatically improves the lesson. Whereas the teacher must invent or recall each time they are needed the many subtle ways to monitor student behavior in other lesson formats, the programmed format permits their immediate incorporation into the printed program.

No one knows for sure how students would react to programmed lessons were they to become standard classroom procedures. Despite how much they really enjoy school, being in school is traditionally supposed to be odious to many students. Once the novelty of the programmed lesson wears off, there is the chance that these students would develop apathy or more pronounced negative reactions to a type of lesson with only a minimum of dramatic and social appeal.

Inherent in the programmed lesson format is another subtle but vitally important weakness. The format is admittedly sophisticated and cumbersome. To use such a format to accomplish basically simple learning creates incongruity. Simple drill may be an adequate format for teaching technical terms, facts, laws, or principles. Exercising the powers of the mind most often exercised in the pursuit of science requires a more complex lesson format. Unless the programmer comprehends the importance of the ability to detect resemblances and differences, to infer new truths, to make comparisons, to exercise disciplined persistence, to retain suspicious criticism, and the other mental processes that seem to be peculiarly associated with the pursuit of science, his programmed lessons are likely to become simply more sophisticated ways to teach a body of material that may or may not be what students deserve to gain from their courses in science.

Repetition, with its threat of aversive redundancy, is essential in the programmed lesson. To avoid allowing this threat to incorporate weakness in the format, as the student receives new information he is encouraged to make finer discriminations in what he has already learned and to apply what he has learned to an increasingly wide variety of situations. A well-programmed lesson expands the student's verbal response into the use of newly acquired concepts to solve problems, build new models, or some other form of less structured response. Eventually, at least in theory, the student is weaned from a highly structured lesson and becomes ready to take off on his own toward a more advanced pursuit of science.

Examples and Illustrations

The first example of a programmed lesson is drawn from work done by Evans, Glaser, and Homme.[5] They argue that the verbal subject material of a lesson can be classified into two classes of statements, which they call RU's (for "rules") and EG's (for "examples"). The programming of a lesson consists of converting the total lesson into these two classes of statements and ordering them in the proper sequence.

SKINNER'S HIGH SCHOOL PHYSICS PROGRAM RECONSTRUCTED ACCORDING TO THE RULEG SYSTEM

Class	Sentence to be Completed	Word to be Supplied
ru + $\widetilde{eg}$	1. To "emit" light means to "send out" light. For example, the sun, a fluorescent tube, and a bonfire have in common that they all send out or _____ light.	emit
$\widetilde{eg}$	2. A firefly and an electric light bulb are alike in that the both send out or _____ light.	emit
ru + $\widetilde{eg}$	3. Any object which gives off light because it is hot is called an *incandescent* light source. Thus, a candle flame and the sun are alike in that they both are _____ sources of light.	incandescent
$\widetilde{eg}$	4. When a blacksmith heats a bar of iron until it glows and emits light, the iron bar has become a(n) _____ source of light.	incandescent
$\widetilde{eg}$	5. A neon tube emits light but remains cool. Unlike the ordinary electric light bulb, then, it is not an _____ of light.	incandescent source
$\widetilde{ru}$	6. An object is called incandescent when _____.	it emits light because it is hot

SKINNER'S HIGH SCHOOL PHYSICS PROGRAM RECONSTRUCTED ACCORDING TO THE RULEG SYSTEM

Class	Sentence to be Completed	Word to be Supplied
ru + r̃u	7. It has been found that an object, an iron bar, for example, will emit light if its temperature is raised above *800 degrees Celsius.* Therefore, we say that above _____ (temperature) objects will become _____.	800° Celsius incandescent
ru + r̃u	8. An electric light bulb produces light when the fine wire, technically called a *filament,* inside the glass is heated to incandescence. This means, then, that the fine wire or _____ must exceed a temperature of about _____° Celsius to emit light.	filament 800
	9. Etc.	

A second example of programmed lessons is adapted from the early work of Jay A. Young.[6] Students use his programs by placing a small index card over the answers which appear near the margin and moving the card downward as the items are studied.

VAPOR PRESSURE

1

Liquids evaporate, and the gas, or vapor, that is formed by the liquid that has evaporated can be recondensed—forming the liquid again. The relationships between and among the original liquids, the vapor, and the condensed vapor are worth thoughful consideration. We shall study these matters here, but to understand the discussion, you must first know what the word, pressure, means. If you do, continue on.

2

To begin, consider an Erlenmeyer flask, about half filled with water, as illustrated in figure 1. If we let the flask stay on a laboratory bench for several days and then examine it, we will find that the water _____.

has evaporated, or, is gone

Figure 1

3

The water in the flask evaporates because the molecules of water are constantly moving about, in one direction and then in another, downward, sideward and _____.

upward

4

Consider one of these molecules, one that is very near the surface of the water in the flask. If it is moving downward or side-

ward, it will not leave the liquid water. But if it is moving upward
and is going fast enough, or, if moving downward or sideward,
it is bumped upward (by another molecule) hard enough, then
it will _____ the liquid water.   leave

5

Eventually, if enough time is allowed, _____ of the molecules of water will evaporate, and no liquid water will be left
in the flask.   all

6

For a moment, we shall change the subject and consider a deck
of cards, thoroughly shuffled. If you are asked to pick a card from
the deck, the chance that any one card will be selected is the
_____ as the chance that any other card will be selected.   same

7

The motion of the molecules of water in the flask is random.
The chance that any one molecule near the surface will escape
is the _____ as the chance that any other molecule near the
surface will also escape.   same

8   constant,
Or, since there are millions of molecules near the surface of   regular,
the water in the flask, as one escapes, and then another, and   or, the
another, and so on, the rate of escape is not first, say, fast, and   same at
then slow, but rather the rate of escape of the molecules is_____.   all times

Whether a teacher who has not been especially trained in programming lessons can create the scripts for machine teaching is a
question on which there is divided opinion. The next example was
produced by a teacher who, although she enjoyed adequate mastery
of the subject matter and knew something of how students react to
problem-solving assignments, had no training or experience in programming. The format of this programming uses underlining to call
attention to key terms and blanks (parentheses) for responses.

DETERMINATION OF EMPIRICAL AND MOLECULAR FORMULAS

Let us suppose for a time that we are engaged as part of a research team of
chemists in a laboratory. Our job is to assist in identifying unknown products
which are formed by experimental reactions. There is a very orderly procedure which we learn to follow in determining these formulas.
1. The (formula) which tells us the elements present and the ratio of their
atoms in each molecule is called an empirical formula.
2. The (empirical formula) then tells us two things: the (elements) present
and the (ratio) of their atoms in the molecule. It is the simplest type of
formula.
A bottle arrives in the laboratory one day containing a product formed by
a reaction in the bacterial research department. The product is a liquid and

our chemist friends rapidly determine that the liquid contains only three elements. That is, each <u>molecule</u> of the liquid contains only 3 kinds of atoms.

3. The three types of (atoms) are carbon, hydrogen and oxygen. The chemcal symbols for these elements are:

(<u>Carbon</u> .... C)
(<u>Hydrogen</u> ...... H)
(<u>Oxygen</u> .... O)

4. We have now <u>one</u> of the requirements for determining our (<u>empirical</u>) formula. We know what (<u>elements</u> [or <u>atoms</u>]) are present. We must next determine the (<u>ratio</u>) of these atoms in each molecule.

5. Our first step is to calculate the <u>percentage</u> of each of these 3 (<u>elements</u>) in the compound. We want to know the percentage by <u>weight</u>.

6. Percent is, briefly, parts per <u>hundred</u> parts. Thus, if we have 25¢, we have 25 (<u>per cent</u>) of a dollar.

We have performed the following calculation:

$$\frac{25 \text{ cents we have}}{100 \text{ cents in a dollar}} = .25 \times 100 = 25\%$$

7. Similarly, if a baseball player hits 14 home runs in 100 times at bat, he has hit home runs

$$\frac{14 \text{ home runs}}{100 \text{ times at bat}} = (\underline{.14}) \times (\underline{100}) = (\underline{14\%}) \text{ of his}$$

times at bat.

Exactly the same calculation is carried out with each element in our compound. Our analysis tells us that in each 100 grams of our liquid, they have found

```
 40 grams of carbon
 6.6 grams of hydrogen
53.4 grams of oxygen
```

8. So we can easily calculate the (<u>percentage</u>) of each element.
For carbon:

$$\left(\frac{40 \text{ grams of carbon}}{100 \text{ grams of liquid}} = .40 \times 100 = 40\% \text{ carbon}\right)$$

For hydrogen:

$$\left(\frac{6.6 \text{ grams of hydrogen}}{100 \text{ grams of liquid}} = .066 \times 100 = 6.6\% \text{ hydrogen}\right)$$

For oxygen:

$$\left(\frac{53.4 \text{ grams of oxygen}}{100 \text{ grams of liquid}} = .534 \times 100 = 53.4\% \text{ oxygen}\right)$$

9. List your answers below using the chemical symbol for each element.

(40% C)
(6.6% H)
(53.4% O)

10. These are the (percentages) of each element present in our unknown liquid.

We must now obtain a more absolute relationship for these elements. We can do this by dividing the percentages by the atomic weight of each atom.

11. Thus if carbon has an atomic weight of 12,

$$\frac{40}{12} = 3.3$$

and hydrogen has an atomic weight of 1

$$\left(\frac{6.6}{1} = 6.6\right)$$

and oxygen has an atomic weight of 16

$$\left(\frac{53.4}{16} = 3.3\right)$$

12. We have the ratio 3.3: 6.6: 3.3 because we have compensated for the differences of atomic weights by (dividing) these weights into the (percentages) of each (element) in our mystery liquid.

However, because we are dealing with whole atoms and because we must express our empirical formula in the simplest possible terms, we must express our ratio in small, whole numbers.

13. Thus, we divide each quotient by the smallest quotient. This is our third step.

Let us now make these calculations

for carbon $\dfrac{3.3}{3.3} = 1$

for hydrogen $\dfrac{6.6}{3.3} = 2$

for oxygen $\dfrac{3.3}{3.3} = 1$

14. Using our chemical symbols we could write our empirical formula as $C_1H_2O_1$. The subscript 1 is not necessary, however, so we can write our formula simply (CH_2O).

15. A word aside here. Had we been working with some compound whose elements we found by the above calculations to exist in a ratio such as 1:3.5:1, a further operation would be necessary. We would have to multiply by a number which would give us the smallest possible whole number ratio. In this case the number is (2). Our ratio would then be (2:7:2).

16. Let's summarize the steps which we have taken to determine the (empirical) formula.

1. Calculate the (percentage) of each (element) present in the compound.
2. Divide the (percentage) of each (element) by its (atomic weight).
3. (Divide) each (quotient) obtained by the (smallest quotient).
4. If the numbers obtained are not small (whole) numbers, (multiply) each by a number which will express the ratio in the smallest possible (whole) numbers.

17. These steps we have now taken to determine that the empirical formula of our unknown liquid is (CH_2O).

18. However, when we try to decide just what this compound is, we find that we must know, not only the (ratio) of the atoms in the molecule but also the actual number of each atom present.

As an example of something similar let us suppose a new family has moved into the neighborhood. A friend tells us that for each three humans, there is one cat and one dog. Using a sort of shorthand we can write the "formula" for the household as

$C_1 H_3 D_1$.

However, we don't really know just how many of each creature is present in this household. But if our friend tells us also that there are 15 members of our imaginary household, we can make some calculations which will give us a more accurate picture.

19. Let us first add up the number of members represented by our "empirical formula."

Dogs   1
Cats   1
Humans   3
Total   (5)

If we divide the number of members by this quotient we obtain the number (3)

$$(\frac{15}{5} = 3)$$

We can then multiply each number in our empirical formula by (3) to obtain the true numbers of each type of member in the household. Thus:

Dogs: ($1 \times 3 = 3$)
Humans: ($3 \times 3 = 9$)
Cats: ($1 \times 3 = 3$)

Our "formula" is

$D_3 H_9 C_3$

This is exactly what we do for our unknown liquid if we wish to know the true molecular formula.

We ascertain from our analytical chemists that the molecular weight of compound is 60.

We can compare this with the weight expressed by our empirical formula if we multiply the <u>weight</u> of each atom by the <u>number</u> of this atom in the molecule.

Carbon: $(12 \times 1 = 12)$
Hydrogen: $(1 \times 2 = 2)$
Oxygen: $(1 \times 16 = \underline{16})$
The total is $(\underline{30})$

We then (<u>divide</u>) the molecular weight by the weight expressed in our (<u>empirical</u>) formula.

$(\dfrac{60}{30} = \underline{2})$

Our compound is (<u>twice</u>) as heavy as expressed in our empirical formula. We must then (<u>multiply</u>) the number of each atom by (2).

The correct molecular formula is thus $(C_2H_4O_2)$

We can review these steps thus:

1. Calculate the empirical formula (<u>weight</u>).
2. Divide the (<u>molecular</u>) weight by the (<u>empirical formula</u> weight).
3. Multiply each atom's number in the (<u>empirical formula</u>) by the quotient obtained in Step (#2). This gives us the actual number of each (<u>atom</u>) in each (<u>molecule</u>).

For Discussion and Further Study

1. What psychological principles, assumptions, and premises are particularly involved in programmed learning?

2. Does the quotation from Turner "teach" what a programmed lesson is?

3. Discuss the potential of programmed lessons for stimulating the curiosity of students, collecting evidence bearing on a problem, proposing hypotheses, designing experiments, interpreting data, and applying principles to new situations.

4. Develop a programmed lesson for a commonly taught high school or elementary school science lesson. What problems accompany its development?

5. Is the programmed lesson format significantly related to other educational materials that have been developed to expedite individual learning?

References

1. Eugene Galanter. "Programmed Learning and Teaching Machines." Paper presented at symposium, "Tomorrow's Teaching," January 13–15, 1961. Oklahoma City: Frontiers of Science Foundation, 1962, pp. 28–30.
2. Chester A. Lawson, Mary Alice Burmester, and Clarence H. Nelson. "Developing a Scrambled Book and Measuring Its Effectiveness as an Aid to Learning Natural Science," Science Education, 44 (December 1960), pp. 347–58.
3. Joseph Turner. "A Machineless Teaching Machine," Science, 134 (August 25,1961), p. 531. Reprinted by permission of the American Association for

the Advancement of Science and Joseph Turner. Copyright 1961 by the American Association for the Advancement of Science.

4. Laurence M. Stolurow. *Teaching by Machine*. Washington: Government Printing Office, DHEW–USOE Cooperative Research Monograph No. 6, 1961, p. 150.

5. J. L. Evans, L. E. Homme, and R. Glaser. "The Ruleg (Rule-Example) System for the Construction of Learning Programs." A report prepared under the Cooperative Research Program of the U.S. Office of Education at the Department of Psychology, University of Pennsylvania, 1960. (Mimeo.)

6. Jay A. Young. "Programed Instruction in Chemistry." King's College, Wilkes-Barre, Pennsylvania, 1961. (Mimeo.)

36

The Individual Project

It seems probable that project teaching insures attainment of more aims, gives a greater possibility of learning in general, should induce better learning "growth," insures increased expenditure of effort on the part of pupils, develops greater initiative and independence, gives greater opportunity for "socialization," teaches pupils to think for themselves and develops the "problem solving attitude," encourages a wider range of reading, provides better for the needs of pupils of varying capacities, and provides better opportunities for real and genuine teaching, and for teacher growth than in traditional types of teaching.[1]

Ralph K. Watkins 1923

There are indications that the individual-project method tends to develop traits of industry and initiative which are not revealed by the usual objective-test marks. . . . The pupils taking courses in high-school physics vary widely in capacity, interest, vocational expectancy, chronological age, character-trait ratings, marks in previous school courses, year in school, time available for school work, number of previous sciences studied, and home environment. One course will not fit the needs of all, unless the course is planned to care for these individual differences. . . . Provision for specialized activities or projects is a workable method of caring for individual differences and in this experiment resulted in much desirable activity and many concrete evidences thereof.[2]

Archer W. Hurd 1933

On the basis of class averages, the test results with the seven classes indicate that the accomplishment of the project classes, measured by standardized tests was slightly better than that of the non-project classes, although the average intelligence rating of the latter was almost seven points higher. Pupils in a project class do get and retain information on the material which is reported to them by other pupils. Nearly three-fourths of the number of pupils expressing a preference, voted in favor of the project method.[3]

Ellinor Garber 1922

Science Fairs tend (1) to focus attention not only of pupils but also of the entire community on science; (2) to encourage and inspire in youth the desire for scientific experimentation; (3) to recognize talented youth without exploiting them; and (4) to encourage further work in the field of science in college and industry.[4]

Norman R. D. Jones 1953

The young person with talent often discovers himself through the excitement and satisfaction of tackling a scientific problem, experimentally.[5]

Watson Davis 1951

Although "individual" retains meaning, the term "project" is no longer reserved for a planned undertaking calling for constructive thought and action. Current usage finds almost any undertaking being referred to as a project. Keeping a notebook can be a project. So can making a poster or decorating a bulletin board. In some instances, by being assigned to an individual student, a lecture demonstration becomes an individual project. Similarly, if a student is allowed to choose one rather than another laboratory exercise, he has adopted the project method.

The science "fair" or "congress" has been a flourishing activity during recent years. It has done much to bring student and public attention to science projects. This activity, however, has contributed much toward accepting any undertaking as being a science project. A science fair or congress, to be successful, must emphasize an exhibit. In some cases, the preparation of the exhibit becomes the primary goal if not the entire science project.

A few authors hold out for limiting the use of the term "science project" to small-scale genuine excursions into the pursuit of science. Within these limits, the student must investigate "something—what it is and how it happened, is happening, or might be made to happen." The goal is to do on a small scale what practicing scientists do on a larger scale. The student's project differs from the scientist's project only in degree of sophistication.

Strengths and Weaknesses

Basically, the value of an individual science project is determined by how much of the spirit of science and its strategy the student gains from the time he invests. The information he gains is worth something but since, in most cases, it could have been gained more efficiently by consulting authority, it is in his manner of gaining it that one must seek justification for the more expensive project approach.

Much depends on the perspective of the person who is determining the value of an individual project. The puzzling event or circumstance that can arouse a boy's or girl's curiosity cannot be expected to justify the attention of an experienced scientist. Youngsters' hypotheses may be horribly naive, but they deserve the intellectual stimulation that comes with creating them. Their experiments may be clumsy replications of things done long ago under much better controlled circumstances. But again, even the most sophisticated scientist knows the value of occasionally proving something for himself. Finally, the information gained by a student on his first excursions into science may be much less trustworthy than that which he could have read in any standard textbook or encyclopedia. But how can he come to know the concept of trustworthiness of knowledge without exploring the pathways of its creation?

Although a student can gain private and personal value from almost any excursion into science, those projects return greatest value that can be exhibited in science fairs or reported in appropriate journals. These are the students' counterparts of the conventions, conferences, and literature that allow practicing scientists to communicate.

What might be considered a weakness of the individual-project method is the likelihood that it will throw other things out of perspective. The graduate student who becomes caught up too early by the fascination of his own research project can be expected to slight courses that would have provided fundamental knowledge. The threat of specialization at the expense of general education becomes of even greater significance at the secondary school level.

Examples and Illustrations

The first illustration has been adapted from a seventh-grade girl's report of her science project.

PROBLEM: *Why Are Nature's Sands Colored?* One day last spring we were out in the woods looking for early wildflowers. We happened upon a large sand bank and I noticed the bright colors in the sand. I began wondering about the different colors in the sand.

OBSERVATIONS: *I. At the Sand Bank.* There are many kinds of gravels mixed in with the sand. The stony sand that first comes out of the bank is really very hard, but when given a chance to weather it becomes quite soft. This is especially true in the yellow and purple colors. The red-orange sand is gritty hard.

All of the sand is brighter when it first comes out into the air. It seems the purples were wet like clay but the whites were dry like sea shore sand even though both colors came from the same place. The different layers of sand are not uniformly thick. The red may be two feet thick where the white is two inches and these figures can switch at some other spot.

II. Taken from "Gravel and Sand Deposits of Eastern Maryland." The sedimentary rocks under the coastal plain near Washington comprise the several formations of the Potomac group, somewhat more than 600 feet thick; sand and sandstone apparently restricted to old stream channels or beaches and dark clay and sand.

The Magothy formation overlying the Potomac east of Washington consists of gray or yellow sand and brown sand with local gravel or pudding stone. The Potomac group is composed of irregular alternations of sand and clay. Iron oxide forms ironstone.

The capping area is a mixture of gravel, sand, and reddish loam. In Terrace Gravel there is not much red loam. The Patapsco or the lower formation includes large bodies of sand mostly light colored and gravelly, grading into clays of red, white and other colors.

HYPOTHESES: After due consideration, I decided the five most probable hypotheses are:

1. The ocean and various large streams at one time covered this land bringing in salts and plant life which colored the sands.

WHY ARE NATURE'S SANDS COLORED?

2. The rocks under the soil were different colors and caused sands to be colored when they decayed.
3. Earthquakes mixed the soil causing fallen leaves to discolor the soil.
4. Glaciers have scooped different layers and brought them together in the sand bank.
5. Decaying plant and animal material on top of the soil exposed the soil to discoloring minerals.

EXPERIMENT: The book I read mentioned iron oxide. My dictionary told me that yellow iron oxide is $Fe_2O_3H_2O$ and that red iron oxide is Fe_2O_3. Perhaps heating the yellow oxide would turn it red. It did. I then heated the yellow sand in a test tube to see if it would turn red. It did and water appeared in the test tube. I also heated some of the red sand and it turned redder.

INVESTIGATION: I wanted to know where the sand pit sand came from. So I put a spot of creek bed sand on a slide, some crushed rock, and some sand pit sand. After examining them under the microscope, I decided the sand pit sand resembled the creek bed sand most but the sand pit sand was more rounded. Since I knew where the creek sand and crushed rock came from, I can now guess better where the pit sand was formed.

CONCLUSIONS: Nature's sands, at least the ones I studied, seemed to be

FIGURE 11. Although science projects begin with puzzling observations in nature and proceed through hypotheses and investigations, science fairs provide additional, albeit extrinsic, motivations.

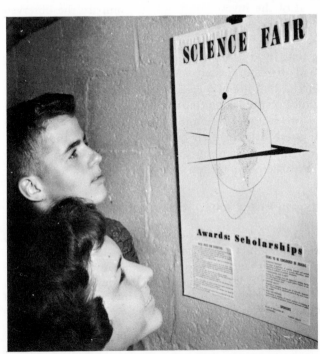

colored by iron oxide. Since iron oxide comes in different colors, sands may be different colors. My conclusions can be wrong if there are other minerals which change from yellow to red when heated.

My investigation suggested that iron oxide was added to the sand after it was made. I believe the sand pit sand came from streams and rivers since it had been rolled around more than the sand from a small creek.

For my next science project I would like to find out where the iron oxide came from and how it was changed in nature.

One advantage pronouncedly inherent in the individual project format is that it in itself imposes practically no limit on the achievement of a student. When this format is applied, each student can begin at whatever level his background permits and then advance to whatever degree of sophistication his time, abilities, and resources allow. To illustrate this point, the project based on a study of the colors of sand can be compared with the following report of a student's investigation of a radioactive decay phenomenon.

At the time of the investigation, the student was a high school junior enrolled in the usual chemistry course. He had participated in competitive science fairs, and one element in his motivation was to complete an investigation the report of which would be a worthy science-fair entry. In this he was successful; the project received national recognition. It is obvious that the boy enjoyed the advantage of guidance above and beyond the content of standard secondary school science and mathematics courses. Several phases of his work were completed in nearby university laboratories and he maintained a small-scale but somewhat specialized laboratory in his home.

The general goal of the investigation was to compare the observed and theoretical decay rates of an unstable isotope. A more specific purpose was to observe the somewhat more complex case of radioactive decay in which a long-lived isotope (lead-210, half-life of 19.4 years or lead-212, half-life of 10.6 hours) yields a decay product of much shorter half-life (bismuth-210, half-life of 5 days or bismuth-212, half-life of 60 minutes). The choice of the lead-bismuth reaction permitted chemical separation of the two isotopes by simply taking advantage of marked differences in the solubilities of their common salts. The student's report begins with definition of terms and an argument regarding the theoretical nature of the phenomenon being investigated.

DEFINITION OF A RADIOACTIVE EQUILIBRIUM

In the members of a radioactive decay series, a radioactive equilibrium is the situation which prevails when the ratio between the amount of successive members of the series remains constant. This means that a radioactive species decays into another radioactive species (which in turn, decays into another) at a rate so that the amount of species into which the original species decays remains constant relative to that species. The half-life of the original species (referred to as the parent) must always be longer than its decay product species (referred to as the daughter). Depending on the half-lives, an equilibrium may be formed between the daughter and its decay products. This can go on until a stable isotope is reached.

Introduction

The two general classes into which equilibria are divided are the secular and the transient. In the former, the half-life of the parent element is very much longer than the half-life of the daughter (or successive element). There is no appreciable change in the amount of parent, while the daughter element is constantly decaying and being regenerated. The parent element in the transient equilibrium, however, has a sufficiently short half-life, so that its decay is not negligible. Intuitively speaking, in a radioactive equilibrium, the rate of disintegration of the daughter equals its rate of regeneration by its parent. This definition does not hold well for the transient since the amount of daughter being regenerated by the parent is constantly decreasing with the half-life of the parent.

The concept of a radioactive equilibrium applies with equal validity to many successive decays of elements possessing the necessary half-life relationships. The common connotation is, however, a relationship between two immediately adjacent members of a decay series.

At this point in his report, the student reviewed the mathematical derivation of equations describing the radioactive decay of isotopes in equilibrium. His report continues.

This research project is a study of the actual conformity of the theoretical equilibrium with the actual equilibrium. For all practical purposes, an equilibrium is an activity on an instrument which detects a certain percentage of the decaying components. Therefore, under the same counting conditions, the activity of a source in, or forming, an equilibrium may be used to measure the activity of a component or components in the equilibrium. Above these fluctuations the problem to be solved here is how close these equilibrium activities compare with what is expected.

The study is divided as follows:
I. The activity of two radioactive isotopes in equilibrium
   A. By sampling, detect fluctuations.
   B. By a χ^2 test (or an equivalent test) determine the validity of the null hypothesis that there is no significant variation.
II. The properties of equilibria
   A. By chemical separation, observe the stability of the growth of the daughter in a pure parent fraction.
   B. By chemical separation disturb the equilibrium and observe the mode in which the equilibrium reforms.
III. Analysis of energy distributions of beta emitters.

Several pages of the report were devoted to identifying the statistical procedures used to determine whether discrepancies between observed and theoretical decay rates did or did not lie within the limits of randomness associated with the conditions of observation. The investigator then described the preparation of his samples and data collecting procedures.

Procedure

Two sources with the Pb^{210} and Bi^{210} secular equilibrium which had been in equilibrium for a year were used. (Referred to as source I and source II). Separation of Bi^{210} and Pb^{210} as chlorides. Prepare 130 ml solution of .5N Hcl Add 3.68 grams of radio-lead nitrate. Heat the solution to free $BiCl_3$ from the $PbCl_2$ crystals and allow to cool. Remove some solution with a pipette and plate on a nickel plate. The sources are then covered with scotch tape to cut out the alpha particles from the Po^{210}.

Throughout all the work in this paper, the sources were counted (lcm) at a distance from the end window geiger tube. The activities are strictly the beta from bismuth since the beta from the lead has too small of an energy to be counted, and the polonium alphas can not reach the tube. Twenty samples of ten readings each were taken simultaneously for the two sources over a 24 day period. The counting was done by a preset count method (this records the time required to obtain a preset number of counts; 1000 counts in this case).

After plotting his data and subjecting them to statistical analysis to establish significance and confidence levels, the investigator concluded:

When two isotopes form an equilibrium, there is a tendency for activity of the daughter to assume a constant value (or a stable value relative to the parent as in the transient equilibrium). The deviations from the constant or stable equilibrium activity form a fairly normal distribution. The variability of the daughter is much greater than would be expected with a Poisson variable with variance equal to the mean. On the basis of the difference between the actual and Poisson variance, there is a definite variance above that expected in the daughter activity. This added variance is directly attributed to the parent which is generating the daughter. Therefore, this activity of the daughter in an equilibrium varies normally around the theoretical constant or stable value with a variance that is greater than what is expected by the Poisson distribution. When a deviation of greater than $2\sqrt{x}$ (about 95 per cent confidence) is observed, it is not necessarily an abnormality.

At this point, the investigation turned to the general properties of equilibria between two isotopes. The report then reviewed the radiochemical procedures that were carried out during the investigation.

The Separation of Pb^{210} and $Pb(SO_4)$
    A. Place 5 ml of $Pb(NO_3)_2$ with 20 ml of .2 M HNO_3 in 100 ml beaker
    B. Add 10 ml of 5 N HNO_3 and then add 2 ml of .3 M $Bi(NO_3)_3$
    C. Mix 20 ml of 1 N H_2SO_4 with solution
    D. Swirl solution as $Pb(NO_3)_2$ precipitates

E. Remove supernatant with pipette and place in a separate 150 ml beaker

F. Rinse Pb(SO₄) with 20 ml of 1 N H_2SO_4 twice, each time removing supernatant and placing it in the supernatant beaker

G. Make final rinse with water, repeat E

H. With vacuum system, remove $PbSO_4$ onto a small piece of filter paper. (see comments)

I. Remove filter paper, add gum arabic, place on planchet, dry with a heat lamp

Separation of Bi^{210} as $Bi_2(C_2O_4)_3$

A. To the supernatant from II E-G-F, add 10 ml of $H_2C_2O_4$ and precipitate $Bi_2(C_2O_4)_3$

B. Using vacuum system again, remove $Bi_2(C_2O_4)_3$

C. As in II, I. prepare the sample on planchet. . . .

Separation of Ba^{137}

A. Add Cs^{137} in solution to centrifuge tube

B. Add 1 ml of $Ba(NO_3)_2$ carrier

C. Add 1 ml of 1 NH_2SO_4 and quickly centrifuge

D. Remove supernatant and wash with 1 ml of 1 N H_2SO_4, again

E. Centrifuge and remove supernatant

F. Wash with 2 ml of water, remove supernatant

G. Break end of centrifuge tube in planchet

H. Add methanol, gum arabic, and ignite

I. Cover and count

Separation of Cs^{137}

A. Pour supernatant into planchet and evaporate with heat lamp

B. Count

Combined separation of Pb^{212} and Bi^{212}

A. 20 ml of .5M $Th(NO_3)_4$ and 5 ml of .1 N HNO_3 in crucible

B. Electrolyse solution at .1 amp, 5-6 V ten to fifteen min.

C. Remove cathode and rinse in water

D. Boil cathode in 1 ml of concentrated HNO_3

E. Remove cathode, neutralize with NH_4OH and evaporate in planchet

F. Count source

G. Pour residue in crucible into waste bottle

Separation of Pb^{212}

A. Same as II A. B. above; C. D. also same

B. Add 1 ml of .1 N $Pb(NO_3)_2$ and 1 ml of .1 N $Bi(NO_3)_3$ after cathode is boiled in HNO_3

C. Add 6 drops of 18 M H_2SO_4 and evaporate

.D Add 1 ml of H_2O and transfer to centrifuge tube, centrifuge, wash precipitate with 2 ml of .2 N H_2SO_4

E. Remove supernatant to other centrifuge tube

F. Rewash $PbSO_4$ precipitate twice with 2 ml of 1 N H_2SO_4 each time adding washings to solution in E.

G. Dissolve precipitate in 5 drops of concentrated HNO_3 evaporate in aluminum planchet with heat lamp
H. Count

Separation of Bi^{212}
A. Add 2 drops of concentrated $NH_4 OH$ until $Bi(OH)_3$ precipitates
B. Wash precipitate three times in H_2O
C. Dissolve $Bi(OH)_3$ in concentrated HNO_3 and evaporate in aluminum planchet
D. Count

Analysis of the observed decay rates obtained from these sources led the investigator to conclude:

Conclusion

The natural tendency of radioactive equilibrium is to form from a state where the parent is in excess and decays into the daughter until the equilibrium is formed. When the situation is reversed, this equilibrium again forms, but only with great variation in the daughter activity. This is an instability which arises from the disturbance of the equilibrium and the natural tendency to reform.

Continued contemplation of this conclusion caused the investigator to hypothesize that the observed discrepancies could be due to defects in his counting system. A more courageous hypothesis, however, questioned the generally accepted concept that no fluctuations occur in the rate of radioactive decay. This hypothesis led the investigator to experiment with the decay of Cs^{137} and Bi^{210}. Series of absorbers cut from aluminum foil permitted an analysis of the energies carried by separate particles ejected by these nuclides. From the data obtained, the investigator concluded:

The beta distribution of the Bi^{210} daughter in the secular equilibrium shows abnormalities in its beta distribution when in equilibrium with its parent. The parent Cs^{137} however exhibits nothing other than what would be expected. The abnormalities in the Bi^{210} distribution may arise in the actual decay process itself. Therefore, it is possible for abnormalities in the day to day activity to arise from fluctuations of the number of beta particles of energies above .20MEV. When data is available, it will be possible to determine which stratum or strata the most variation arises from.

In the summary to his entire investigation, the student included references to additional work that, in his mind, should be done.

The activity of a daughter exhibits fluctuations which do not entirely conform to the expected errors in counting rates. These fluctuations are related to the way in which the parent produces the daughter. These values themselves may have a definite correlation to a stratum of energies in the overall distribution. The daughter activity in an equilibrium can be represented as a Markov chain. This work will be included in a supplement to this work. Also other radiochemical separations will be done on other secular and transient equilibria. From these data a more complete picture of the stability of radio-active equilibria will be formulated.

Fifteen carefully prepared graphs added to the general impression that this student did a scholarly piece of work. The general tone of his report endorses the individual project as a format that is adaptable to the school classroom and laboratory and provides opportunities for students to advance far beyond the levels of study and instruction available to rank-and-file students.

For Discussion and Further Study

1. Are there features of the spirit and structure of science that are particularly subject to contradiction by clumsy administration of the science project format? Conversely, does the gifted administration of this format promise to singularly nurture any of these features?

2. Is the hypothesis expressed in 1923 by Watkins more or less valid today?

3. What should a teacher do when a student expresses interest in investigating a topic and the teacher knows that the student lacks an adequate background of knowledge dealing with the topic?

4. Is there a modification of the individual project format that can be appropriately assigned to all members of a class?

5. What hazards accompany encouraging students to prepare sometimes elaborate exhibits of their work on projects for public display or competition?

References

1. Ralph K. Watkins, in Francis D. Curtis. *A Digest of Investigations in the Teaching of Science.* Philadelphia: P. Blakiston's Sons & Company, 1926, pp. 99–100.
2. Archer W. Hurd, in Francis D. Curtis. *A Third Digest of Investigations in the Teaching of Science.* Philadelphia: P. Blakiston's Sons & Company, 1939, pp. 125–29.
3. Ellinor Garber, in Francis D. Curtis. *A Digest of Investigations in the Teaching of Science.* Philadelphia: P. Blakiston's Sons & Company, 1926, p. 64.
4. Norman R. D. Jones. *Science in Secondary Schools Today.* Washington: National Education Association, National Association of Secondary-School Principals, 1953, p. 165.
5. Watson Davis, "The Interpretation of Science Through Press, Schools, and Radio," *Science Education,* 36 (March 1963), 79–83.

Appendix

Selected Readings

The following list of textbooks is included as a historical supplement for the use of those who may wish to document curriculum developments dating back to the period when science began to assume a more important role in the secondary schools of the nation.

The authors decided to terminate the listing at 1936 because since that date there has been a proliferation of textbooks, and also between 1931 and 1960 three yearbooks on the teaching of science have been published by the National Society for the Study of Education. These publications document fully the curriculum developments since the 1930's.

1918   Brownell, Herbert. *Text-book in General Science.* The Macmillan Company.

1918   Fall, Delos. *Science for Beginners.* World Book Company.

1918   Smith and Jewett. *An Introduction to the Study of Science.* The Macmillan Company.

1918–   Hodgdon, D. R. *Elementary General Science.* Hinds, Hayden, and
1922   Eldrige.

1918   Downing, E. R. *Field and Laboratory Guide in Biological Nature Study.* University of Chicago Press.

1919 Synder, W. H. *Every Day Science with Projects.* Allyn & Bacon.

1919– Van Buskirk and Smith. *The Science of Everyday Life.* Houghton
1925 Mifflin Company.

1919 Patterson, A. J. *Studies in Science.* Row, Peterson & Company.

1919 Trafton, G. H. *Science of Home and Community.* The Macmillan Company.

1919 Hodgdon, D. R. *Junior General Science.* Hinds, Hayden and Eldridge.

1920– Hessler, J. C. *Junior Science.* Books I & II. Benjamin H. Sanborn &
1921 Company.

1920 Downing, E. R. *Field and Laboratory Guide in Physical Nature Study.* University of Chicago Press.

1921 Hunter and Whitman. *Civic Science in the Home.* American Book Company.

1921 Bedford, E. A. *General Science. A Book of Projects.* Allyn & Bacon.

1921 Barber, F. D. *Lessons in Science.* Henry Holt and Company.

1921 Simmons and Gale. *First Book of General Science.* The Macmillan Company.

1922 Tower and Lunt. *Science of Common Things.* D. C. Heath & Company.

1922 Hunter and Whitman. *Civic Science in the Community.* American Book Company.

1923. Washburn, C. W. *Common Science.* World Book Company.

1923 Hunter and Whitman. *Civic Science in Home and Community.* American Book Company.

1923 Bowden, G. A. *General Science,* with Experimental and Project Studies. P. Blakiston and Sons Publishing Co.

1923 Bergeman, L. *Everyday Physical Science.* L. Bergeman, Cedar Falls, Iowa.

1923 Hunter and Whitman. *Civic Science Manual.* American Book Company.

1924 Caldwell, Eikenberry and Glenn. *Laboratory Problems in General Science.* Ginn & Company.

1924 Hooton. *Junior Experimental Science.* Warwick & York.

1924 Loevenguth, J. C. *Syllabus for General Science.* World Book Company.

1924 Nichols, M. L. *Science for Boys and Girls.* J. B. Lippincott Company.

1924 Webb and Didcoct. *Early Steps in Science.* Appleton-Century-Crofts.

1924 Curtis, F. D. *Manual of Experiments in Elementary Science.* Charles E. Merrill Books.

1924 Pieper and Beauchamp. *Natural Science for Seventh and Eighth Grades.* A Guide Book. Scott Foresman.

1925 Synder, W. H. *General Science.* Allyn & Bacon.

1925 Pieper and Beauchamp. *Everyday Problems in Science.* Scott, Foresman & Company.

1925 Caldwell and Meier. *Open Doors to Science.* Ginn and Company. For 7th and 8th Grades.

1925 G. Lombard Kelly, *One Hundred Experiments in General Science.* Elkay Company, Augusta, Ga.

1925 Pieper, Beauchamp and Frank. *Natural Science for the Ninth Grade.* (Biological) A Guide Book. Scott, Foresman & Company.

1925 Clement, A. G. *Students Laboratory Manual and Notebook in General Science.* Iroquois Publishing Company, Syracuse, N. Y.

1925 Weckel, Thalman, Rivett, and Vernon. *Home and Community Science.* Row, Peterson and Company.

1926 Bowden and Powers. *General Science, with Experimental and Project Studies.* Revised and rewritten. P. Blakiston and Sons Publishing Co.

1929 Caldwell, O. W. and Curtis, F. D. *Introduction to Science.* Ginn & Company.

1930 Hunter and Whitman. *Problems in General Science.* American Book Company.

1931 Bowden, Garfield. *Foundations of Science.* P. Blakiston and Sons Publishing Co.

1933 Obourn and Heiss. *Science Problems of Modern Life,* Book 1, Webster Publishing Company.

1933 Obourn and Heiss. *Science Problems of Modern Life,* Book 2, Webster Publishing Company.

1936 Skilling, W. T. *Tours Through the World of Sciences.* McGraw-Hill.

INDEX